Family Therapy
and
Disturbed Families

Family Therapy
and
Disturbed Families

Editors

Gerald H. Zuk & Ivan Boszormenyi-Nagy

Research Associates, Family Therapy Project
Eastern Pennsylvania Psychiatric Institute

SCIENCE AND BEHAVIOR BOOKS, INC.

577 College Avenue, Palo Alto, California 94306

Fifth Printing 1973

PREFACE

This book might well be dedicated to Harry Stack Sullivan who, in the words of Gordon Allport[1], "perhaps more than any other person, labored to bring about the fusion of psychiatry and social science," for it is, and is an outgrowth of, an attempt to promote a useful exchange among interdisciplinary workers—psychiatrists, psychoanalysts, psychologists, sociologists, and cultural anthropologists—on the nature of pathogenicity in social systems, particularly the family, and on the method of treatment known as family therapy.

Such interdisciplinary exchanges give cognizance to an assumption that has come to be generally accepted in the dialogue between psychiatry and social sciences: that the various professional groups have special contributions to make to the interpretation of relevant phenomena; even more, they have special contributions to make to the interpretation of what is relevant. One might wish that the dialogue had been more fully developed by this time, but such processes are apparently slow to mature because of the many obstacles that must be overcome.

This volume makes available papers[2] read at a conference planned by the editors and entitled "Family Process and Psychopathology: Perspectives of the Social Scientist and Clinician," which took place at the Eastern Pennsylvania Psychiatric Institute (EPPI) on October 9-11, 1964, bringing together more than fifty prominent investigators. In August 1963, one of the editors (G. H. Z.) began to sound out a number of leading social scientists and clinicians who were working primarily with the family system on the possibility of a national conference at which an exchange of views in depth could

---

[1] See the footnote by Allport on pp. 135-136 of *Tensions That Cause Wars*, edited by Hadley Cantril, Urbana, Ill.: Univer. of Ill. Press, 1950. See also Sullivan's book *The Fusion of Psychiatry and Social Science*, New York: Norton, 1964, a collection of his papers prepared by a committee at the William Alanson White Psychiatric Foundation.

[2] The exception is the paper by Don D. Jackson.

be made. Response was immediate and enthusiastic; the need for such a conference was established, and intensive planning began early in 1964. The support and sponsorship of the conference by EPPI was enlisted and a proposal, subsequently approved, was made for additional financial support to the National Institute of Mental Health.

The emphasis in the conference was to be on prepared papers followed by discussions in which the authors, within the context of the main theme—the nature of pathogenicity in social systems—were to develop a line of thought of continuing and special interest to them. We made this request of the authors because we believed the time was ripe to attempt an accommodation of different views in the field— or ripe at least for workers to more boldly confront each other with definitive statements of their views so that the possibilities for accommodation or for a more unified theoretical outlook could be evaluated. We consider this book and the conference out of which it grew as steps toward such a goal.

Among the authors are representatives of major theoretical positions in the field today. There are communication or system theorists: those concerned mainly with the interrelation of verbal and nonverbal behavior in interpersonal relations and with the definition of systems of relating or communicational networks. There are role theorists: those concerned mainly with the problem of how personal identity is formed in the forge of family, society, and culture. There are ego theorists: those concerned mainly with bridging the gap between the individual's intrapsychic existence and his relation to the outer world. Also in the volume are individuals who combine aspects of two or more of these theoretical orientations.

Numerous factors might make it difficult to set up a useful exchange among these theorists, let alone a confrontation or accommodation. One such factor is the different training and professional experiences of the social scientist and clinician. Another is the lack of a suitable and accepted "language" to encompass the phenomena of the field. (Several of the papers, especially in Section I, stress this point.) Still another factor, obviously related to those already mentioned, is a persisting need to make fundamental departures from established notions of change in social systems, of "personality change," and of normal-abnormal behavior. In spite of these factors, we are sure the conference was a useful encounter; certainly most of those present were deeply involved in it and felt that they gained in understanding.

In most of the papers, family therapy serves as an important source of observations or ideas, or as a means to pinpoint methodological problems affecting the main issue of the book. In the last decade, the introduction of family therapy has increased the interest of clinicians in studying the family as a social system, but they have lacked an adequate conceptual framework to help them deal with the complexities of the problem. In an attempt to explain the family sys-tem, they have tended to fall back on theories that were really de-veloped to explain the individual. Social scientists have a rather long tradition in the study of the family. However, as Spiegel and Bell[3] have pointed out, "Isolated aspects of the total picture—se-lected traits of the relationship of the parents and child—have been extensively investigated, but such relationships are almost always dealt with out of context, as if the family-as-a-whole did not exist" (p.114). There are now, however, social scientists who are investi-gating more complex social systems than the dyad and who have found in family therapy a useful arena for this task.

Besides the hoped-for "therapeutic" effect of bringing these workers together for a formal and informal exchange of views, other substantive aims of the conference were: a stock-taking of the field, an attempt to rework or reevaluate some of the concepts or methods that have proved especially useful, and an attempt to formulate new ideas. We believe the papers show a measure of success in fulfilling these aims of the conference, which are also the aims of this book.

The four papers in Section I—those by Bell, Haley, Jackson, and Lidz and Fleck—are oriented to the problem of stock-taking, al-though the reader will quickly recognize that they are not limited to stock-taking. They introduce the reader to the field of specialization, provide historical referents and contrasts, and suggest issues, areas, and special problems that need to be dealt with.

The six papers in Section II—those by Ackerman, Boszormenyi-Nagy, Brodey, Sonne, Titchener, and Zuk—address themselves more specifically to the problem of describing pathogenicity in the family system. They attempt to define such concepts as change in individu-als and families, and mental "health" and "illness" in close-relating persons, families, and other social systems.

The three papers in Section III—those by Fisher and Fisher, Opler, and Sanua—examine the relationship among pathogenicity, sociocultural phenomena, and the family or marriage system. Some papers in this section focus especially on methodological problems in evaluating the interrelationships.

The five papers in Section IV—those by MacGregor, Paul, Ru-binstein and Weiner, Shapiro, and Warkentin and Whitaker—are di-rected especially to clinical or treatment-related issues. They ex-

---

[3] Quoted from the chapter "The family of the psychiatric patient" in *American Handbook of Psychiatry, Vol. I.*, New York: Basic Books, 1959, Pp. 114-149.

plore the theory and technique of family therapy and the therapy of married couples.

The section headings are somewhat arbitrary, although we believe them to be quite useful for purposes of organization. The reader should expect overlap: that is, a paper carried in one section may touch on the subject matter of another section, although not as centrally as on the subject matter in the section in which it is listed.

The papers of this book have been substantially revised and expanded from those originally read at the conference in October 1964. The cooperation of the authors in reworking their papers is greatly appreciated. The editors are especially pleased that many of the authors thought that the conference "process," especially the formal and informal discussion of papers, helped to focus their thinking and facilitated the job of revising their papers for the book.

Special problems of integration of material and the tendency for material to be uneven in style and quality are inherent in edited books. We have tried to deal with the problem of integration by spelling out what we consider the main issue and sub-issues of the book in this preface, and by arranging papers in an order of logically interrelated yet relatively discrete sections. We have tried to deal with the problem of evenness of style and quality by enlisting the services of prominent and distinguished contributors to the field, and through our editorial suggestions to authors. We believe that there are substantial individual contributions in each of the sections, and that each section contributes a substantial weight to the whole of the book.

We believe the reader will find the papers consistently well-written and compact statements. One editorial policy which we think enhanced the chances of concise and elegant prose was our request to authors to keep papers within a limit of twenty-five typewritten pages, which rule was adhered to in almost all cases. Exceptions occurred in two of the papers of Section III, presentations dealing with the cultural context of the family, which required reference to extensive literature and numerous comparisons of cultural practices.

In a few cases authors presented what were essentially condensations of views presented previously in book or monograph form or in a series of papers. This practice also was in accordance with our editorial policy, since a condensation of this nature requires an extensive reorganization and careful selection of material; in other words, it too is a creative act.

One of the difficult editorial questions has been whether to include the discussions of papers and issues in addition to the papers themselves. Several conference participants felt that the discussions were significant contributions; others thought that their value was restricted to maintaining the growth of the group process. Open discussions of issues seldom lead to solid, well-organized conceptual frameworks, but they often contain honest questions and convictions spontaneously offered about issues that seem to matter a great deal to the participants. One such key issue was that of the definition of what can be called, somewhat inaccurately perhaps, "pathology" in families.

In our review of the discussions it became obvious how difficult it is to create the conceptual edifice of the underlying value orientation that guides the social scientist and clinician in their work "intuitively." A discussant who is a cultural anthropologist suggested that "crazy" families may be found among both cultural maximizers of and deviants from central normative expectations of a given society. A synthetic approach was then debated: can the combination of various family dynamics terms, e.g., pseudomutuality, double-bind, family skew, etc., be brought together in a meaningful, reciprocally clarifying and contour-sharpening manner? One of the sociologists thought they could not; a prominent psychoanalyst thought they could.

One group of comments suggested that concepts of family pathology, like any scientific concepts, should have operational validity. One participant suggested that predictive questions can be useful heuristic devices in our effort to tease out the important dimensions of family dynamics and pathology. Another, however, questioned the usefulness of predictive studies or even of efforts directed at testing definitive hypotheses at the present stage of knowledge. He suggested that long-term, descriptive studies are needed for observing which families produce illness.

Taking a rather radical position, one psychoanalyst declared that pathology makes no sense when applied to families. He stressed the importance of developing a wholly new conceptual system for describing the truly subjective, experiential components of relationships rather than the purely observable aspects of behavior. A sociologist was another proponent of subjectivism as a source of new conceptualizations: he suggested that one should start conceptualizations from one's own family experience and from direct work experience, if necessary, in complete disregard of the conceptual systems of others.

The consensus of views expressed in the discussion was that the unifying conceptual language of close relationships and their pathology remains to be born.

This sample of viewpoints was compiled from over a hundred pages of typewritten transcripts of discussions. A consistent, productive discussion of central issues would have been difficult because, in our opinion, there is a lack of fundamental and agreed-on concepts for the description of the meaning of relationships. The participants might easily have gotten lost in tangentially relevant issues and incompatible points of view. Our concern about just such a potential hazard caused us to limit the amount of discussion time at the conference, to emphasize individual presentations of prepared papers. As it turned out, the discussions, even though limited, did produce a rich divergency in points of view that probably accurately reflects the condition of the field at this time; it certainly influenced the thinking of those who formally prepared papers for this volume by providing contrasting views, new information, and suggestions about where special emphasis was needed.

We felt that the possibility of productive discussion would not end with the conference but would continue indefinitely in private talks and in later correspondence between the participants, and in the development of further conferences, which might be devoted to clinical or methodological issues (as contrasted with conceptual issues, which formed the central issue in our conference). Undoubtedly the conference laid the groundwork and set a standard for future conferences; this is perhaps the single most important criterion of success of the plan we developed.

We hope this book will recapture for the reader some of the excitement and sense of expectation of new accomplishment that pervaded the conference out of which it grew.

Gerald H. Zuk, Ph.D.
Ivan Boszormenyi-Nagy, M.D.
Editors

Philadelphia, Pennsylvania

ACKNOWLEDGEMENTS

The papers in this book were read in their original form at the conference on Family Process and Psychopathology: Perspectives of the Clinician and Social Scientist. We acknowledge with thanks the sponsorship of the conference by the Eastern Pennsylvania Psychiatric Institute (EPPI), representing through its Board of Trustees the five medical schools of Philadelphia, and the EPPI Medical Advisory Board, which generously offered the facilities for the meetings held October 9-11, 1964. The conference was also made possible by funds from the Commonwealth of Pennsylvania, and from the National Institute of Mental Health through Grant MH 10004-01.

We acknowledge with thanks the help of the Planning and Arrangements Committee of the conference which, in addition to the editors, consisted of: William A. Phillips, M.D., Medical Director, EPPI; Richard E. Schultz, Ed.D., Business Administration, EPPI; Anthony F. Wallace, Ph.D., Professor and Chairman, Department of Anthropology, University of Pennsylvania.

We acknowledge with thanks the services of special discussants whose remarks highlighted the papers and stirred a deeper exchange of views: Ray L. Birdwhistell, Ph.D., Murray Bowen, M.D., James Framo, Ph.D., Ronald Laing, M.D., Otto Pollak, Ph.D., Albert Scheflen, M.D., Ross Speck, M.D., Fred L. Strodtbeck, Ph.D., Anthony F. Wallace, Ph.D., Lyman C. Wynne, M.D., Ph.D., and Israel Zwerling, M.D., Ph.D. The incisive comments during the discussion periods of Andrew Ferber, M.D., Alfred Friedman, Ph.D., and M. Peter Laqueur, M.D., were also most helpful in furthering the goals of the conference.

We wish to extend our thanks to Mrs. Elizabeth Haley for her editorial efforts in behalf of the book. Miss Mary Patton was responsible for the revising of reference lists and footnotes throughout, and for many other editorial details. Mrs. Rita Tocci was most helpful in the conduct of our correspondence with contributors.

CONTRIBUTORS

NATHAN W. ACKERMAN, M.D., Director, Professional Program, The Family Institute, New York, New York.

NORMAN W. BELL, Ph.D., Chief, Social Science Department, McLean Hospital, Belmont, Massachusetts.

IVAN BOSZORMENYI-NAGY, M.D., Director, Family Therapy Project, Eastern Pennsylvania Psychiatric Institute; Associate Professor, Department of Psychiatry, Jefferson Medical College, Philadelphia, Pennsylvania.

WARREN M. BRODEY, M.D., Research Affiliate, Massachusetts Institute of Technology, Cambridge, Massachusetts; Member of the Faculty, Washington School of Psychiatry, Washington, D.C.

RHODA L. FISHER, Ph.D., Research Psychologist, Syracuse Scholastic Rehabilitation Program, Syracuse, New York.

SEYMOUR FISHER, Ph.D., Professor of Psychology, Department of Psychiatry, Medical School, State University of New York at Syracuse, Syracuse, New York.

STEPHEN FLECK, M.D., Professor, Department of Psychiatry, Yale University Medical School, New Haven, Connecticut.

JAY HALEY, M.A., Research Associate, Mental Research Institute; Editor, Family Process, Palo Alto, California.

DON D. JACKSON, M.D., Director, Mental Research Institute, Palo Alto, California.

THEODORE LIDZ, M.D., Professor, Department of Psychiatry, Yale University Medical School, New Haven, Connecticut.

ROBERT MacGREGOR, Ph.D., Director of Research, Family Therapy Project, Medical School at Galveston, University of Texas, Galveston, Texas.

MARVIN K. OPLER, Ph.D., Professor of Social Psychiatry, Department of Psychiatry, Medical School, State University of New York at Buffalo, Buffalo, New York.

NORMAN L. PAUL, M.D., Director of Family Therapy, Boston State Hospital; Private Practice, Boston, Massachusetts.

DAVID RUBINSTEIN, M.D., Research Scientist, Department of Clinical Research, and Member, Family Therapy Project, Eastern Pennsylvania Psychiatric Institute, Philadelphia, Pennsylvania.

VICTOR D. SANUA, Ph.D., Associate Professor, Wurzweiler School of Social Work, Yeshiva University, New York, New York.

ROGER L. SHAPIRO, M.D., Chief, Section on Personality Development, Adult Psychiatry Branch, National Institute of Mental Health, Bethesda, Maryland.

JOHN C. SONNE, M.D., Research Associate, Philadelphia Psychiatric Center; Private Practice, Philadelphia, Pennsylvania.

JAMES L. TITCHENER, M.D., Associate Professor, Department of Psychiatry, University of Cincinnati College of Medicine, Cincinnati, Ohio.

JOHN WARKENTIN, M.D., Ph.D., Senior Psychiatrist, Atlanta Psychiatric Clinic, Atlanta, Georgia.

OSCAR R. WEINER, M.D., Psychiatrist; Member, Family Therapy Project, Eastern Pennsylvania Psychiatric Institute, Philadelphia, Pennsylvania.

CARL A. WHITAKER, M.D., Professor, Department of Psychiatry, Medical School, University of Wisconsin, Madison, Wisconsin.

GERALD H. ZUK, Ph.D., Research Scientist, Department of Clinical Research, and Member, Family Therapy Project, Eastern Pennsylvania Psychiatric Institute, Philadelphia, Pennsylvania.

CONTENTS

PART I

Central Issues
and Historical Perspectives

TERMS OF A COMPREHENSIVE THEORY OF FAMILY PSYCHOPATHOLOGY RELATIONSHIPS

Norman W. Bell, Ph. D.

As one surveys the work that has been done over the past decade on the relationships between individual pathology and the dynamics of family life, one cannot help but be impressed. A minor explosion of knowledge (minor in size but not significance) has taken place. In both the psychiatric and the social science professions, investigators of high caliber have been attracted to the field. At long last, the Holy Grail of ability to handle the <u>family as a unit</u>, conceptually and clinically, is in the grasp of some and within the reach of many. And the cross-fertilization of the social sciences and psychoanalytic psychiatry, begun so long ago, appears now to be producing fruit.

It would be interesting to analyze the shifts in philosophy of science and associated cultural and social changes that have produced this blossoming. Clearly, there have been significant changes in our concepts of the interrelatedness of different levels of phenomena (changes which have gone on under the names of general systems theories, general theories of action, and so forth), changes in the openness of various professions and their accessibility to each other, and changes in technology, which have made the recording and processing of large amounts of data possible. These changes, of course, have been made possible by courageous imagination on the part of many individuals, whose work was respected and supported. It seems to me that the history of such changes should be written; but beyond noting that this has been largely an American movement, it is not my purpose to dwell on history here.

DEFICIENCIES OF CURRENT FAMILY RESEARCH

In the midst of such self-adulation, we must also take a hard look at ourselves; take stock of where we stand now and what our future course will be. From such a critical stance we may be able to recognize several features of current family work.

2

1. We have not yet developed a widely-shared common language with which to communicate. If one tries to go from one investigator's work to another's, one is caught between many concepts and generalizations that sound similar but are not the same. To take only the most obvious example: the concept of role is used by almost all writers in the field, but the connotations are more numerous than the writers. Similar difficulties are encountered with many key concepts, such as complementarity, norms, functions, etc. Of course, not all concepts need have a single meaning; concepts that point in a proper direction are also useful. In the early stages of an enterprise demanding individualistic efforts, private languages are perhaps to be expected; but in the long run, a common language has greater power.

2. We have not stayed in touch with fellow scientists in such fields as genetics and epidemiology. Initially, it was probably necessary to break with their ways of thinking and investigating. But perhaps we have insulated ourselves too well from the potentials that their developing knowledge and techniques might bring to us and, what is equally important, from what ours might bring to them. Having studied our 18 cases for 8 years, should we not have a few concepts that could be taken over for investigation on a large scale? Some of our hardheaded colleagues would like to study the incidence of double-binds, schisms and skews, pseudo-mutuality, or boundary failure in a stratified random sample of schizophrenic patients, but find our concepts incapable of being operationalized.

3. We have been slow to recognize the impact of that to which we pay so much lip service: namely, scientific method—control groups, replication, generalizability, operational definitions, and so on. Again the complexity of the phenomena with which we deal makes it difficult to approach the ideal we hope for, but perhaps the difficulties have been exaggerated and our imaginativeness dulled. To cite a single example: the study of birth-order effects, so popular a generation ago, had become barren. Important though birth-order is, it seemed to be so static and condensed a variable that its effects were nonspecific and of little general use (Spiegel & Bell, 1959). But by using multivariate techniques for the analysis of attributes of large samples of schizophrenic patients, Solomon and Nuttall (in press) have recently come up with findings regarding the variations in effects of birth-order by social class, ethnicity, and family composition that may revive the interest of dynamically-oriented investigators. At another pole, the cross-cultural studies of Caudill (1963) on birth-order effects in Japan also represents a skillful blend of dynamic notions put to a more adequate test than most of us have been willing to undertake.

4. But perhaps the most troublesome obstacle on the path toward genuinely comparable and additive work is the lack of consensus on what has to be attended to in our formulations: that is, what are the components of the system or systems with which we must be concerned. On the one hand, we all agree that illness may profitably be viewed as a symptom of group functioning, and that the group has a developmental history. But on the other hand we seem to begin with the presence of a disturbed individual and add further dimensions haphazardly. In the work of one investigator, systematic data on current relationships with extended kin are to be found; in another's, no data whatever are available. Similar complaints have been or can be made about the consideration and/or reporting of data in social class and ethnic background (Sanua, 1961), current relationships with neighbors, schools, and churches, and even within-family relationships that appear not to be central to the investigator's theory. It is this tendency of theories to be oriented to a narrow range of phenomena that I find so discouraging. For example, there is something paradoxical about taking the theoretical stance that schizophrenia is a symptom of family dysfunction, yet building theories that define schizophrenia in terms of an individual's defects in communication, thinking, or ego functioning and looking to the family milieu merely for the prodromal and precipitating factors.

Naturally, it cannot be expected that all studies will be directed to all possible variables. Since we deal with such complex phenomena, the variables that can potentially be attended to are limited. It is perhaps unrealistic to expect that a study of the precipitants of schizophrenic episodes in the here and now of family interaction will give systematic data on the character formation of grandparental generations and ethnic background. But when we cannot be sure that the investigator even knows whether there are grandparents alive, or from what ethnic group the family comes, we are faced with many questions about what the data mean.

Some investigators are wont to reply that what is important will be represented in family interaction. Since (so the argument runs) the family is reacting to their existential reality, including the living past, we must study that reality. Such a formulation may be useful clinically. Sometimes it is espoused, and quite as legitimately, by those who have never advanced past observing and treating the individual. But this argument presents many problems: how can we generalize and arrive at propositions worthy of the name of science?

The other common argument is that we must first develop a theory or unifying theme to guide our observation. This ignores the fact that theories are constructions of our minds, and have a certain capacity to guide us to confirming data. What I would submit is that there is a pretheory stage, a stage of deciding what our theory must be about, what territory it must cover, what terms it should have. Until we are all building theories about the same set of phenomena, our theories are likely to grow like snowflakes—complex, beautiful, individual, but still only snow. What is offered here is a list of the kinds of terms and propositions that have been dealt with by one investigator or another. Someone has seen them as important in one case or another. The question is whether they are important for all of us, in all cases. This list is offered with no feeling of finality and no conviction that the terms are stated in the best way. In some theories and some problems, these terms may best be stated as structural characteristics; in others, as processes. For some purposes they may be seen as associated background variables; for others, as intervening variables; for still others, as central variables. The danger (and tendency) is that they get tacked on haphazardly as we make our personal blends of longitudinal and cross-sectional, intrapsychic and interpersonal concepts. My hope is that by finding the bricks we can build a stronger and larger edifice.

ELEMENTS OF A COMPREHENSIVE THEORY

1. Bowen, following Hill and others, has stated with admirable clarity that "schizophrenia [is] a process that requires three or more generations to develop" (p. 352). Others have commented in a similar vein about the frequency of obsessive-compulsive character structures in the parents of schizophrenics; still others, on the higher prevalence of some types of pathology among the upwardly-mobile descendants of lower-class immigrants. Such findings would lead us to believe that there ought to be in our comprehensive theory a set of terms and propositions which specify the kind or kinds of social and cultural backgrounds and psychological development that are necessary for, or conducive to, the future status of parents of a disturbed offspring.

Of course, it is always possible to push the question back another generation and ask what were the early character development and experiences of the parents of children who grow up to become parents of disturbed children. But in practice such an infinite regress can be avoided by empirical testing of how many generations need to be considered before predictive power falls below a statistically significant level. Alanen and his Finnish colleagues (Alanen et al., 1964), have been able to make significant progress in just this area by very skillful use of epidemiological data.

Ideally, retrospective studies should be checked by prospective studies. Prospective studies are costly in time and money, but skillful selection of populations makes them possible.

2. Some case histories reveal a remarkable ability of families to transmit neurotic and psychotic patterns, and of their offspring to find mates with whom the patterns are recreated. The selection of mates is, of course, never a random process, though the sociological and psychological factors involved are only beginning to be studied with large enough populations to map out the territory. Though we can only "experiment" statistically, it seems feasible to set up testable propositions regarding the increase or decrease in the probability of psychopathology when a given type of woman is paired with various types of males. At least our theory should cover this aspect, not with descriptive statements about the neurotic choice of a partner, which can always be made from retrospective data concerning identified cases, but with more general propositions regarding classes of cases.

3. Once marital partners are chosen it is likely that some characteristics of their interaction patterns are already determined, but some "freedom" (in the statistical sense) remains. That is to say, the forms of attachment and detachment, the division and integration of labor, the security and insecurities emerging in the relationship, are characteristics that develop over time. Presumably there are branching points, which, once past, the system is committed to. Current work, for instance, by Rausch et al. (1963) on the crisis of intimacy that engagement and marriage brings, or by others on the crisis that the birth of a child brings, begins to show promise that a set of propositions in this area could be formulated.

4. In the past much attention has been focused upon the kinds of experiences which, suffered at particular stages of development, reduce the possibilities of a child remaining apathological for his lifetime. This area has clearly been the core of studies to date. No one ignores this order of data and we have no dearth of propositions relevant to the issue of the psychosocial development of identified patients. What seems necessary is a good deal of organizing and sifting so that the generic features of pathogenic families stand out more clearly.

5. Whenever overt pathology occurs in an individual or in a family, there are virtually always sufficient (if somewhat ad hoc) reasons to account for it. What appears in admission histories under the label of "Precipitating Circumstances" often seems to me an exercise in rationalization rather than a convincing argument as to why the "break" (itself frequently magnified) should have occurred at this particular time and could not have occurred at other times.

Undoubtedly, accidental factors play a part. But the constancy of the relationships between rates specific to age, sex, mental status, social class, and so on, suggest that some determinate factors are operating.

In the field of psychiatry, it is difficult to be aware of, let alone study with care, negative cases — cases in which the pathogenic factors have been present but the expected pathology does not manifest itself. The possibility exists, and should be built into our comprehensive theory, that there are some types of family system which reduce as well as enhance the likelihood of overt pathology appearing. Closely related is the question of why some cases move rapidly to overt pathology while others hover for long periods between covert and overt pathology. Many psychologists now distinguish between process and reactive schizophrenia. The distinction may seem overly static and individual-centered to a family-oriented investigator, but this may be a dimension of schizophrenia that could be stated in terms of family structure and process.

6. Currently there are differences of opinion about how frequently overt pathology appears in a single child, or, conversely, is latently present in most children in a family and overtly recognized and defined as being in one child. Lidz's work on this topic (Lidz et al., 1963) is compelling by reason of its depth and care, but the size and special nature of his example make it uncertain how far his conclusions can be generalized. If we may assume that the differences in opinion one finds are not merely products of the methods used, we need some terms to account for the differential propensity of families to diffuse or encapsulate psychopathology. Here again some epidemiological studies, designed and analyzed with care and intelligence, might reduce our uncertainty.

7. It is commonplace to observe that there are differential outcomes once overt pathology has occurred, that some cases reconstitute rapidly and others slowly, if at all, and that some cases appear to recover substantially and others remain impaired. Most attention has been given to factors endogenous to the sick individual as the explanation of different courses of illness. Solomon and Nuttall's studies of social factors associated with the classification of schizophrenics along the process-reactive continuum hint at the complexity of this area and how it can yield to sophisticated analysis. Perhaps we may hope that a set of propositions relating family life and differences in outcome will find systematic place in a comprehensive theory of schizophrenia.

8. Illness is a state that redounds upon the family quite as much as it is stimulated by the family. In the literature the stress is most heavily put on the disorganizing effects of illness, although

the recent work of Sampson, Messinger, and Towne (Sampson et al., 1962) suggests that overt illness and hospitalization can serve to halt schizogenic processes in the family. In any event, throughout all stages of response to illness, from initial "normalizing" to ultimate resort to experts, there is variation in how families cope with and react to the presence of deviance. Differences in readiness to see deviance as illness, readiness to hospitalize, and response to the separation that hospitalization involves need to be accounted for in a general theory.

9. One aspect of the occurrence of illness and hospitalization that seems to have been largely neglected revolves around the new set of adaptive problems that arises when a family has to deal with a treatment institution. Then the family, that prototypical primary group, has to engage in a complex set of exchanges with a secondary organization of considerable complexity. As Zucker and I suggested in a recent paper (Bell & Zucker, 1964), there is a range of responses observable among families. The task is one in which some families cooperate and others merely obstruct; in which some families are stable in their responses and others are very changeable; from which some families learn new patterns of internal processes and others do not. Intuitively and often imprecisely, treatment agents use facts of this order in their assessments of families and in their treatment and discharge plans. Perhaps this order of family operation can be formulated clearly enough to become part of a comprehensive schema of family functioning.

10. Our list of types of terms to be included in a general theory of family life and psychopathology would not be complete unless it contained some specification of the types of therapeutic intervention which are possible and promising. What types of family system are immune to influence introduced through therapy of one member (or a number of members)? What types of family system can efficiently be altered by family therapy?

CONCLUSION

These, then, seem to me to be the tasks to which a comprehensive theory must be devoted—devoted without any a priori assumptions that some terms are more central, important, or interesting than others. As was said originally, this list may be incomplete and the tasks may not be formulated in the most profitable way, but at this time these considerations seem less important than trying to lay out the blocks of propositions with which we must ultimately deal, not one at a time, but as an interrelated set.

It will be noted that I have eschewed mixing any grand theoretical mortar which might hold the blocks together. In part, this is because the work is too difficult. We deal with a wide range of individual and group phenomena from longitudinal and cross-sectional perspectives. We know how to begin to think of them: as linked, open systems, as transactional fields, and so on. The next steps are more uncertain. To date, the emphasis has been upon detailed elaboration of the dynamics of parts of the total set. The alternative, or rather the complement, may be to put the essentially clinical insights and formulations into a form which would allow testing on a wider scale by our more hardheaded colleagues. In the privacy of my study, I sometimes try to see beyond the organizing, cataloguing and evaluating work that must be done, to the day when we can set up a series of contingent propositions. The form might run something like this: if a mother had an infancy and youth marked by a, b, and c, and she is coupled with a father whose infancy and youth were marked by d, e, and f; if they chose one another for g, h, and i reasons; if their early family formation involved j, k, and l experiences; if . . . and so on . . . then the probability of an oldest male child becoming schizophrenic will be X. Obviously such a formulation is, in actuality, a long way off. My faith is that if the total territory is staked out, our individual explorations will be more productive. We may be destined to examine small sections, but we must make our efforts more cumulative.

REFERENCES

Alanen, Y., et al. The transmission of psychotic and neurotic patterns in the family. Paper read at the First Int. Congr. of Soc. Psychiat., London, August 1964.

Bell, N. W., & Zucker, R. A. Family-hospital relationships in a state hospital setting. Paper read at the First Int. Congr. of Soc. Psychiat., London, August 1964.

Bowen, M. A family concept of schizophrenia. In D. D. Jackson (Ed.), The etiology of schizophrenia. New York: Basic Books, 1960. Pp. 346-372.

Caudill, W. Social background and sibling rank among Japanese psychiatric patients. Paper prepared for the Second Conference on the Modernization of Japan, Bethesda, Md., January 1963.

Lidz, T., et al. Schizophrenic patients and their siblings. Psychiatry, 1963, 26, 1-18.

Rausch, H. L., et al. Adaptation to the first years of marriage. Psychiatry, 1963, 26, 368-380.

Sampson, H., et al. The mental hospital and marital family ties. Soc. Prob., 1961, 9, 141-155.

Sanua, V. D. Sociocultural factors in families of schizophrenics: a review of the literature. Psychiatry, 1961, 24, 246-265.

Solomon, L., & Nuttall, R. Sibling order, premorbid adjustment and remissions in schizophrenia. J. nerv. ment. Dis., in press.

Spiegel, J. P., & Bell, N. W. The family of the psychiatric patient. In S. Arieti (Ed.), American handbook of psychiatry, Vol. I. New York: Basic Books, 1959. Pp. 114-149.

TOWARD A THEORY OF PATHOLOGICAL SYSTEMS

Jay Haley, M. A.

At this time psychiatry would appear to be undergoing a basic change in orientation. Quite possibly the change is a discontinuous one, which can mean that the knowledge and training necessary for the previous orientation is not helpful in dealing with the developments yet to come. To describe a change of this kind while it is happening is difficult, but the emerging ideas are becoming sufficiently clear to be contrasted with the past point of view.

METHOD

In the past it was assumed that a science of man could be developed by studying a man in isolation from his fellows, by examining him as he dealt with strangers in artificial group situations, or by analyzing the ideology of the society he inhabited. Primarily man as an individual has been the focus of study; the goal has been to describe and classify the individual in terms of his body type, character, personality, clinical diagnosis, and so on. The nature of this focus has severly limited the possible explanations about people and why they do what they do. Putting the individual person alone in a frame, the investigator attempted to explain all there was to know about him without including other people in the picture; to explain "why" someone did what he did, it was necessary to postulate something inside the person, such as instincts or drives or emotions. If a person behaved peculiarly, it had to follow that there was an internal defect or the person was experiencing conflicts within himself, such as conflicts between opposing drives or needs. If a person changed in psychotherapy, then something inside him must have changed, such as an increase in understanding or a shift in perception. When men of different cultures were compared, the individuals were contrasted on the basis of their ways of thinking or their values and beliefs. The influence of psychiatric ideology upon social theorists usually led them more in the direction of the indi-

11

vidual and further from a social orientation. Within psychiatry there was an absolutely basic assumption that the problem was how to diagnose and treat the individual patient.

In the last decade in psychiatry the frame around the individual has been broken, and questions about "why" a man does what he does are being answered in terms of the context of relationships he creates and inhabits. The reasons for this change have been the continuing emphasis upon interpersonal relations over the years and the recent development of ideas about systems. The change is a shift in focus from the individual and his nature to the habitual and systematic patterns of behavior men develop when dealing with their intimates. The direct manifestation of this change is in the field of family research and family therapy.

In the last few years, for the first time in history, married couples and whole families are being brought under systematic observation. Family members are observed actually dealing with one another. The research problem is how to conceptualize the repeating, responsive behavior in this ongoing social network in such a way that statements about regularities in the interchange will hold true over time. The problem is no longer how to characterize and classify these individuals; it is how to describe and classify the habitual patterns of responsive behavior exchanged by intimates. Can one categorize the typical processes in the group, describe changes if they occur, and differentiate one organization from another? With this focus, the "cause" of why someone does what he does is shifting from inside him to the context in which he lives. The question of whether a family containing a psychiatric patient is a different type of organization from another family is a question of whether there is a system of interactive behavior which provokes, or requires, one or more members of the system to behave in a way that could be classified as psychopathological. A similar question is whether there are discernable trends in relationships that predictably lead to violence or divorce and the dissolution of the family. These questions have relevance beyond the family research field. Insofar as any group of men have a history and a future together (for example, research groups or business organizations), the type of exchanges generated in the system may determine whether there will be amiable relations and productive work or a disturbed and unhappy group of participants. In the larger social scene, the family of nations may develop patterns of exchange that predictably lead to disruption and war. For inquiry into these questions, the focus must be shifted to the exchange of acts in a relationship and away from the description of man as if he were autonomous. This means breaking new ground.

If we take seriously the accusation often made that the psychological and social sciences, as contrasted with the physical sciences, are still in the dark ages, there is an analogy between what is happening today and what happened in the physical sciences in the seventeenth century. What had survived from Greece at that time was an interest in the orbits of the planets and a theory that the planets moved in circular orbits around the earth, the center of the universe. In this period, certain men began to doubt the explanations of the ancients about these orbits, and yet they had few actual observations of planet movements and they were even uncertain whether such observations were necessary. They had no conceptualization of physical laws as a framework for the observations available to them, and they were handicapped by a variety of past theories, including theories that the planets were propelled by angels. A further difficulty was the opposition to new points of view shown by an establishment of knowledgeable people who had an investment in the ancient theories. Yet within a relatively short time the orbits of the planets were accurately determined and from this effort came the laws of Newton, which had relevance far beyond this particular question and influenced the entire nature of scientific investigation.

Today in the field of social relations we appear to be in a remarkably similar situation. Some people have begun to doubt the past theories about human beings, such as the idea that men are driven by instincts, and yet there are few factual observations of people in "orbit" in their intimate relationships. Many people are even uncertain whether such observations are necessary. We also have no conceptualization of laws of social relationships, if such regularities exist, as a framework in which to place the few observations that we do have. In addition, our current establishment of knowledgeable people has a large investment in the past theories of the individual as an autonomous being.

In that earlier scientific endeavor, there were several steps necessary before the problem could be solved. First of all, it was necessary to make a bold shift in the focus of attention. Copernicus did this when he suggested that planets orbited around the sun rather than the earth. To take this necessary step, men had to revise basic assumptions about man and the universe. The current shift of focus in psychiatry from the individual to the social network he inhabits could be said to be comparable to the shift from the earth to the sun as the center of the universe. It is a bold step, and many people react almost religiously against the idea that man is not the focal point but is rather helplessly responding within his network of ongoing relationships. Those who protest say the importance of the individual is being overlooked and he is being made a mere element in the system, just as they said man was diminished if his planet was not the focal point of the universe.[1]

The natural scientists' second step was to begin to doubt the statements and observations of the ancients and to collect accurate observations of the movements of the planets. Kepler obtained these "facts," and after immersing himself in them was forced to abandon the ancient idea of circular orbits and to conclude that the planets moved in elliptical patterns. This discovery of the shape of the orbits made possible the formulation of a new set of causal explanations. Today we have begun to doubt the statements and observations of our own "ancients" but we have hardly begun the task of collecting our observations. Despite the large number of books on marriage and the family, which describe what families are supposed to be like, it is only in the last few years that investigators have actually begun to bring families together and to observe the members dealing with one another. We have a great many opinions, which are adaptable to any causal explanation, but we will need many years of observing and testing families in operation before we have sufficient observations to refute a theory.

The final step of the men of earlier times was to derive from their new observations new generalizations sufficiently broad to include the idea that what occurred in the heavens also occurred on earth. In this way they delineated laws of nature that had wide application in many fields of endeavor. Now we, too, are beginning to assume that the idea of a coalition between family members is relevant to coalition patterns in any ongoing social group and that patterns in a marriage could be relevant to those of international relations. That is, we are beginning to seek laws, or regularities, which hold true in any system of relationships with a past and a future. It is this possibility that makes research on the family appear potentially so rewarding.

We can hope that it will not take as long to develop a science of human relationships as it did to develop the physical sciences, because we have that vast attempt to guide us. However, we should also not assume that we can jump the preliminary steps necessary and have a sophisticated theory of human relationships appear full

---

[1] A similar response was made to Freud when he suggested that the idea of man's being unable to control his own mind was the third great blow (after a sun-oriented universe and a descent from animals). Freud argued that man was driven by unconscious forces within himself which he was helpless to control. The current family-oriented view in psychiatry would also argue that man is helplessly driven, but by the people around him in the system he inhabits. Perhaps this diminishes man even more, since the "cause" of his behavior is no longer even located within him but in the outer context. However, this point of view also implies that he participates in creating that context.

blown in all its grandeur. Over time, we will need the three factors necessary in any scientific endeavor: (1) we must have a collection of facts — observable events which either occur or do not occur, (2) we must be able to formulate those facts into patterned regularities, and (3) we must devise theories to account for these regularities and be willing to discard past ideas if they handicap us in our efforts.

Regarding the collection of facts, in family research it is not yet clear what the relevant "facts" are or what the best method is of collecting them. When studying families, if we confine ourselves to observable events we have only the behavior of family members as they respond to one another: their bodily movements and vocal intonations, their words and acts. If we extend our "facts" to include unobservable events, then we have the emotions, attitudes, expectations, and thought processes of the participating family members. Agreement has not yet been reached as to which of these types of data are most appropriate. Additionally, we face the problem that our "facts" are determined by the ways in which we collect them; there is not agreement about how to proceed in family research. There are three general methods of collecting data: (1) using the self-report of family members about their families obtained either by questionnaire or by interview, (2) bringing family members together to study them in operation, with the data consisting of observations by human observers who attempt to reach agreement on what they see happening, and (3) placing families in communication networks where their behavior is recorded on instruments. These three different schools of family research are obviously going to collect different "facts" about families.

A further difficulty in family research is the problem of formulating some sort of theory as a guide for the type of observations to make and the kind of methodology to use. We need to conceptualize formal patterns of human relations in such a way that we can ultimately collect data which will verify whether or not certain patterns actually occur. At this time we must conceptualize with only a minimum number of observations of families in operation. Yet we must speculate on the basis of what we have and then decide what sort of approach might support or refute our speculations. A speculation will be offered here about a characteristic pattern which appears evident in pathological systems.

Although men have not focused upon the systematic study of relationships, they have observed each other in action for many years and we might assume that if some aspect of ongoing relationships was truly important it would be emphasized in past literature. There exists a formal pattern that has been noted so often that it has been given a name, "The Eternal Triangle," and has been the focus of man's attention to psychiatry, religion, and politics, as well as in the fiction he has created to express his life experiences. It seems, in fact, to be the only relationship pattern that has been named in folk speech. Perhaps its importance is based on the fact that the essential learning context of the human being is triangular: in the usual biological family unit, two people unite to create and rear a third.

In the family research of the last decade there has been a progression from descriptions of individuals to descriptions of dyads (such as mother and child) to triadic descriptions (such as parents and disturbed child). Larger family groupings, for example a quadrad, have not been emphasized, despite a move toward studying the entire family network. The extended family is usually discussed in terms of the smaller units. For example, the influence of the grandparent generation is usually discussed in terms of the influence on a parent of his mother and father. This focus on a maximum unit of three people would seem to be partly because of the complexity of larger units and partly because the triangle appears to be a "natural" unit.

THE PERVERSE TRIANGLE

If we take the triangle as our unit of study in a family or in any ongoing social system, we can raise the question of what sort of triangular arrangement will generate what could be called a pathological system. In this case "pathological" means a system that will lead to the dissolution of itself or to violence among the elements, or indicates elements which behave in ways that appear peculiar and inappropriate. In terms of the family, a pathological system is one resulting in continual conflict, in divorce, or in the kind of symptomatic distress in one or more family members that requires community attention. If we examine the past literature and activities of man, we find that there is a triangle of this sort—it can be called a perverse triangle—that has long been taken for granted without being made explicit. These are its characteristics:

1. The people responding to each other in the triangle are not peers, but one of them is of a different generation from the other two. By "generation" is meant a different order in the power hierarchy, as in a human generation of parent and child or in an administrative hierarchy such as manager and employee.

2. In the process of their interaction together, the person of one generation forms a coalition with the person of the other generation against his peer. By "coalition" is meant a process of joint action which is against the third person (in contrast to an alliance,

in which two people might get together in a common interest independent of the third person).

3. The coalition between the two persons is denied. That is, there is certain behavior which indicates a coalition which, when it is queried, will be denied as a coalition. More formally, the behavior at one level which indicates that there is a coalition is qualified by metacommunicative behavior indicating there is not.

In essence, the perverse triangle is one in which the separation between generations is breached in a covert way. When this occurs as a repetitive pattern, the system will be pathological. This concept is not being offered as something new but rather as a more precise formulation of what is becoming commonly assumed in the literature on pathology and the family.

As an illustration, in the area of administration it has been taken for granted that a breach of generations will make difficulty in an organization. It is said if a manager "plays favorites" among his employees the organization will be in distress. Put in terms of a triangle, the manager in such a case is forming a coalition across generation lines with one person against his peer. If he merely forms an alliance with an employee, the problem does not necessarily arise, but at the moment he sides with one against another while simultaneously denying that this is happening, the system will become pathological.[2]

This illustration is a rephrasing of a point made in most administrative manuals: the administrative levels in the hierarchy must be kept separate for the proper functioning of an organization. There is one other point assumed in good administrative procedure: communication should not jump levels. That is, an employee should not be allowed to "go over the head" of his immediate superior and contact a higher superior. Once again, this idea can be rephased in terms of a breaching of generations: a coalition between a higher and a lower level against a middle level in the power hierarchy. It is assumed that such breaching should not take place and that if it occurs secretly as a consistent pattern, the organization will be in distress.

---

[2] If one seeks a "cause" of the distress in terms of the individual, it could be put in terms of an unresolvable conflict, or paradox, for the person coalesced against. A generation line or administrative level is implicitly a coalition among peers; employers are in coalition with others on their level and employees are in coalition with others on their level. Within that framework, if an employer and employee form a coalition against another, the other is faced with two conflicting definitions of the situation: (a) his fellow employee is in coalition with him as part of the natural framework of administration, but within that framework (b) his fellow employee is siding with the employer against him. Being forced to respond when there is a conflict between these two different orders of coalition creates distress.

One would expect that if this perverse triangle were causal to pathological systems it would not only be avoided in organizations but it would be assumed to be important in the field of psychopathology, and this is obviously so. In psychiatry, one finds the perverse triangle, slightly rephrased, as the central thesis in psychodynamic theory. In psychoanalytic theory and in much of psychiatry it is argued that the Oedipal conflict is a focal point in the cause of psychiatric distress. The origin of this idea is particularly pertinent here. Sigmund Freud at one time proposed that hysteria was the result of a sexual assault on the patient by an older relative. In this sense he proposed that there was a breaching of generations which should not have occurred and, insofar as it was a secret act, could be considered a covert coalition across generations. However, he then discovered that in certain cases the sexual incident could not actually have happened, and he shifted from the idea of a familial cause of this malady to an intrapsychic cause—a fantasied wish for the sexual act. This was the birth of the Oedipal conflict, the wish of the boy to have sexual relations with his mother and the consequent fear that his father would not take this coalition kindly and would castrate him. The Oedipal conflict became a universal explanation of the neurosis.

In essence, this conflict, as in the play from which Freud drew the name, can be seen as a coalition across generation lines which is covert or denied. The action of the play Oedipus consists of the lifting of the secrecy of this breaching of generations. Thanks to Freud, one can discover this pattern in most of the drama and fiction man enjoys. If one analyzes the content of popular moving pictures, one notes that the theme of the younger man coalescing with a woman against an older or more powerful man is so common that it is standard procedure. The outcome of this triangle seems to vary with different decades, perhaps reflecting changes in the authority structure of the culture. As another of the endless variations, we have Lolita, where the older man secretly coalesces with the girl against her mother. One might expect that the essence of dramatic conflict resides in the secret coalition across generations, perhaps because the audience recognizes the danger of it. It could be argued that this pattern is portrayed symbolically as a reflection of the incest tabu, but one could also argue that the incest tabu is a product of the recognition that cross-generation coalitions result in distress for all participants in the family network.

In the psychiatry of the past, which focused upon the individual, the triangle was considered of basic importance, and when we turn to the newer approach of the relation of pathology to the family we find a similar emphasis common in the literature. Many family descriptions are cast in a framework of individual description, but implicit in them is a view of pathology nestling in a perverse triangle. For example, it has long been suggested that a disturbed child is a product of parents who are in conflict: the child is caught between them by being in coalition with one or the other. When the mother is described as overprotective and the father as passive, the implication is that mother is siding with child against father, who remains withdrawn. The mirror picture is presented, where father and child are in covert coalition against a difficult mother. Generally, the inability of parents of a disturbed child to maintain a common front to enforce discipline is a reflection of their inability to maintain a separation between the generations. A similar breach of generations appears in the case of the disturbed child who associates with his parents but avoids his peers.

It is also becoming more common to read in the descriptions of the extended family a similar pattern occurring in the next generation in disturbed families. It is often pointed out that there is a cross-generational coalition by a parent with a grandparent, usually phrased in terms of an excessively dependent relationship. For example, the husband's mother is said to be constantly in the picture, and while the wife pushes him to assert himself and keep his mother in her place the husband indicates that his mother isn't really a problem (thereby denying the coalition against his wife). Commonly, too, in the disturbed family a wife is said to be excessively involved with her mother in a coalition against her husband. In folk speech we find the situation a problem sufficient to produce the "mother-in-law jokes."

The existence of a coalition between a disturbed child and a parent occurs so often in conjunction with a coalition of one of his parents with a grandparent that one might suggest they are inseparable. That is, it could be stated as a hypothesis that a breaching of generations with the child will coincide with a breaching at the next generational level. (Often, too, it will coincide with a coalition of child and grandparent against parent.) If such a triangle at one generation always accompanies a similar one at the next generational level, we can suspect a regularity in networks of family relations where the patterns in any one part of the family are formally the same as those in some other part.

Anyone who has observed or treated abnormal families assumes that the ways the parents form coalitions with the child against one another appears "causal" to the disturbance in the child. The idea is also present, with a slight translation, in the studies of the hospitals where patients are sent for treatment. Some years ago Stanton and Schwartz noted in their study of the mental hospital (Stanton and

Schwartz, 1954) that a conflict between an administrator and a thera-pist was a "cause" of a patient erupting in a disturbance. This re-sult can also be seen when one staff member sides with a patient against another staff member in a perverse triangle.

If we use the triangle as a unit of study and break down a family network into its triangular components, a rather awesome complex-ity appears. In an average-size family where there are two parents and two children, and each parent has two parents, this group of eight people composes 56 triangles. Any one person in the family is involved in 21 family triangles simultaneously (and this does not include aunts and uncles, neighbors and employers). Every one of the 21 triangles in which parents and children are involved carries the possibility of a coalition across generations. If the occurrence of a secret coalition across generations is indeed pathological, the potentiality for disturbance is exceedingly high in any family.

An analysis of a family network in terms of triangles also re-veals that any one person in the family is at the nexus of a large number of these triangles. He is also the only person at this par-ticular nexus. The fact that no two people are in the same position in a context, even in the same family, raises profound questions about whether individuals can be compared. To say that a neurotic is different from a psychotic implies that the context in which they live is comparable. If it is not, the two people cannot be compared. All attempts to classify individuals into types have assumed that they face essentially the same situations and that therefore differ-ences must be within them. This assumption was made without any investigation to determine whether different individuals face the same situations. The family evidence being gathered indicates that different individuals live in quite different worlds.

If we assume that an individual's behavior is adaptive to his in-timate relationships, it follows that he must not behave in one tri-angular group in a way which will disrupt another triangular group-ing in which he is involved. For example, his behavior in the triangle with his parents will have repercussions in the triangle with his grandparents. In fact, the way a person relates to any one pair in the network will influence the response to him of any other pair. In a family where all the triangular groups consist of amiable members, the situation does not appear complex. But let us suppose that a child is at the nexus of two triangles, or groups, which are in conflict. Suppose, for example, that if he pleases his mother and her mother he will disturb his relationship with his father and his mother be-cause the two groups are in conflict. To behave adaptively, the child must maneuver in such a way that his behavior in one group does not disrupt the other. If one imagines that all 21 of the triangles the child inhabits are in conflict with each other, and if the child is at the nexus of all these conflicting groups, then to adapt and survive in such a network he must exhibit strange and conflictual behavior. It is possible to explain the symptoms of schizophrenia as adaptive to this kind of conflicting set of groups. In fact, it appears that this way of looking at the family system could ultimately lead to a social description of any symptomatic behavior—a translation of psychopathology into the language of social behavior.

SCHIZOPHRENIA AS A CONFLICT OF GROUPS

A way of explaining schizophrenia was offered some years ago by a research group in which I participated. It was noted that schizophrenia could be described as a disorder of levels of communication: the patient qualified what he said or did with an indication that he was saying or doing something else, and then qualified this meta-message with yet another which conflicted (Haley, 1959). That is, schizophrenic behavior was described as a disorder of Logical Types in the Russellian sense. It was hypothesized at that time by Gregory Bateson that the patient must have been raised in a learning context of conflicting levels of communication. This context was labeled a double-bind situation (Bateson et al., 1956). The idea proposed was that the schizophrenic had been raised in a situation where he faced conflicting levels of message from a parent or a combination of both parents with an injunction against commenting on this conflict or leaving the field.

At that time I was particularly interested in attempting to correlate more precisely the behavior of the schizophrenic with his situation in his family to investigate whether schizophrenia was a form of adaptable, responsive behavior. To collect data on this point, it was necessary to accept the reports of the family members about what had happened in the past during a psychotic episode. Alternatively, one can observe the occurrence of psychotic symptoms in the patient during the course of family therapy and examine the situation in which the symptoms erupted. Such an incident can be used here to illustrate the familial context of a schizophrenic.

A schizophrenic daughter improved sufficiently to be sent home from the hospital on a trial visit, and her parents responded to this situation by separating. Mother left father (but called him and told him where she was going) and she asked her daughter to go with her (even though at the time she was saying she could not tolerate her daughter's company). When her mother made this request, the daughter faced a situation in which she had to choose between her parents and either stay with father or go with mother. The daughter's solution was rather complex. She went with her mother, but when they arrived at their destination, her grandmother's home, she called her father. The mother then protested that this meant she was siding with the father against her, and the girl said she had only called the father because when she said goodbye to him she had given him an odd look. A characteristic symptom of this daughter was her "odd looks" and the question was whether this behavior was irrational or adaptive, given this situation. The girl's behavior became more extreme when the father came and reclaimed the mother. The girl was asked by her mother to go to the store, and declined. The grandmother did the errand, and while the mother and father were in the other room discussing the girl's refusal, the girl began to scream. She was then rehospitalized.

At one time, the daughter's behavior might have been explained as adaptive to a situation where there was a conflict of family rules. The rule was that the daughter was not to form an open coalition with either father or mother, and yet the separation forced her to break her rule. She could not merely do nothing because that would have meant staying with her father. Her solution was to have a symptom—the odd look—which solved the problem of how to avoid siding with either parent.

In terms of the larger family context, it is possible to see a family "rule" in a somewhat new way. Repetitive behavior between two people can be seen as not merely the following of an arbitrary rule that has developed between them but as a product of responses in other parts of the family. That is, a rule not to have an open coalition with mother or father can be seen as a response to the consequences among other family members if the coalition occurs.

Examining the larger context in which this girl was living, and focusing upon only the most important people in her life—her parents and two grandmothers—we see that she was involved in a group of ten cross-generational triangles. It would be possible that none of these triangles would involve cross-generational coalitions. The grandmothers might keep out of the parental difficulties, the parents might maintain a separation between themselves and the daughter, and the daughter might not attempt a coalition with either parents or grandparents but would confine her associations to her peers. Quite the opposite extreme was apparent in this situation. Impressions from family interviews indicated that all family members were involved in a consistent pattern of perverse triangles. The two grandmothers bid against each other for the daughter, the father's mother sided with him against the wife (she had once offered the wife a cash bribe to leave her son because she could take better care of him), and the daughter was constantly siding with her mother's mother against her mother and staying with her on visits home from the hospital. The most apparent and persistent cross-generation coalitions occurred in the triangle of the girl with her parents. Father accused mother and daughter of being against him, which they denied. Mother accused daughter of being in coalition with father against her and cited sexual play between them, among other activities, as proof of this. Generally the parents behaved as if there were no generational differences with the daughter.

The amount of struggle and conflict between the different family triangles appeared extraordinary and was complicated even further by the mother's sisters, who were also continually intervening in the family affair. When the girl was forced by this physical separation to choose between her parents, her response carried repercussions throughout the wider network of family triangles. If she went with her mother or if she did not, she was faced with a situation where her response would not only be condemned but she would provoke open disruption in the extended family. For example, to go with her mother also meant joining the mother's family against the father's family, joining one grandmother against another, and joining grandmother against father. At the nexus of warring family factions, what would be an "appropriate and normal" response to this situation? It would seem to be one in which the girl should behave in one way to satisfy one faction and another way to satisfy another, and then disqualify both ways by indicating she was not responsible for what happened in any case. Such conflicting communication would be diagnosed as schizophrenic behavior.

PERSISTING TRIANGLES

Assuming for the moment that a pathological family system consists of a network of perverse triangles, questions arise about how a family got that way, why the members persist in behavior that is disturbing, and how one may go about changing such a system. It seems doubtful that the "cause" can be sought in the behavior of any single individual or even that of a set of parents. The pattern undoubtedly is passed down over many generations. However, the pattern must also be continually reinforced if it is to continue. At a minimum, two people each of a different generation must cooperate to perpetuate it.

One might look upon the situation as one in which at least two people are dissatisfied with the status quo. If a wife is pleased with her association with her husband she is not likely to attempt to join child or parent against him. In a sense, such a coalition is an attempt at a change. Yet there is a perduring quality even in this attempt at change, because to breach generations in an attempt to change continues the family situation which leads to dissatisfaction. However, if one examines the question of "cause" in terms of dissatisfaction, he is focusing once again upon the individual. Such a focus usually indicates an avoidance of looking at the larger context. When one shifts to the larger view, alternative explanations appear that make "cause" appear more complex. For example, it is possible that the wife joins child against husband not merely because of internal dissatisfaction but as an adaptive response to her relationship with her parents. To maintain stability in relation to her parents, she may find it necessary to join child against husband because an amiable relationship with her husband would have repercussions in the way she is dealing with her parents and the way they are dealing with each other. In this sense, "cause" is a statement about regularities in larger networks. [3]

The argument that the extended family has less influence today because many generations do not live under the same roof is not necessarily valid. Young people may marry and settle in their little box in the suburbs, but they are not out of contact with their extended families. Anyone who has dealt with disturbed couples or families knows that communication takes place and repercussions occur in the extended family no matter how geographically distant the members may be.

When one examines an idea of this sort and thinks about how to verify it with more than impressionistic data, the basic problems of family research arise. Suppose we wished to test the hypothesis that families which exhibit violence, dissolve in divorce, or produce members suffering from psychopathology all characteristically exhibit covert cross-generational coalitions. In the past we might have assumed that we need only ask the family members the right sort of questions in order to determine whether the perverse triangle is more frequent in "abnormal" than in "normal" families. Now it is becoming more accepted that the self-report of family members can be used, at most, as an indicator of an area of research and not as a means of validating a hypothesis. (This is particularly so when one is concerned with levels of behavior that involve denials.) It seems necessary to bring the family members together and study the network in operation. One must precisely define "coalition" and "generation," and devise a context that will generate an opportunity for coalitions while providing a means of denying their existence.

---

[3] It would seem superfluous to bring to the question of "cause" of psychopathological behavior anything about the person's history, past conditioning, or internalized images. An adequate description of the present family network should be sufficient.

Then one must place family members in this context to determine whether or not such coalitions occur in a variety of family triangular groupings, and do this with a sufficiently large sample of families to be able to make statements about differences at some designated level of significance. If one uses human observers to observe families and guess whether coalitions are occurring there is always the possibility of bias. If one does not use observers, he must devise a situation where instruments will record the results—and the use of instrumentation to record multiple levels of communication is difficult. Yet ultimately if we are to bring rigor to this sort of study we must provide the opportunity for covert coalitions as they are defined in that context (Haley, 1962). Devising such an experimental procedure and testing an adequate sample is, let us say, a challenging task.

Granting the complexity of the data in the field of ongoing relationships, we have on our side the fact that such relationships appear to contain enormous redundancies. If we can describe and test a systematic pattern in one segment of a family, we should find echoes of that pattern throughout the other parts of the system. We appear to be dealing with networks as tightly organized in repetitious patterns as the orbits of planets.

FAMILY THERAPY

The tightness and rigidity of the family network become particularly evident to therapists attempting to bring about change in whole families. As with individuals, family studies indicate that flexibility is synonymous with normalcy and rigidity with pathology. It would seem to follow naturally that the more severe the disturbance, the more rigid the family pattern; change appears to be brought about more easily with minor pathologies than with families of schizophrenics. Had we more elaborate theories of the technique of family therapy, we might have more success with severely disturbed families. It would appear, however, that such theory will only be built over time.

The various methods of family therapy that have appeared would seem to have one factor in common: a focus on the problem of coalition both within the family and between therapist and family members. It is generally assumed that it is unwise for a therapist to join one member of a family against another. Yet it also appears that members of disturbed families are exasperatingly skillful at provoking a therapist to side with them and at antagonizing him to side against them. In terms of the point being made here, a therapist is causing rather than resolving a disturbed system if he joins in such coalitions while denying that he is doing so. Insofar as the parents consult him

as an expert, he is of a different generation, a different order in the
authority hierarchy. Should he join the child against the parents, as
many novice therapists are tempted to do for reasons of sympathy
and individual orientation, he is instituting a pathological system
and repeating the usual patterns of the family. [4] The danger that
the coalition will be a secret one is particularly present with those
therapists who side with the child but deny it because they know they
should focus upon the whole family.. One way to analyze family therapy is in terms of a process of the therapist constantly disinvolving
himself from coalitions with family members as these occur in all
their subtle variations. The art of family therapy seems to be that
of developing ways of siding with all family members at once, or
of clearly taking sides with different factions at different times
while acknowledging this, or of leaving the coalition situation am-
biguous so that family members are uncertain where the therapist
stands. Family therapists seem to recognize, either consciously or
by intuition, that generations should not be breached, and that denial should not take place if a breach does occur.

The tightness of organization in the disturbed family also indicates new possibilities in family therapy appearing on the horizon.
If all parts of a family network are responsive to change in any one
part because of the tightness of the organization, then a certain
freedom appears with regard to which set of family relationships to
focus upon in family treatment. Certain factions of a family might
be more accessible to change than others. In schizophrenia, for
example, the parents and schizophrenic child might be the triangle
most resistant to change so that treatment of another section of the
family could produce better results. Yet to suggest this possibility
indicates how rapid a change has been taking place in psychiatry.
Not many years ago, it was thought a waste of time to attempt psychotherapy with a schizophrenic. More recently, it has seemed point-
less to treat only the schizophrenic, because of his involvement with
his parents (and the hospital staff), who should also enter treatment.
Now it is conceivable that the schizophrenic could be treated without
ever entering therapy since a change in him is assumed to be brought
about if another part of the extended family in which he lives is
changed. Although such an idea might appear extreme, there is a
recent precedent for it. Disturbed children were once treated as
the problem; then the parents were given individual treatment in

---

[4] A similar danger occurs with individual therapy where the therapist declines
to see the family members of his patient. A spouse may find himself faced with a
coalition between an authority and the relative (with all information about the
relationship funneled through the relative). A disturbance in the family system can
be perpetuated by this secret cross-generation coalition.

addition; and finally, parents and child were treated as a group. Recently it has been so taken for granted that the disturbed child is a "product" of the marital problems of the parents that the child is excluded and only the parents treated. This shift toward assuming that the "cause" of an individual's behavior resides in the context in which he is living reflects the extensive changes that have taken place in the basic orientation of psychiatry in less than a decade. Only that long ago was it suggested that the symptoms of a patient are a product of, and serve a current function in, a unique type of family. If families with abnormal members have a special type of organization, as family research is now attempting to document, then the argument that symptoms are responsive behavior to a particular context is supported (in contrast to the past view that psychopathology is only a product of something askew inside the individual). The consequences of this different point of view must inevitably permeate psychiatric thinking. In diagnosis, the change will be toward including more than one person in the diagnostic category. In treatment, the assumption is developing that one person cannot change unless the context of a relationship in which he lives also changes, which leads to more treatment of marital pairs and whole families as a natural consequence. It is possible that individual theory can be extended to include the relationship, but the current confusion in the field when attempts are made to bridge between the two points of view indicate that this is doubtfully possible and that future developments in psychiatry will represent a discontinuous change from the past.

REFERENCES

Bateson, G., et al. Toward a theory of schizophrenia. Behav. Sci.,
    1956, 1, 251-264.
Haley, J. An interactional description of schizophrenia. Psychiatry,
    1959, 22, 321-332.
Haley, J. Family experiments: a new type of experimentation.
    Fam. Proc., 1962, 1, 265-293.
Stanton, A. H., & Schwartz, M. S. The mental hospital. New York:
    Basic Books, 1954.

ASPECTS OF CONJOINT FAMILY THERAPY[1]

Don D. Jackson, M. D.

The subtitle of this presentation is: "Lolita was not Oedipal but Electracal." I expect you to take the subtitle seriously, since in capsule form it contains all the important points I hope to establish in this presentation. Let me list briefly what these points are before attempting to discuss them.

1. The story of <u>Lolita</u> was both a superbly written novel and a treatment of a "shocking" subject. This combination often applies to psychiatric and psychoanalytic presentations and was best exemplified by the ceaselessly stimulating writings of Freud.

2. Although the book is called <u>Lolita,</u> the story is actually about the people with whom she interacts, as well as about Lolita herself. It is a superb novel because it does not deal with Lolita as if she were a beautiful, sexy young fiend who fastens herself upon otherwise unwilling victims. Nabokov writes tellingly of the mother and of the narcissistic Humbert. Comparing this presentation with another story of a young girl, <u>The Bad Seed,</u> is much like comparing an organicist's description of the autistic child with that of a family researcher.

3. Freud, in discovering the Oedipal triangle, almost ventured into interpersonal theory. However, he made an irrevocable step into an intrapsychic position and partly as a result of this, he did little with the "Electra complex." For though it made sense that the boy saw his father as a rival and desired to possess his mother, it made little sense to reverse the picture and have the young girl child getting rid of her mother in order to possess her father; Freud did not follow up this problem. The utilization of conjoint family therapy has altered the psychoanalytic view of the Oedipal complex and made it a much more interpersonal and dynamic relationship than merely an intrapsychic one. In the story <u>Lolita</u>, you will re-

[1]Presented in somewhat different form as the First Edward A. Strecker Lecture, Philadelphia, Penna., November 21, 1964.

call that Humbert was an apparent villain who intended to seduce a poor innocent child. Instead, Lolita led him around by the nose. Freud deserves credit for indicating that the child is not merely a hapless victim, but also contributes to his own destiny. In contrast, a family therapist would place the child's behavior in a context— such as a relationship between parents that invites a divide and conquer tactic from the child.

4. The essence of a scientific revolution lies in a new discovery that does not fit existing knowledge. One example par excellence is the electrical revolution, and I shall use this as an analogy to the situation in psychiatry in which study of the family has yielded data not provided by intrapsychic theory. Naturally, there are creaks, groans, and occasional cries of anguish as these new findings are put in place alongside existing theories. Not only was Lolita an impudent upstart pitting herself against older and wiser folks, but Nabokov's treatment of a difficult and seamy subject helped revolutionize English literature—a revolution climaxed, perhaps unfortunately, by Candy, a funny but bad novel, and a host of recent pornographic potboilers.

5. Clerk-Maxwell's important theories in electromagnetics were not sufficient to explain all the phenomena with which students of electricity were confronted. When Einstein's ideas were promulgated, a scientific revolution occurred. The jump from the idea of an electromagnetic field of force to the incredible dimensions of Einstein's thinking, while revolutionary, in no way violated the importance of Maxwell's contributions. There has been some question about how much Freud was influenced by the physics of his day, and it is interesting that Maxwell wrote a paper on the governor in 1875. You may remember that his argument was that the electrons in a container do not move at the same speed; that some are fast and some are slow, with the average speed being a statement about the temperature of the gas. He proposed the hypothetical possibility of a trap door separating two parts of the container, with a demon opening and closing the door. When a fast electron came through the demon opened it and let it pass, but when a slow one came along he closed the door and kept it out. In this way the temperature of the two sides was changed merely by a selective process, and thus overcame the second law of thermodynamics. Jay Haley points out that Freud's description of the intrapsychic process makes an interesting comparison with Maxwell's governor. If one sees the ego as the faster electrons and the id as the slower, more primitive ones, and the superego as the trap door or censor who lets some ideas through and prevents others from going through, then one might say that the average temperature of the individual is the re-

lationship between id and ego. On the other hand, the family researcher might be happier with Einsteinian-type ideas: that is, that the trap door in the individual may determine his processes, but that these processes themselves are being influenced by the relative strength of other vectors in his world. There are probably finite laws of human group behavior existing in any family that, regardless of the culture, have a great deal to do with the human condition. Some of these basic laws or rules of human interaction are just beginning to be touched upon, and I will present later on some further speculations about such rules.

LOLITA IS MORE THAN ONE GIRL'S STORY

In 1951, shortly after coming to Palo Alto, I had a Lolita-like patient whom I was preparing to cure on the couch. The fact that she was the last part of my supervised analytic work and therefore the stepping-stone to or the wall between me and the Analytic Society (depending on how the case came out), made me as nervous as a priapic nudist. The day that this recently married young woman of 18 (who seemed five years younger) and I were to begin our work together, her mother telephoned me to announce that her daughter was a terrible liar and that therefore I should not believe anything she said in the analysis. I responded to this unwarranted intrusion into my patient's privacy and mine with annoyance, but without a realization that the mother had already set up a situation in which she was a part of the therapy.

If you wish at this point to note some relationship between the situation I have described and Lolita, Humbert and Lolita's mother, I will not dissuade you. This turned out to be a very difficult case, one that I partially reported on in the Psychoanalytic Quarterly (Jackson, 1953). Although I mentioned the parents in this article, I did not actually see them with the patient. It would never have occurred to me.

This patient, like some of Freud's early cases, reported a sexual trauma involving her father. I chose to hear this report as a wish, and busily fiddled with the patient's motivations while reporting happily and dutifully to my supervising analyst. During one session, the patient became silent and seemed fearful. She could not be persuaded to talk. She went home and took 50 grains of seconal, but did not die because, fortunately, I had had a presentiment that something was amiss and, not being able to reach her by telephone, had gone to her house in a rather non-analytic fashion, found the comatose young woman, and administered first aid, and called an ambulance. I pumped out her stomach with mixed emotions consisting of "I'll save you—damn you!"

The patient later reported that she had seen the shadow of a penis on the wall during the previous session, assumed that I was behaving in an improper fashion, and was terrified. She became frightened again in the telling of the story, and I knew of no way to prove that I had not been guilty. This episode remained unsolved as did the additional fact that she was in a filmy nightgown during her pill-taking fiasco. This, too, seemed difficult to broach without giving satisfaction to her obviously exhibitionistic wishes. However, the analysis went rocking along, with most of the time being spent on the patient's childhood. She assured me that there were no problems with her husband, and I did not meet him until much later.

Early one morning, I was pursuing sweet dreams when the household was brought rudely awake by the sound of crashing glass. A sizable rock had been thrown through the front room window. I ran out the door, either in hopes of uncovering the cause of this intrusion or simply because I couldn't help running, but heard only the sound of a car driving away. There was no doubt in my mind that it was my Lolita.

I knew that I had done something wrong, but being naturally benevolent and having played the game by the book, I couldn't imagine what it was. In due time, it emerged that the patient had sensed that I did not believe her story of the episode with her father, and it became equally apparent that she was having current problems in her marriage which we were not discussing.

I started seeing the patient in face-to-face interviews, and except for the fact that she plopped herself into my lap on one occasion, things began finally to add up. It dawned on me that she not only had a sexual trauma but was still seductively pursued by her father, hated by her mother, and treated with masterful indifference by her husband. However, by the time I got around to seeing her with her husband, he had become rather disenchanted with her and the marriage and did not choose to participate in marital therapy. In an effort to save the marriage, and perhaps her therapy, she went on good behavior, he became mollified, and they are still living together some eleven years later (as indicated by their Christmas card).

I don't think I've had a case, or not more than two or three others, in which I put so much time, energy, and anxiety. It did not occur to me until years later that I was picking up the tab for the rest of the patient's family. Her husband, sister, brother, mother, and father were all willing to stay out of it, provided I could bring about some change that would make life more peaceful for all of them. Since I wrote this, my "Lolita" telephoned me to say that her mother had a serious cardiac condition and wasn't expected to live. She insisted on her daughter's visiting daily and used the visits to beg forgiveness for past wrongs.

IT WAS NOT AN ELECTRA COMPLEX
BUT A COMPLEX OF RELATIONSHIPS

Thomas Kuhn (1962) makes the point in his book The Structure of Scientific Revolutions (in which he uses the electrical revolution as a model) that changes in conventional beliefs occur not from some slowly moving philosophical cause or from step-by-step research, but from a new discovery that represents a departure or a break-through. Such a break-through occurred for me in relation to the above-mentioned patient. Once I started seeing her as a family-surrounded individual with real life problems in the present, my entire attitude toward theory and therapy was altered. I recognized, for example, that the therapist who is behaving benevolently in an attempt to be helpful may, in fact, not always be doing the best thing for the patient and the significant others. Lolita's mother gave her "too much" freedom, and in this case I erred in the same way. People can only change in relation to other people, and unless the therapist plans to live with the patient for the rest of his life, he owes it to the patient and the significant others that attention be paid to interactions between them, so that change can begin and be sustained within their ambient family, and not just in his cloistered office. In fact, if the successful therapy of an individual results in the breaking-out of symptoms in one of his significant others, then little may have been gained (a situation I reported on at length in 1954).[2]

THINGS ELECTRICAL AND ELECTRA'S COMPLEX

The psychoanalyst would be curious about Lolita's sexual drives and the unconscious meaning of her choosing a much older man. The family therapist would probably first focus his attention on the mother and then on her relationship to Humbert—coming only at last to Lolita's part in the interaction.

You will remember that the wave and particle or photon theories of light were once hotly debated. They are now both accepted and are both equally useful, depending on the particular phenomenon that the

---

[2]"The Question of Family Homeostasis", presented as the Frieda Fromm-Reichmann Lecture, Veterans Administration Hospital, Palo Alto, Calif., January 1954.

physicist is studying. <u>There has, however, been no successful merging of these two theories, so that it has been necessary for each group gradually to accept the views of the other</u>. The natural analogy here is the situation in psychiatry where psychoanalytic and other individual theories of behavior now find themselves competing with the findings of those in family research, and vice versa.

I suspect that the problem here is severalfold and that we must face it squarely before there will be continued progress and rapprochement between the two points of view. Some of the major issues and difficulties are the following:

1. Family therapy is a very different technique from psychoanalysis. It requires a different kind of effort on the part of the therapist and it requires, in general, a different sort of personality, a different kind of schedule arrangement, fee, and so on. There are those who have been waiting in the wings of the psychiatric stage and who now embrace family therapy like a sailor discovering a blonde on a desert island. There are those psychoanalytic experts who resent their illegitimate child and who would wish to banish him from their home altogether. However, these are the extremes at each end of the continuum, and in the center is a large group of therapists who are willing to practice whatever the situation calls for. The problem of embracing two different theoretical situations remains; this is not always easy to do. I do not feel, personally, that therapy and theory are necessarily closely related; and certainly, therapeutic practice rarely eventuates from theory. It was not until Freud had already placed someone on the couch that he then decided there were good theoretical reasons for doing so. On the other hand, his magnificent contributions regarding childhood sexuality and dream analysis, and the important later contributions of a host of analysts on ego psychology, are in no way dependent on the use of the couch. I would say, therefore, that the apparent antithetical issues between psychoanalysis (as the foremost individual psychological theory) and family interactional theory are more apparent than real and are fostered by differences in technique, not by true incompatibility of theory. The theories deal with <u>different subject matter</u>, and though both attempt to present a theory of therapy, their frames of reference are entirely different.

2. Second, let us go back to light theory for a moment. It is obvious that photons get together in waves and that waves have different properties than individual photons. That is, the phenomena have to be accepted as discontinuous in order for the physicist to make sense of them. There seems to be a reluctance in psychiatry to accept family interactional theory and intrapsychic theory as discontinuous. For example, work done at the Mental Research Insti-

tute indicates that families are surprisingly rigid systems. The work of Jay Haley (1964) in particular demonstrates that the more "pathological" the family, the more rigid a system they have. Yet when a psychiatrist deals with an individual from one of these families he does not necessarily see him as rigid. He tends to think of him in terms of motivation, in terms of gratification of needs, in terms of individual philosophy, goals, and so on.

The concept of "role," which psychiatrists have borrowed from other behavioral scientists is undoubtedly a useful one. However, the concept "role" sings a siren song that the unwary psychiatric mariner may carelessly heed, much to his own peril. If we see an individual in our office, alone, and this individual is the father of a family, we might attempt to assess him on the grounds of how well he is fulfilling the "father role." We are apt to find ourselves assessing his masculinity, his virility, his assertiveness, his sexuality, and his apparent ability to serve as a strong, masculine model for his children. In fact, there is a cultural assumption that the father is the servant of instrumentality and that the mother is the expressive one. How the father actually functions in his family may be a problem of an entirely different order. Thus, Leik (1963) studied twenty-seven trios consisting of mother, father, and daughter. He rated the father's behavior in his real family, and then had observers rate father when he pretended to be the father in a family made up of a wife and daughter not actually his. He discovered that the father behaved "more like a masculine father" when he was with a simulated family than he did when he was with his real family. In the "normal" families we have studied at the Mental Research Institute, [3] I have been impressed that the mothers' and fathers' roles do not appear to be too different. "Masculine" and "feminine" are terms I would personally like to see banned from the psychiatric lexicon. It is unfortunate that so many psychiatric disorders have been attributed to a passive, nonmasculine father or a dominant, nonfeminine mother.

There are almost no dyadic words in the psychoanalytic vocabulary. This means that when we talk to a colleague or attempt to write a paper we are apt to find ourselves describing a collection of individuals in a family rather than emphasizing the unique aspect of a family—namely, its interactional and system properties. The general semanticists have warned us for years about the word becoming the thing. If you are in disagreement with this point, try a little experiment. Discuss with a colleague what went on between a mar-

[3] U.S.P.H.S. Grant MH 11-362-01 (formerly M O-4916) received from the National Institute of Mental Health.

ried couple that you were interviewing conjointly. Notice how you will ascribe motivation to one partner <u>and then ascribe the other spouse's behavior to this assumed motivation!</u> We say: "She was nagging him so he clammed up." A therapist will remark: "The father was being hostile and the whole family got anxious." Great Shades of Freud! What does this mean? For one thing, it means we have some bad habits to break before we can even <u>think</u> inter-actionally. In <u>Games People Play</u> Eric Berne (1964) has helped us with this problem by the invention of game titles that are clever and often ring a bell with a therapist. However, even Berne's titles need careful reworking because they consist of a number of individual-oriented games and some game titles that are too general to be of much use in talking about a particular piece of family interaction. Of course, when we come to the problem of studying a "normal" family, we have almost no language whatsoever.

IS THERE A REAL REVOLUTION OR A MERE UPRISING?

One of the difficulties of being a scientist is that one never knows what part of the road he is on or, to put it another way, how far along the road he is, since he cannot predict what will come after. Thus, as I mentioned earlier, the enthusiasm that greeted Clerk-Maxwell's electromagnetic theories in no way told these sci-entists that they were merely at the beginning of a truly great revo-lution in electrical theory. Therefore, I must make clear that I shun the obvious opportunity to make comparisons between the enormous leap from electromagnetic ideas to the theory of relativity and the state of things vis à vis intrapsychic and interpersonal theories. We may not be anywhere near that far along. Instead, let me go back to the year 1740 and the discoveries of Benjamin Franklin in regard to the Leyden jar. It was this particularly intriguing and enigmatic piece of equipment that led many people of Franklin's day to become dissatisfied with the current theories of electricity. The Leyden jar itself had been born by chance or by accident; the fluid theorists wanted to bottle electricity, and stumbled upon this piece of apparatus, which they then could not explain. This is not unlike the "accident" of conjoint family therapy (Bell, 1961). Frank-lin set up a paradigm that had a remarkable effect at that time, since it suggested which experiments would be worth performing and which, being directed to secondary or to overly complex manifestations of electricity, would not. As Kuhn (1962) states (page 18):

". . . only the paradigm did the job far more effectively, partly because the interschool debate ended the constant reiteration of fundamentals and partly because the confidence that they were on the right track encouraged scientists to undertake more precise, esoteric, and consuming sorts of work. Freed from concern with any and all electrical phenomena, the united group of electricians could pursue selected phenomena in far more detail, assigning much special equipment for the task and employing it more stubbornly and systematically than electricians had ever done before."

It is well known that conjoint family therapy was an accident. Yet, until someone did it, until someone actually brought a family together for treatment, the doubts and fears and complaints of many therapists for many years about individual therapy amounted to naught. There were scattered papers on the reluctance of the father to attend collaborative therapy sessions even when cute social workers were provided. The difficulties in collaboration between the child's therapist, the mother's therapist, and the father's therapist were explored and debated, but nothing new was done about them. Nothing new was done about them, except that a kind of family therapy was invented in which the collaborating therapists were brought together by another therapist and supervised. When the therapy family ironed out its problems, the patients improved. When several people in various parts of the country began seeing families in conjoint family therapy (without knowledge of each other), an instrument was born which, like the Leyden jar, inspired its originators to understand the very article that they had created. Some understanding has eventuated—much of the work remains yet to be done. Still, let me list a few things (but not in order of their importance, since I wouldn't know that) that I consider have eventuated already from our still young and imperfect technique.

1. Just a few years ago there existed only two papers in the literature on the siblings of schizophrenics. In these papers it was claimed that they were normal, and the schizophrenics' abnormality was then accounted for on a genetic basis. Now we have a number of reports by therapists who have gotten to know the schizophrenics' siblings and find that their perfectness is, as our group has titled it, "counter-schizophrenic." These siblings are allowed by the family rules to set up a diametrically opposite picture from the identified patient. Singer and Wynne (1965a, 1965b) have shown in their studies that the thinking habits of the patient are not greatly different from those of his siblings and parents—even though the other family members function in the outside world.

2. The idea of "sick family" and not just "sick patient" has brought up such remarkable questions as: "What are we doing when we give the identified patient drugs?" It seems so natural, so ob-

vious, to medically oriented people that a sick person needs medication that, until recently, except for the studies of Henry Lennard, [4] there has been almost no consideration of the effect on the family of the patient's altered chemical state. If drugs calm him down and improve him in terms of obvious functioning, it is not always a blessing to other members of the family. If drugs cloud and bewilder him, then he is harder to relate to than ever. If he is helped to relate more effectively, then other family members may regard this as an intrusion or as some kind of deviant behavior. Some years ago I mentioned giving pills to a depressed patient's wife instead of to him (Jackson, 1961). Perhaps when we understand family interaction, this will no longer seem an unusual procedure.

3. Family therapy did not create, but certainly has augmented, the notion of more activity on the part of the therapist. The old idea that therapy had to take place five times a week in order to be "deep" has been challenged by many authorities, and the activity of the analyst has increased, as reported in the writings of Menninger, Saul, Szurek, and others, so that some psychotherapists are comfortable seeing families and individual analytic patients.

4. There is a new field just beginning and it is called Family Experimentation. The data is not collected by assuming that relevant information can be gained by asking people questions about themselves and their motivations. The assumption is made that individuals must relate with each other through patterned behavior or redundancies, and that these behaviors can be described as rules. Fortunately, modern technology has made it possible to machine-measure some of these redundancies and thus to escape from the always present phenomena of observer bias.

5. The observations of family therapists point to phenomena that might be called fit, or match, or mismatch. Man is subject to competing tendencies, whether in his intrapsychic motivation, his group behavior, or even in the level and net-like arrangements of his brain. For example, he may be the member of a group, wish the acknowledgment of status that comes with being a leader, and yet shun the responsibility of leadership and the lack of being taken care of that the leader must endure. It is obvious that if marital pairs stay together, they must make some kind of fit. For example, in the congenial marital pair, we note that there are workable quid pro quo's. There is also evidence of trust, and trust may be considered the establishment of rules that are durable over time. If a couple such as this is asked: "How, out of all the millions of people in the world, did you two happen to meet?" and if the husband answers for both of them, the trusting wife will wait for his reply

[4] Personal communication.

because she knows that her point of view will be acknowledged, and invariably it is. This is much in contrast with a couple who monitor each other's behavior constantly, as though the only thing that would make their system workable is careful attention to not letting the other dominate the situation or determine the nature of the relationship. This is what we call a symmetrical couple (Jackson, 1958; Haley, 1963), and they are obvious because, no matter what the content, there is a struggle. It does no good to point out to a symmetrical couple what they are doing, because they will simply incorporate it into their system and claim: "Maybe so, but I don't do it as much as she [or he] does." The concepts of redundancy, of system, of rules, will inevitably result in therapeutic techniques that are apt to be quite different from those described in the ordinary textbooks of psychiatry or psychoanalysis. Whether such techniques are "better" or "worse" is a matter for speculation.

6. You will remember that Lolita, rather than turning out to be a story of the older, wiser man seducing the poor young victim, tells how Lolita herself, with her mother's implicit, if not explicit, backing, turns the tables. Similarly, it is possible in psychotherapy that the therapist, rather than acting like the older, wiser man, the one who is going to introduce something into the patient's head in order to promote maturity, will utilize the patients' pathology as a lever with which to introduce change. This is particularly pertinent to family therapy because the family can reinforce this kind of treatment between treatment sessions. Thus, if mother is a martyr, the therapist, instead of introducing insight as to the origin of mother's masochism, may help mother become more of a martyr and help the other family members to promote this in mother. This is the introduction of a deliberate runaway, and when the situation becomes sufficiently caricatured, the family will be forced to break its own rules in order to take care of the situation. In breaking their rules, they open the closed system and make possible other changes (Jackson, 1963).

7. Further thoughts on therapy include the idea that conjoint family therapy may bring about a more advisory or behind-the-scenes role for the therapist, and that this may have its particular uses in certain cases. Just as some family therapists are consulting with businesses that have administrative and communication problems, so also the therapist may act as a consultant to a family in the business of changing. His position would be to see that certain changes were acted upon, but he would not be directly involved in carrying them out any more than he would be as a consultant to someone else's business. In this type of therapy, the use of ancillary therapists may be quite feasible: for example, it seems terribly un-

fortunate that the mother of the schizophrenic is not given more opportunity to utilize her obvious skills in any but a sick situation. Because the role of the therapist, his status and the cultural folklore about him automatically brings about a certain amount of resistance, it may be that ancillary therapists under his guidance can be more effective in certain situations.

8. The well-family checkup is a technique that has preventative possibilities and is workable with therapists, like Virginia Satir, who are "health" and not "pathology" oriented.

9. There is another therapeutic technique that I think may develop, and that is related to psychodrama. Families have little awareness that they are guided by covert relationship rules, and if one puts them in a play situation where they are carrying out a joint activity, the rule concept may suddenly strike home. This is a slightly different principle from psychodrama as originated by Moreno, but the familiar essence is there, namely, that in playing a game, one can learn some serious or important things that he can't learn while he is being serious.

I conclude with a statement that is obvious, yet needs reiteration. Family study, spurred by the accident of conjoint family therapy, has resulted in a body of data that differs significantly from psychoanalytic data. It is not better or worse, it is different. Premature attempts to wed the two bodies of knowledge will result in a psychiatric Lolita—a theory that appears older, wiser, and more complete than it really is. Lolita was pushed into appearing sexy and thus denied the chance to develop properly. If we wait for our theory to grow up and not attempt to imitate that wiser, older woman, psychoanalysis, then there is a chance for a new and different knowledge.

REFERENCES

Bell, J. E. Family group therapy. Washington, D.C., Public Health Monograph No. 64, Dept. of Health, Education and Welfare, 1961.

Berne, Eric. Games people play; the psychology of human relationships. New York: Grove Press, 1964.

Haley, J. Marriage therapy. Arch. gen. Psychiat., 1963, 8, 213-234.

Haley, J. Research on family patterns: an instrument measurement. Fam. Proc., 1964, 3, 41-65.

Jackson, D. D. Some factors influencing the Oedipus complex. Psychoanal. Quart., 1954, 23, 566-581.

Jackson, D. D. Guilt and the control of pleasure in schizoid personalities. Brit. J. med. Psychol., 1958, 31, 124-130.

Jackson, D. D. Family therapy in the family of the schizophrenic. In M. I. Stein (Ed.), Contemporary psychotherapies. Glencoe, Ill.: Free Press, 1962. Pp. 272-287.

Jackson, D. D. A suggestion for the technical handling of paranoid patients. Psychiatry, 1963, 26, 306-307.

Kuhn, T. The structure of scientific revolutions. Chicago: Univer. of Chicago Press, 1962.

Leik, R. E. Instrumentality and emotionality in family interaction. Sociometry, 1963, 26, 131-145.

Singer, Margaret T., & Wynne, L. C. Thought disorder and family relations of schizophrenics. III. Methodology using projective techniques. Arch. gen. Psychiat., 1965a, 12, 187-200.

Singer, Margaret T., & Wynne, L. C. Thought disorder and family relations of schizophrenics. IV. Results and implications. Arch. gen. Psychiat., 1965b, 12, 201-212.

SOME EXPLORED AND PARTIALLY EXPLORED SOURCES OF PSYCHOPATHOLOGY

Theodore Lidz, M. D. and Stephen Fleck, M. D.

Family studies have opened the way for the development of a new and more dynamic understanding of personality development and maldevelopment, and now make imperative some major reconceptualizations of dynamic psychopathology. Classic psychoanalytic theory together with the genius of Freud pointed the way for a dynamic psychopathology that served as a guide to psychotherapy and psychoanalysis. Relatively few advances based on analytic theory have been made in recent years — an indication, we believe, that the theory no longer provides adequate conceptual guidance. Like New - tonian physics, its very real worth cannot transcend certain limits, and its constructs restrain investigators from moving beyond them. Indeed, we find that a dichotomy between psychoanalytic theory and practice exists that is usually unverbalized and often unappreciated. First, we wish to direct attention to two aspects of theory that impede progress.

Psychoanalytic psychopathology has focused largely upon intrapsychic or endopsychic causes of fixation and regression without adequate attention to the interpersonal and social settings in which the child develops. It has remained encumbered by its early emphasis on biological drives and sources of aberration, so compatible with science at the turn of the century. Whereas the genetic anlage certainly is a determinant of many aspects of the personality, too much was attributed and is still attributed to instinctual patterns and genetically inherited attributes. Little attention has been given in classic theory to the cultural heritage which the child assimilates, and which accounts for many ethnic differences in personality traits. Appreciation that the self emerges and develops in relation to others, who in turn are organized into a social system with institutions and guided by cultural instrumentalities, greatly enhances the understanding of the manifold sources of maldevelopment (Mead, 1934). Remaining essentially oriented to endopsychic and biological determinants, psy-

41

choanalytic theory has based theories of motivation primarily on instinctual drives, as if motivation was solely concerned with past and present needs to regain a psychophysiological equilibrium. It does not take into account an essential attribute of man—that his adaptation rests on foresight and motivation to meet future contingencies. This shortcoming is part of a larger problem that will be discussed later—the virtual neglect of the role of language and its central position in human behavior and personality development.

In an examination of interpersonal and social environment, the importance of the family becomes apparent. It is the primary social unit, the major source of security for the child, and the basic socializing and enculturating agency. Consideration of the family as a central point in understanding the origins of psychopathology does not or should not revive old conflicts concerning biological and cultural determinants of behavior (Lidz, 1962). The family is a necessary outgrowth of man's biological makeup. It is essential for the child's survival, for his learning of adaptive techniques, and for his development of personality characteristics through identification and other mechanisms of internalization. The members of the family, how they relate to the child, and how they interrelate as a family unit establish the patterning of the child's development as a person. In practice, much of psychoanalytic therapy focuses on such family processes and problems. Indeed, unless this were so the use of transference as a major therapeutic lever would be as meaningless as it would be ineffectual. It is time to overcome this peculiar divergence between theory and practice, not because orthodox psychoanalytic theory is so wrong but because it is too limited to conceptualize clinical experience adequately.

A second shortcoming of psychoanalytic psychopathology has been the overemphasis upon developmental phases, and the attempt to understand characterological abnormalities primarily in terms of fixation and regression. Although this concept has been of great value, it leaves out important aspects of normal and abnormal development that do not fit. To take an example: the achievement of a firm identity as a member of one's biologically determined sex is a major determinant of personality development. Of all factors entering into personality formation, the sex of the child is the most significant. Confusions concerning sexual identity are among the major sources of psychopathology. Classic theory had assumed that biological sex largely determined sex role assumptions and explained deviations on the basis of innate bisexuality or biologic inversion. We now know that gender identity depends upon role ascriptions together with the child's identification with a parental figure of the same sex. While gender consciousness is well established by the age of three, the attainment of gender identity is not firm until closure of the Oedipal period, and is not completed until adolescence or later. It is an aspect of development that is not confined to one phase—and contrary to opinion commonly held, it is not determined only by the outcome of the Oedipal transition.

A similar consideration applies to language development, which is all-important to ego functioning and the eventual attainment of identity as an independent and self-sufficient person. The learning of language rests upon the development by the child of a trust in preverbal communication with the mother and continues through adolescence. Vygotsky (1962), for example, has shown that abstract conceptualization does not occur prior to the onset of puberty—or about at the start of high school education.

Psychoanalytic theory also has tended to consider some phases as biologically determined which cross-cultural studies indicate are culturally determined or family determined. There is ample evidence that the "anal" phase and "latency" are not biologically determined and do not seem to exist in some societies, and that the time of the Oedipal crisis varies greatly with the society's family pattern. In general, the attempt to understand the differences in the etiology of various psychopathologic syndromes primarily through differences in their loci and periods of fixation and regression fails to allow for the clinically observable deficiencies in personality structure that can be understood as the result of defects in the teaching and enculturating functions of the child's immediate surroundings—the family. We believe it is essential, therefore, to reexamine the developmental process to ascertain more clearly how the family shapes the personality, and how disturbances in the parental personalities and in the family transactions relate to psychopathological manifestations in the offspring. The scope of the problem is enormous. We have sought to make a start, and wish to draw attention to certain sources of psychopathological developments that require further study, elaboration, and specification.

SOURCES OF PSYCHOPATHOLOGICAL DEVELOPMENT IN OFFSPRING

1. Deficiencies of parents in meeting the child's needs at each developmental phase, including failures in altering their ways of relating in accord with changes in the child's needs. We are here simply emphasizing the interactional aspects of the developmental process that have already been the focus of much research. Family studies have generally recognized that the parent-child interaction cannot be considered only in dyadic terms, for it transpires in a

family unit in which the behavior of every member affects all. In addition to the parents' emotional attitudes toward the child, their nurturant capacities are affected by their marital interaction, their knowledge of children and child-rearing, deficiencies in their own upbringing, and so on.

From among the many factors concerning the nurturant capacities of parents, we wish to note just one that may clarify certain psychophysiologic disorders as well as some problems of schizophrenia. The failure of a mother to discriminate between the child's physiologic needs and her own or her repeated misinterpretation of the child's signals can lead the child to faulty perception of inner stimuli and erroneous "programming" of physiologic processes, as Hilde Bruch has pointed out (Bruch and Palombo, 1961). Although seemingly a dyadic problem, such disturbed interaction between mother and child is usually but part of a broader family problem.

2. A relationship exists between the dynamic structure of the family and the structuring of the personality. We have presented and discussed elsewhere the concept that in order to direct properly the personality organization of a child, the spouses must form a parental coalition, maintain adequate boundaries between the generations, and adhere to their respective sex-linked roles. The proper channeling of drives, the attainment of a firm sexual identity, and the appropriate transition through the Oedipal situation depends upon such factors. Delimitation of behavior is essential to integration.

a. The achievement of a cohesive identity depends upon a reasonably harmonious integration of identifications with two parents. Parents who are irreconcilable in reality can give rise to irreconcilable introjects that create varying degrees of intrapsychic conflict and even of splitting of the personality with alternative "ego" and "superego" formations suited to each parent.

b. The essential identification of the child with the parent of the same sex provides self-esteem only if the object of identification is acceptable to the other parent who should be a basic object choice of the child. Such considerations concern the offspring's achievement of harmony between ego and superego, between self-image and self-ideal.

3. The family must convey the basic instrumental techniques of the culture to the child. Faulty transmission of such techniques diminishes adaptability to the physical and social environment.

a. The transmission of a firm foundation in linguistic meanings forms a particularly critical issue, and its importance cannot be overemphasized. The ability to conceptualize, think, communicate, predict, and plan ahead depends upon word meanings. Confused meaning systems interfere with ego functioning (the capacity to direct the self into the future) because they prevent the child from attaining clear guide-lines. We have discussed elsewhere the importance of words as the critical tool in human adaptation and the family's role in guiding language development (Lidz, 1963). The development of trust in the utility of verbal communication is crucial to normal development.

b. Other adaptive techniques, especially ways of relating to others, are also found to have been conveyed erroneously to patients suffering from various psychiatric illnesses. One aspect of "ego weakness," for example, concerns the lack of proper tools and techniques for relating to and working upon the physical and social environment.

4. The child develops in relation to the institutions of his society as well as in relation to other individuals. The family is the basic social institution, where the child learns or fails to learn the value of subordinating individual needs and drives to the collectivity and gains trust or distrust in cooperative endeavor, marriage, family life, and so on. The wish to participate or to avoid participating in such institutions is a motivating force for interpersonal processes and a directing force in development and further growth. The family must provide opportunities for the child to learn appropriate sex, age, and generation roles at each stage of development. If these roles are idiosyncratic, the set of expectations he will use in relating outside of the family will be misleading and will impair his peer relationships, as well as settling him with unrealistic needs for dependency on or distance from others.

5. Parental styles of behavior, communication, and defense mechanisms play a fundamental part in determining character traits and pathology in children through direct example and through the reactions that such styles produce in the child. Obsessive parents are apt to rear constricted children; parents who teach distrust of others foster paranoid trends; parents who are primarily interested in appearances and with what they and the children can "get away with" promote delinquency; and, as Wynne and Singer (1963a, 1963b; Singer and Wynne, 1965a, 1965b) have emphasized, parents with amorphous or fragmented modes of thinking and communicating are apt to produce schizophrenic children. Parents should define and transmit prescribed, permitted, and proscribed goals and differentiate acceptable and unacceptable means of striving for them. Pursuit of goals unacceptable to society, or of acceptable goals through unacceptable means involves the problem of psychopathy.

46

These are simplistic illustrations of topics that require intensive study.

6. Conflicting cultural patterns in the parents can lead to confused behavioral patterns in offspring, as Spiegel and Kluckhohn (1954) have emphasized. The entire problem of the nuclear family as an adequate representative of the society and its cultural pattern requires exploration. Behavior that is acceptable and sometimes required within the family may be aberrant outside of it.

Whereas we have selected these topics because we have had occasion to focus upon them in our work, we consider that the entire problem of how the infant develops into a person in relation to significant family members and to the family as a social system must become the focal area in the study of personality development and maldevelopment. What seems urgently needed is a conceptual system for thinking about and discussing these matters.

REFERENCES

Bruch, Hilde, & Palombo, S. Conceptual problems in schizophrenia. J. nerv. ment. Dis., 1961, 132, 114-117.

Lidz, T. The relevance of family studies to psychoanalytic theory. J. nerv. ment. Dis., 1962, 135, 105-112.

Lidz, T. The family and human adaptation. New York: Int. Univer. Press, 1963.

Mead, G. H. Mind, self and society from the standpoint of a social behaviorist. C. Morris (Ed.), Chicago: Univer. of Chicago Press, 1934.

Singer, Margaret T., & Wynne, L. C. Thought disorder and family relations of schizophrenics: III. Methodology using projective techniques. Arch. gen. Psychiat., 1965a, 12, 187-200.

Singer, Margaret T., & Wynne, L. C. Thought disorder and family relations of schizophrenics: IV. Results and implications. Arch. gen. Psychiat., 1965b, 12, 201-212.

Spiegel, J. P., & Kluckhohn, Florence. Integration and conflict in family behavior. Report #27, Group for the Advancement of Psychiatry. Topeka, Kansas, August 1954.

Vygotsky, L. S. Thought and language. E. Haufmann & G. Vakar (Eds. and Trans.). Cambridge, M. I. T. Press, 1962.

Wynne, L. C., & Singer, Margaret T. Thought disorder and family relations of schizophrenics: I. A research strategy. Arch. gen. Psychiat., 1963a, 9, 191-198.

Wynne, L. C., & Singer, Margaret T. Thought disorder and family relations of schizophrenics: II. A classification of forms of thinking. Arch. gen. Psychiat., 1963b, 9, 199-206.

PART II
Pathogeny
in the Family System

PREJUDICE AND SCAPEGOATING IN THE FAMILY

Nathan W. Ackerman, M. D.

While treating a family with an only daughter—a girl of 16 years with an early and labile form of psychotic disorder—it struck me forcibly as I watched the family, and also as I viewed over and over the film record of these interviews, that when one part of the family came to life, the other part seemed to die. I am talking now of the sheer flow of affect, not words. The quality of coming to life, affectively speaking, seemed to swing back and forth, pendulum-fashion, from the parents to the daughter and back again. As I studied the process, it became plain that this was a consistent and repetitive pattern. If the young, psychotic girl showed signs of life, the parents literally lay down and died before my eyes; if the parents became vocal and excited, the girl faded away. One part of the family seemed to draw the breath of life at the expense of the other.

Studying the family further, I observed other things. Within a single interview, one could discern critical oscillations in the level of health and sickness. At one point, the patient would be in the depths, the malignant depths, of her illness; at another, she would be more sane than her parents. If one were comparing degrees and qualities of health and sickness between parents and daughter, one might detect a seesaw movement—up on one side, down on the other. I then noticed something else. When the patient, as though making a frantic gesture to heal what ailed the family, tried to take hold of the tense situation and failed, she promptly plunged deeper into her sickness. What I was seeing seemed important. The patient reached out to her parents, made a desperate thrust at mending the warp of relations between her mother and father and between them and herself, failed pathetically, and instantly sank into the trough of her sickness. The rigidity and urgency of the parents' denials and justifications were overwhelmingly powerful. The patient slid into despair, panic, and deeper psychosis.

I asked myself: What is the idiosyncratic character of this type of family, which exhibits such a ferocious prejudice against a free

48

breath, a free movement, in their one child? How was this child scapegoated? Do other types of families show different forms of prejudicial scapegoating? In the area of the relations of family process and psychopathology, can we perhaps trace some specific connections between types of prejudicial scapegoating and types of emotional breakdown? Is it possible, then, to examine a range of family types in terms of the presence within the group of specific emotional allergies, specific intolerances of affect-laden, symbolically perceived qualities of the offspring that lead to scapegoating and breakdown?

The question posed here needs to be seen in a wider framework. In examining the relations of family and individual, we have observed that the family inflicts emotional damage on the patient and that the patient in his turn injures the family. Each defends against the other's urge to blame and punish. We have learned something of the means by which the family may harm the individual. Thus far, however, we have learned little of the other side of the question—the ways in which the patient may harm the family. Now and then we get the dramatic impact of a patient's destructive invasions upon the life of the family, and even see instances of a schizophrenic killing a parent. Yet we have not yet systematically studied the family's defenses against this threat. And though we have discovered something of the family's destructive potential, we know much less of the family's role in promoting healing or recovery. Nor do we know much about what happens when a patient tries to make over a pair of parents, to heal what ails their relationship so that he may recover a livable place in the family.

FAMILY ROLES

Since people make one another sick, they may also make one another well again. We may then formulate a broad question: What is the balance of forces in the relations of family and individual as between a circular process of prejudicial scapegoating and a circular process of healing? Why does a patient break down when the effort to heal the family fails? This kind of conjecture leads to another intriguing question: In the mutual accommodation of family roles, under what conditions is it possible for family members to integrate emotionally into definable roles by which they may escape mental breakdown?

Let us take the argument a step further: Clinically we observe troubled families in which the child is scapegoated and made vulnerable for a breakdown, and we note too that some parents divide their traits, conflicts, fears, and prejudices among their brood of children in a special way. For example, in a group of three daughters whose mother has committed suicide, the oldest is assigned and accepts the role of "the brain of the family." She becomes a lawyer in imitation of her father, who was a judge. The middle daughter fulfills the part of "the body beautiful," destined for a "successful" marriage with a rich man. The youngest becomes "the family renegade," a Bohemian artist who lives in Greenwich Village with a series of men. All three daughters are afflicted with character disorders, but have escaped major mental collapse.

In another family the children take up the roles of "family genius," "family dummy," and "family pet." In another, we find "the ugly duckling" and "the adorable baby doll." In still another, one child becomes an aggressive leader, another is shy and withdrawn, and a third becomes the family clown.

Under what conditions is the integration into these roles protective? Under what other conditions does the assumption of these roles render the individual susceptible to breakdown? What are the spontaneous healing forces which emerge in one or another family type? When is healing effective? When does it fail? When is healing natural and full? When is it partial, distorted, and pathogenic?

In the course of such explorations, we have been impressed with the repeated appearance of a special set of emotional mechanisms that we characterize as prejudicial scapegoating and the emergence of neutralizing forces in the family group. In our clinic study of family interaction, we observe certain constellations of behavior, which we have epitomized as the role of destroyer or persecutor, the role of the victim of the scapegoating attack, and the role of the family healer or "doctor." The destroyer or persecutor uses a special prejudice as the vehicle of his attack. Another member of the family becomes the object of this prejudicial attack, the victim of scapegoating. He sustains an emotional injury which renders him susceptible to breakdown in varying degrees. The family healer or "doctor" intervenes to neutralize the destructive powers of this attack and thereby, in some measure, rescues the victim. We now test the theory that a specific patterning of these emotional mechanisms offers a useful diagnostic clue to the psychosocial identity and emotional health of a given family.

INTRAFAMILIAL PREJUDICE

Close study of the emotional processes of a troubled family group suggests that the kinds of prejudicial scapegoating that are characteristic of a given family become organized in an irrational way around special meanings that are attached to differences among the family members. Prejudice of this kind is of a distinct and private nature. It differs from the common stereotypes of prejudice in the wider community. It is a recurrent and predictable manifestation of the idiosyncratic quality of family life and thus provides a special diagnostic clue to the emotional organization and functioning of a special kind of family. These observations give rise to several questions:

1. What is the special role of prejudicial scapegoating in the life history of a given family?
2. How are the roles of attacker, victim and healer organized within such a family?
3. What is the significance of these processes for the emotional health of the members?
4. What is the relation between this kind of social disorder and the susceptibility to mental disorder?

But before amplifying these questions, we must first make clear our conception of the phenomenon of family prejudice. We distinguish here between two categories of prejudice—private and public. Prejudice within the private life of the family assumes a form quite unlike that encountered in public life, i.e., the familiar antagonisms based on differences of color, religion, ethnic origin, etc. Private, intrafamilial prejudice is of another kind, so subtly different that it is often not recognized as prejudice at all. Yet it is there just the same—real, abundant, intense, far-reaching in its effects. Personal prejudice becomes translated into community prejudice. In turn, however, the anxiety that is aroused by the awareness of public forms of prejudice aggravates the tendency to the formation of private prejudice attached to differences, real and fantasized, among the members of a family group.

In a basic sense, the members of one family may be viewed as the same kind of people. They are, in fact, related by blood. They resemble one another, they have much in common, they share the same way of life. In view of this sameness, one might expect an absence of prejudice among the insiders and a concentration of prejudice against outsiders. This is not the case, however. Among members of the same family group, there are elements of difference as well as sameness. Depending on the idiosyncratic emotional qualities of a particular family, symbolic meanings are attached to these differences, which are then subjectively experienced by some members of the family as a distinct danger. The person showing the difference is felt to be the alien—the invasive stranger who threatens the security of the other members of the group. Sharing this sense of threat, several or most members of the family attack the source of the difference. In the inner life of the family, such prejudice becomes organized around a variety of differences. It becomes attached to the battle between the sexes, or to the struggle of youth and age; to the conflict of money and power with spontaneity and pleasure, or brains with brawn, or political liberal with conservative. At other levels, prejudice becomes attached to such qualities as fatness or thinness, tallness or shortness, intelligence or stupidity, light or dark skin, smooth or hairy skin. Still other prejudices of this kind attach to such matters as habits of eating and dressing, or cleanliness and orderliness.

The question may promptly be raised: Why do we call this prejudice? Are there not valid reactions to difference, legitimate likes and dislikes, preferences and aversions that may not constitute true prejudice? It is true, of course, that people who achieve sound health have a full measure of likes and dislikes, attractions and repulsions. Such attitudes, however, become transformed into irrational prejudices to whatever extent they become rigid, fixed, automatized, and walled off from the corrective influence of the prevailing realities. Furthermore, such prejudice varies in degree. It may be relatively benign or malignant. In their benign forms, such prejudices need not extend to the compulsive urge to hold the self together by breaking down someone else. In point of fact, however, the more disturbed the family becomes, the more it leans toward the organization of malignant forms of prejudice. The significant feature of prejudice is its contagion. Some or even all members of the family may become bound in its organization.

PREJUDICE AND MENTAL ILLNESS

There are significant connections between prejudice and mental illness. Both have to do with human relations and are affected by the struggle to reconcile human differences. Both impair a person's ability to perform his tasks in life, especially that of getting along with other people. Both have a common source in the intimate exchanges of family relationships, the first experience in life for learning to get along with other people. It is exactly the striving within the family group to establish one's position and to win acceptance and respect for one's unique quality that affect the proneness to prejudice as well as to mental illness. Nevertheless, the two forms of behavior are distinct. They evidence themselves in different life contexts. But there is a significant relationship between them. People tending to an emotional breakdown often lean on prejudice as defense to save themselves, to stave off the risk of their own breakdown, to move in the direction of trying to break down another member of the family. There is convincing force for such remarks as, "My wife is driving me crazy" or "You'll be the death of me yet."

We are concerned here with the use of private prejudice as a family defense of the continuity of family functions and as an individual defense against the fright of dangerous exposure. To the degree in which one individual feels incomplete, weak, exposed, and vulnerable, the difference of another can become magnified, symbolically, to the dimensions of a penetrating threat.

Let us return to the questions posed earlier. When the clinician trains his eye on a troubled family, he is immediately struck by the split of the family group into competing emotional alliances. These factions wage their battle around the felt threat of certain differences among the family members. Around these differences there is the patterning of specific family prejudices. In the unfolding of these emotional mechanisms specific functions, or roles, are organized: the role of the attacker, the victim, and the healer. At a given point in time, these roles are fulfilled by particular members and, with the passage of time, by other members. Each is selected for his respective role by unconscious emotional processes within the family. The family destroyer punishes the member of the family whose difference is felt as an offense and a menace to the continuity of family functioning. The member who is chosen as scapegoat suffers an emotional injury and is thus rendered vulnerable to the danger of a mental breakdown. Still another family member enters the role of peacemaker, protector, or healer, rising to the rescue of the victim of the punishing attack. To the degree to which the rescuing member holds the capacity to neutralize the destructive force of the prejudicial punishing assault, he offers to the scapegoated victim some immunity against breakdown. At times, the member who starts out in the role of persecutor may shift into the role of victim or that of healer, and vice versa. Each of these functional roles may be fulfilled at various times by members of the nuclear family or by a relative, a delegate of the extended family.

PREJUDICE AND COUNTER-PREJUDICE

A further step is also involved. In the unfolding of a critical family conflict, a primary prejudice attaching to a conspicuous and threatening difference of one member may evoke a counter-prejudice. In this case, the emotional sequence is attack, defense, and counter-attack. Thus, the emergence of one pattern of scapegoating evokes the emergence of the opposite pattern of attack and scapegoating. Ultimately, reciprocal patterns of attack and scapegoating appear on the scene. The role of family healer then becomes progressively more complicated and may be fulfilled in turn by a series of members of the group. In this context, one direction of scapegoating may be partly counterbalanced by the other. In the long run, however, prejudice, counter-prejudice, and the associated defense mechanisms lead to progressive distortion of family role relationships and impairment of essential family functions. At its core, this is a process that fragments the emotional life of the family and alienates its members.

It is to be borne in mind that we are talking about an emotional mechanism that functions in a selective way. It affects some family members more than others; it predisposes some in the direction of intense family prejudice, while it fortifies others against it. In this configuration of family events, several developments are possible, contingent on the emotional condition of the family. If the condition favors it, there may be a movement toward resolution of the primary prejudice, and, with this, an easing of the scapegoating assault; or, if the emotional matrix so disposes, a counter-prejudice may emerge. Beyond that a range of efforts unfolds, the intent of which is to neutralize and assuage the harm inflicted on the victim of family scapegoating.

If the movement is toward resolution of the primary prejudice, the pressure toward the splitting of the family and the setting up of competing alliances is reduced and the family members are freer to reach out for an improved quality of union and love. On the other hand, if this is blocked, the primary prejudice evokes a counter-prejudice and the function of family healer is stirred to action; it becomes, in fact, an urgent necessity.

But one must bear other alternatives in mind. The prejudicial attack may shift from its original object to another member of the family. One prejudice may be substituted for another. The attack may be displaced from the family scapegoat to a new target outside the family.

The vicissitudes of control of intrafamilial prejudice are the paths along which the emotional split of the family group achieves a specific pattern. One part of the family pits itself against another. Therefore, prejudice and counter-prejudice formations need to be correlated with the split of the family into warring segments, with the conflict over differences and the methods of coping, and with the unconscious selection of particular family members as scapegoats and others as rescuers. On occasion, a member tries to avoid being sucked into the family conflict; for his own safety, he seeks to remain unaligned with either faction, but this attempt at neutralism must, in the long view, fail. The root of "nonintervention" is emotional isolation and alienation; it disconnects the feeding line. The denial of connection is unnatural and cannot long survive. Often, it cloaks a concealed alignment and implies an attitude of fickleness and betrayal. Such a member may erratically shift alliances from one side of the family to the other. In such a family matrix, acting-out becomes not merely a unit of experience in which one member lives out the unconscious urges of another but also the vehicle for the discharge of shared aggression as one family alliance does battle with another.

It is, therefore, of the essence to identify specific forms of family prejudice, the roles of persecutor, scapegoat, and healer, the competing family alliances, the specific conflicts around which the battle rages, and the types of group and individual defenses that are mobilized to neutralize the destructive results of scapegoating.

HYPOTHESES:

1. Disturbed families tend to break up into warring factions.
   a. Each family member allies himself with one or another of the factions.
   b. Each faction competes for dominance.
   c. Each faction represents a preferred family identity and value system relating to goals, role expectations, and role complementarity.
   d. Each faction attaches specific meaning to individual differences and organizes around them specific devices of prejudicial scapegoating.
2. A leader emerges in each faction.
   a. Each leader epitomizes the family identity and values of his faction.
3. A particular family member is chosen as the victim of the prejudicial attack.
   a. Some individual quality of this member becomes a symbolic expression of a perceived threat to the family on the part of one of its factions.
4. A defensive counterattack is mobilized.
   a. The scapegoat allies himself with another family member and asserts an opposed form of prejudice.
   b. To the extent that this defensive alliance succeeds, the primary scapegoat minimizes his own injury at the expense of another. He may shift from the role of scapegoat to the role of persecutor.
   c. To the extent that this defensive alliance fails, the primary scapegoat finds himself undefended and alone.

1) He becomes progressively more vulnerable and may suffer a breakdown.

2) He shifts to the role of healer; if this suceeds, he may nullify or reduce his vulnerability.

5. A member of the family unconsciously is selected as the "healer."

   a. He provides the emotional antidote to the destructive effects of the prejudicial assault.

   b. He may be motivated to accept this role because it offers the protection required for his own safety.

6. The health-sickness continuum is influenced by the shifting balance of the effective struggle between factions toward:

   a. Entrenchement of valid values of family identity and equilibration of family functions that enhance genuine loyalty, sharing, and growth.

   b. Entrenchment of progressive, irrational, competing prejudices, tightening of family organization, and constriction of roles that reduce emotional nourishment of all members.

To families under study, it is useful to apply the following questionnaire:

QUESTIONNAIRE:

1. What is the prejudice?
   Does it express itself overtly or covertly?

2. Is there a single scapegoat?
   What qualities and/or differences of the intended victim are felt as threatening?

3. Is the prejudicial assault relatively amorphous?
   Does it shift from one intended victim to another?

4. In relation to the dominant prejudice pattern, does the family line up in warring factions? Specify.

5. Is there one member of the family who consistently enters the role of attacker? Specify.

6. Does a pattern of counter-prejudice emerge?

7. Who enters the role of counterattacker — the intended victim of the primary pattern of prejudicial scapegoating or another member entering the role of family healer? Or is the process relatively amorphous?

8. What are the effects of the primary prejudice? To what extent are they cohesive or disruptive?

9. What are the effects of the counter-prejudice? To what extent are they cohesive or disruptive?

10. Identify the conflicts related to the primary pattern of prejudicial scapegoating and to the counter-pattern.

11. What spontaneous healing forces emerge? Who in the family epitomizes this function?

12. Appraise the healing. Is it partial or complete, pathogenic or healthy?

RELATIONAL MODES AND MEANING

Ivan Boszormenyi-Nagy, M. D.

The family therapist, more than any other psychotherapist, has to be concerned with the determinants and the meaning of relationships. Insofar as a relationship defines interactions as well as subjective feelings of identity, its meaning must be based on a dyadic model: the relating self and the other to whom the self is related. On the one hand, relating can be thought of as a form of observable behavior , but its true meaning can be inferred only from what we know of each relating person's private fiction about the meaning of the relationship with that particular other. This paper is concerned with the structures of subjective meaning in close relationships and the implications of these structures for personal identity.

A combative psychotic boy, who had been treated conjointly with his family for over a year, appeared especially aggressive toward his father in one of the sessions. Later in the same evening, his father could not control his own anger anymore and hit the boy for the first time since he grew up. For the observer during this session, the boy's behavior toward his father was that of a series of constantly threatening and belittling aggressive statements. As it turned out, however, the deep significance of this interaction and the subsequent beating was that it restructured the relational engagement between father and son: it proved to this boy of 220 pounds that his father cared, and consequently his sense of identity was subjectively defined as a child again. From a threatening sense of psychotic loss of identity, he managed to escape into a regressive but experientially meaningful identity.

Relating has an active and a passive aspect. The other is needed because I want to perceive him as the "ground" against which my person becomes distinguishable as a figure. I want to make him an object for myself as subject; I may want him as an object for my instinctual strivings, for my identity delineation, and for my security needs. In other words, being a self obliges me to express myself and I actually become an entity in the process of expressing

58

myself to another entity. Sensory deprivation amounts to expressive deprivation; it is object deprivation as well as deprivation of the meaning of the self. The lonely person can only express himself by turning to the object of his fantasy in daydream or hallucination, or to his own body through hypochondriac preoccupations that serve as internally available grounds for the meaning of his self. The dialogue of the isolated or perceptually deprived person is truncated; its feedback components can come only from such others as are internalized.

Although personal fictions and private meanings are essentially inaccessible to direct observation, they can be inferred from overt communication since they are context setters for what the person is about to communicate in a given relationship. It is also true that the structure of any given relationship tends to become itself a determinate of matching self-fictions. For example, a young man may fall in love with a girl because, though outside his awareness, the girl reminds him of certain of his mother's features. Conversely, a real other can be recruited to match an internal "relational need template" (Boszormenyi-Nagy, 1965), e.g., in what is called "projection" or "transference" in clinical usage.

Projection and transference are regarded, for our purposes, as examples of relational choice rather than mainly as distortions of person perception. In fact, the so-called "nagging" wife may very well know, for instance, that her husband has corrected his careless driving habits, while she continues scolding him for his past and therefore potentially present or future tendencies toward the same fault. Like the deluded psychotic who "knows" the facts but is unable to correct his notions, the meaning of this wife's self-delineation may be unconditionally linked to her expressed relational need template: e.g., a husband who is a "bad object." Consequently relational needs can be categorized according to needs for (a) an object of one's drive and (b) an object of one's specific need-configuration as a basis of self-delineation. [1]

The latter need can be called "ontic" dependence on a certain other. By this is meant that my full self-meaning depends on a fitting other, regardless of whether I am, in effect, dependent on the other. Thus, in order to experience myself as a leader, I need those who depend on me; as a healer, I need those who need my help. The essence of the relational complementation between any two persons

---

[1] Ernest Jones (1953) cites Freud as having stated: "An intimate friend and a hated enemy have always been indispensable to my emotional life; I have always been able to create them anew, and not infrequently my childish ideal has been so closely approached that friend and enemy have coincided in the same person" (p. 10).

lies in a "dialogue of needs" which guarantees that the relationship will not turn into a one-sided exploitation. Naturally, in addition to expecting certain attitudes, members of a family can manipulate one another to act in accordance with their private relational needs and expectations. Thus, the expectations of the various members are in competition for mastery.

This situation may be illustrated with a relationship based on two competing need templates: that of A for a "bad" object and that of B for a "good" object. For example, a masochistic man and a maturely heterosexual woman may discover, to their disappointment, that they cannot develop a working complementarity of roles. Each may try to "convert" the other by the assignment of fitting, expected object roles, yet neither is willing to oblige the other by actually conforming to the desired object role. If the couple don't break up, they can either continue their struggle, or the masochistically inclined partner will ultimately win because the resulting overall "badness" of their mutually frustrating relationship will provide a context that favors his object role assignment needs.

An important factor in relating is the formation of and the degree of completeness of a boundary between the relating partners. A self-other or ego boundary is often conceptualized as cognitive in nature, as exemplified in the infant's learning to distinguish between self and object. Perhaps it is easier to describe the affective and motivational ingredients of this boundary if we think of the child's learning the boundary between the two interdependent realms of "I" and "mine" rather than I and other. Cooley (1956) quotes Emerson's statement about friendship in what appears to be a similar emphasis on the value of the boundary between the self and the other: "Friendship requires that rare mean betwixt likeness and unlikeness that piques each with the presence of power and of consent in the other party. . . . Let him not cease an instant to be himself. The only joy I have in his being mine is that the not mine is mine. There must be very two before there can be very one" (p. 154).

Emerson's expression, "Let him not cease an instant to be himself" can be interpreted in a number of ways. On the one hand it certainly is a formulation of friendship or love that does not presume fusion or merger as its basis. On the other hand, he who remains himself and "not mine" in a sense will become mine nevertheless. That is, he will become mine, but not in the sense of a passive object of possession or a dependent appendage who lacks a will of his own. Or, to put this conflictual state of affairs in other words: I want the object of my friendship (possession) to remain a free agent (subject) of his own will.

A similar conflict is familiar to observers and therapists of families. The underlying ambivalent attitudes lead to the picture of contradictory messages which Bateson et al. (1956) named "double-bind." The conflicting wishes of possession and separateness can also lead to a vicarious fusion of motivations as exemplified by the phenomenon described as "superego lacunae" by Johnson (1949). In these cases the pattern of the child's acting-out is determined by the parent's superego configuration, as though the self-other boundary between parent and child were defective. Family therapy uncovers many other unconsciously collusive motivational systems which, in the extreme case, form what Bowen (1965) describes as "undifferentiated family ego mass."

Sartre, in his Being and Nothingness (1956), develops a complex and sophisticated picture of the reciprocal conflict between lover and loved one. Each wants to possess the other as an ontological basis of his own existence, but wants to possess the other as a free agent rather than an automaton. In other words, both relating partners are a mixture of constitutive, active (subject) and constituted, passive (object) aspects, and each can say of the other with Emerson: "The not mine is mine." From the vantage point of his own experience, each can use the other as his constitutive object, by means of whom (and perhaps at the expense of whom) he can assert himself. He, in turn, can be used by the other as the latter's object or point of reference. One thing is certain as a consequence of the dialectic nature of personal experience: I need an other as the outside reference point or ground of my existence.

These rather abstract structural properties of the relationship experience are of considerable significance for the interpretation of certain clinical problems. For instance, when a woman complains that her husband lacks understanding, it is important to know whether she means that she misses his active inquisitive interest or his receptive availability and capacity to listen to her whenever she has something to say. Does she, perhaps, want a better harmony of the latter two processes in a well-functioning dialogue? Does she express a desire for a merger or fusion with the person of her husband?

Family members may question each other's capacity for loving. One may claim that the other uses the word "love" to mean selfish receiving while he himself means giving or give-and-take of emotional exchanges. Further, people's preferences may be divided between loving and being loved—between being the subject or the object of love.

It is unfortunate that the language of subjective relational experience is so inadequately developed. When a lover talks about loving or being loved, he knows he is describing very important subjective experiential differences. Such subjective relational meanings are the object of this paper, even though a more systematic language may appear to lack the desirable subjective experiential freshness.

Family pathology, or, perhaps more precisely, relational psychology, is badly in need of a comprehensive conceptual outlook capable of integrating our emerging knowledge of transactional or multiperson motivational systems with the individual-based outlook of classical Freudian personality theory. The subjective experience of one's personal identity is meaningful only in a dialectical, intrinsically dyadic context. On the other hand, the concept of a dyadic relationship cannot be restricted to the sphere of social action, particularly since Freud's structural theories have illuminated the great importance of intrapsychic relationships. By introducing the concept of superego as a quasi-personal, internal psychic representation, Freud established a relational framework as one of the most important intrapsychic structural dynamics. By means of the intrapsychic images of my parents, I carry the meaning of old relationships into my current relating to the other. This is the way he becomes meaningful to me. The other treats me the same way. In other words, my actions and attitudes toward the other will be determined by the constellation of my relational "need templates," a term I have used to describe certain aspects of internalized relationship orientations (Boszormenyi-Nagy, 1965).

To the extent that my need templates represent the core of my personality and my self is equal to the configuration of my relational need templates, I am what I need to make of other people. The fact that I have an emotional investment in seeing people fit my need templates (transference distortion) differentiates me from a camera, which has no need to project an image upon the objects it is directed at. Of course, I could not be a self if I were simply to register objects like a camera. Each person's identity evolves as a changing series of relational need templates. In this sense, we can think of the "regressed" psychotic as a person whose identity is composed of wishful constellations that we feel should properly characterize a child or at least the hidden and not the publicly observable tendencies of the grown-up.

Psychotically regressive need templates usually have an element of sensual specificity. A 17-year-old in-patient reported that she was constantly preoccupied with a desire to be held in the soft arms of a woman with soft breasts, and to be bottle-fed at the same time. Once she saw in a magazine an illustration of a woman psychiatrist holding a grown-up patient in her lap while the patient was being fed from a bottle. My patient was ecstatic about this picture and she pasted it in her scrapbook. Gradually as the weeks passed, another daydream emerged as most meaningful: the fantasies pictured tall women who had to go through the torture of various humiliating treatments. Finally, she imagined the violent death of her parents and siblings in a fatal car accident. The two phases of this young woman's wishful imagery represented a transition from being a passive object to being an observer of what is done to others. These need templates, of course, can be analyzed according to their derivation from their instinctual roots. However, from the vantage point of relational meaning, they represent two distinct modes: in one, the self is the object; in the other, the tall women and the patient's family are the objects. The first of the two modes seems to be a more common structural property of wishful imagery of psychotic females. Several other patients had the wish to be held by their mother and one to be masturbated by her mother at the same time. A psychotic young man demanded that his mother sit at his bed and massage his jaw for hours because he claimed his jaw hurt him.

The reason for calling these primitive need expressions "relational" need configurations is complex. It is probable that they become fixated because they had a gratifying value at a certain earlier life phase, probably in early childhood. What is the most important single gratifying quality of these memories, however? As shown by the work of Harlow (1962) on monkeys, an inanimate, nonresponsive environment can produce an autistic-like monkey out of the experimental baby monkey. The lack of live monkey mothers resulted in growth that made the young adult's instinctual life disorganized, psychotic-like. Somewhat in the manner of psychotic humans, these young adult monkeys became incapable of sexual intimacy as well as motherhood. Whether the early life experience of our patients did actually contain an excess of loneliness or an exaggerated vulnerability for it, the wish configurations of being held and fed are reminiscent of the wishful components of loneliness and separation anxiety states. Their significance might very well lie in the reassuring effect of possessing someone who "responds."

Even though the response to the hungry and lonely infant's needs primarily means physical care and satisfaction of biological "instincts," no one could deny that the response yields a most significant psychological contribution as a byproduct. In the process of being taken care of, the infant obtains the first opportunity for ego-boundary formation: i.e., identity formation. Through her caring responsiveness, the mothering adult appears on the horizon as someone whom the child "has." The possession of predictable response on the adult's part leads to the development of "basic trust" (Erikson, 1959), the foundation of all later social functioning and identity.

The effect of having or possessing people is one of the most important known, experientially crucial factors in the etiology of a variety of psychiatric conditions. The loss of a parent, sibling, or child, or the birth of a child are among the most frequent "precipitating causes" of depressions, schizophrenic episodes, and so on. With the loss of a relationship goes part of our own self-delineation; with the loss of the ground, the definition of the figure is also lost, at least partly. It follows logically that family or other close relationships are constantly subject to opportunities and disappointments concerning deep object-possessive needs and expectations. In fact, much of the intrafamilial struggle cannot be adequately described in terms of conflict, love, hostility, and so on. The real struggle is to possess a secure ground for one's sense of selfhood—and that ground consists of the other.

The arrested social growth of the delinquent or psychotic child can make him a most useful and covertly rewarded "captive" object, although on an instrumental or practical level the child's behavior may represent pure nuisance for the parent (Boszormenyi-Nagy, 1962). Through his being and remaining a captive object, perhaps one unconsciously representing a parental introject of the parent, the child remains a delineating ground or object for the parent's self. Conversely, the child, by accepting a "negative ego identity" (Erikson, 1959) defines himself as an entity, at least as an object to the parent.

Recurrent acts of delinquency or other forms of negative identity choice are the clearest examples of a need for a certain type of identity at all costs. Even if the pragmatic or instrumental consequences of one's actions are detrimental, as long as one's identity delineation is contingent on a certain type of socially undesirable action, one will continue to act it out repetitiously. "Repetition compulsion" obtains a new explanation if we look at it as a manifestation of man's universal "need of symbolization": i.e., need for definable meaning (Langer, 1948, p. 32). Repeated actions help create the symbolic reference point of our autonomous self, whereas being the target of the actions of others can only define a nonautonomous self. The slave is a slave because he is depended on by his master while not being allowed to depend on his own right to possess another. In a dialectical, relational sense, autonomy is a paradox; it is an innerly sensed freedom achieved through dependence on those vis-à-vis whom we realize the assertion of our needs. As Rapaport (1958) points out, autonomy from the environment is a different concept from autonomy of the ego functions vis-à-vis the instincts.

The other or the others are antithetical and indirect constituents
of the self, rather than merely its dichotomous, or moulding, context. I become defined as a parent when confronted by a child. As a
child, I am implicitly confronted by a parent. If I were a closed
existential system, my own parent-self could satisfy the self-delineation needs of my child-self. Of course, the notself-referents of
my self can also be internalized, and, within limits, they can substitute for real, external others. It is the main assumption of this
paper that it is essential to conceive of the self as arising vis-à-vis
the antithetically complementing others, whether the other is a
real person or an internalized replica like, for instance, the superego. This point of view has broad implications for the understanding
of relational dynamics.

I would like to examine the vicissitudes of the choice of an other
as context or ground in the self's struggle for its delineation or
existence. For the sake of simplicity, this exploration will be mostly
confined to two-person relationships.

Figure 1 represents six modes of relatedness, arranged in a
hierarchic order.[2] The diagram is used chiefly to indicate the subjective symbolic structuring of the self's position in the various
dyadic self-delineating relationships. This type of subjective symbolic structuring has to be distinguished from the concept of the unconscious fantasy. The former is a mode in which the figure-ground
matching of two complementing relational positions is programmed;
the latter are context-setting contents, viewed from the intrapsychic
vantage point of one individual. Each consecutive step in the diagram
represents a more satisfactory mode of relational self-delineation
or boundary formation. Each segment of circle corresponds to a
physical individual. Each broken line represents an ego boundary,
achieved through a contraposition of self and other. This simple
antithetical relationship is complicated by the circumstance that both
self and other can be either subject or object, depending on the
relative positions of the participants with regard to autonomy and
assertive use of the relationship. The arrows indicate the directional and dynamic quality of the object-role assignment inherent in
being a subject. The solid lines between subject and object imply
available but not utilized relational "opportunities." The first two
of the six relational modes are dyadic in structure, though they do
not involve more than one physical person. The third mode is a
nondialectical "intersubjective fusion" and does not lead to the

[2] Reproduced with permission from *Intensive Family Therapy: Theoretical and Practical Aspects*, Boszormenyi-Nagy and Framo (Eds.), Hoeber Medical Division, Harper and Row, Inc., 1965.

formation of an ego boundary. The fourth and fifth modes represent asymmetrically incomplete evolvements of dyadic relationships. The sixth mode symbolizes a potentially fully symmetrical social relationship that is qualitatively different from and more than the sum total of Modes (D) and (E). Experienced by both participants as a dialogue, the sixth mode is the basis of a working feedback system of mutuality and growth.

Intrasubject Boundary

This first drawing represents the least adequate form of self-delineation, which can appear for only short intervals as a defense against the threatened loss of a sense of self. Manneristic expressions such as: "I guess I don't feel like that" or "as I have so often said" are examples of these fictive splits between parts of the self. It is as though one part of the self were looking over the shoulder of the other. It is probable that some aspects of hypochondriac preoccupations are vested with this type of intrapsychic self-defining significance. The body and its functions are thereby partly experienced as aspects of the sensing subject, although in delusional forms of hypochondria they are experienced as objects (Szasz, 1957). Schizophrenic personality fragmentation can appear in the form of an unproductive intrapsychic quarrel of disparate selves that does not result in any enduring ego-boundaries.

Internal Dialogue

The self is confronted here with the internalized others, the introjects. The internalized others may be regarded from the point of view of subject or object. A typical example of an internalized other is the superego. As subject, its message, the voice of conscience, can make one squirm and escape into a variety of "symptoms." Viewed as object, one can attempt to negotiate with one's conscience and even manage to bribe it occasionally. Intensive, enduring states of guilt represent typical examples of helpless exposure to a superego behaving as subject.

Hallucinations and delusions clearly have the structuring of an ego-internal object relatedness. In praising the reliability of his voices, one schizophrenic patient sounded like he was advertising the advantage of internal friendships over the less reliable external ones he encountered. We are all familiar with the variety of internal others we encounter during our dreams. In a systematic study on the direction of threat in dreams and direction of aggression in psychotics, Framo et al. (1962) demonstrated a correlation between two subject-object dimensions: patients who were the objects of threat in the manifest content of their dreams were more apt to make others objects of aggression through their actual behavior.

In summary, internal relationships differ from transitory intrapsychic boundary formations in that the former represent manifest motivational conflicts as the foundation of internal self-delineations. The impact of pangs of conscience or delusional convictions, for example, can lead to serious consequences. They can make a person pay a high cost for their endurance. One has to learn how to live with one's internal others just as with real others. In reality, every real interpersonal relationship is interwoven with internal relationships as reference points for meaning.

Merger

This condition is partly responsible for the one described as confusion of relating with identifying. An area of primary identification is an area of lacking ego-boundaries. Certain members of a family, usually the mother and one or several children, may consciously think of themselves as one we-subject. Naturally, they can be a we-object, as when a mother has a tendency to react to any paternal discipline of the children as aggression against herself. In its more subtle motivational aspects, merger can be achieved through unconscious collusion or vicarious participation in the feelings or actions of the other. Recovering psychotic patients may be seen to shift from a preoccupation with delusional internal objects to a merger-like identification with the doctor or nurse. In a somewhat less conscious form, the person who loses his father through heart attack, can merge with him by having a lifelong disposition for medically unexplained cardiac pain. The fantasied pain has assumed the significance of a lasting tie with the deceased—a borrowed ego-boundary. It is probable furthermore, that a certain amount of merger with people who are important for us may be necessary for building up the experiential contents of the self as subject. In terms of families, shared "family myths" (Wynne et al., 1958) may represent a merger of several members vis-à-vis others who are represented through complementary roles or positions.

Being the Object

The concept of object relationship implies a directional property; it hinges on A's capacity for making B his object as well as B's capacity for becoming an object vis-à-vis A as subject. Being a context for someone else's self-assertive or self-delineating projects can be preferable to being isolated from all meaningful ties with people. One may sense an implicit danger in such a passive role, however, and one can become exploited by, or a captive of, the other unless one insists on an equal chance for reciprocation.[3] In order to be accepted, adolescents often assume the role of the clown too willingly. It has been reported that prisoners who were kept in indefinite periods of total isolation recorded even periodic tortures as welcome evidence of their worth, at least in the role of the hated enemy. Children may willingly accept an assigned parent-like role that serves as an outlet for the transference needs of their parents. When the child grows up, however, such unilateral role exploitation may result in desperate, unconscious revenge motivations in the form of delinquent or psychotic behavior. As another example, many women sense deeply that the role of a wife and mother is essentially that of a martyr, and that to fulfill this martyr role, they must renounce their own personal ambitions and become merely a ground or context for the strivings of their husbands and children.

Being the Subject

On this more accomplished relational level, the only significant missing element is a need for capacity for the empathic recognition by the subject of the other's needs for being a subject too. One participant may succeed in assigning the role of an object to the other, without giving due consideration to the other's autonomous existence. More specifically, as _exclusive_ subjects we avoid becoming a context for the other's self-delineating relationship needs, while we manage to "use" the other for our internal needs. Usually, the person is not fully aware of his tendency to assign object roles to others. A typical example of this tendency, especially if it is done by two or more people, is the phenomenon of scapegoating. The scapegoat is not given a chance to reciprocate and use the scapegoaters as objects for his own self-assertive strivings.

Some people are masters of using other persons' statements as a takeoff point for something completely different from what they wanted to say, thus totally overruling the meaning of the other's statements. Words can even be put into someone else's mouth without regard for the intention of the owner of the mouth. Transference "distortions" can be regarded as attempts at making the other a certain type of object. Being a subject can be considered as a relational

---

[3]Barnes (1959) quotes the cuckold from "The Baker's Wife" as a beautiful example of someone thinking of himself as a captive object: "How can I bake bread when I am busy being deceived?" (p. 57).

mastery, but often a dubious one; it demands that the other exist
for the one who is the subject.

Dialogue

The last diagram depicts a symmetrical and, therefore, a more
stable relational mode than the preceding five. A prototype is the
freely developing heterosexual involvement in which the more the
male can realize his masculinity, the more he tends to offer the
female a chance to play her counterrole fully. Perhaps here lies
one of the explanations of the significance of the Oedipal conflict:
in order to become a man, the boy must establish a role position
in opposition to the mother, and not find a role in imitation of the
father alone. Or, the doctor finds his role reinforced by the patient
whose sickness makes him an object of the patient's needs. Many
people, while seeming to ask for advice, ask only for a dialogue
with someone. The give-and-take of an exchange of responses renders the decision-making process more secure.

A fascinating question about the dialogue is whether it can exist
asymmetrically: i.e., fully from the reference point of one participant only, while the other experiences the dialogue merely as object. This may be possible if one partner does not or cannot assert
his own autonomous needs while adapting himself to the role of a
desired object of the other. In a decompensating marital pattern,
for instance, the suspicious and malicious partner can produce a
realistic suspiciousness in the other one in accordance with his or
her own internal needs, creating thereby an emotional climate in
which the other's needs for reciprocal admiration become irrelevant.
Or the delinquent child by his self-destructive behavior may satisfy
his parent's transferred infantile revenge needs vicariously, while
the child cannot satisfy his own needs for a genuinely growth-pro-
moting parent. Thus, while one party gets feedback fitting his needs,
the other is incapable of extracting the same from the first one.

Family therapy offers a new vantage point for exploring the
directional aspects of relational engagements. The family therapist
can observe the specific ways in which a particular relationship may
consist of two asymmetrical, partially internal dialogues. Yet one
member's originally objectionable self-delineation needs and modes
of relating may gradually find reinforcement through fitting him as
object of the other member's needs. Therapeutic work with families
requires new levels of analytic insight. Fundamental self-delineation
needs express themselves through fixated, more or less archaic
patterns of complementary behavior. A new type of behavior can be
adopted only if it is capable of satisfying both persons' needs for

self-demarcation. The simultaneous examination of both participants' undesirable subject and object roles may result in the uncovering of specific obstacles to the genuine dialogue.

According to the theory here presented, the dynamic structure of relationships is not to be founded on the fiction of individual persons as interacting entities. A more comprehensive view of relationships takes into account that a rhythmic oscillation of the dialogue is not only a function of the individual but a condition of his existence. As the philosopher Heinemann (1954) put it: "Respondeo, ergo sum" (I respond, therefore I exist).

The response structure of the dialogue can be considered as a communication system. It is important to study patterns of communication as expressions of meaning, but the essence of the relational dialogue is on a deeper layer than communications. It lies in the nature of the fundamental engagement of relational positions as part of each participant's striving for meaning.

My reason for such close consideration of certain modes of the relational process originates from the recognition of certain often-overlooked dialectic aspects of social motivations. What I chiefly wanted to convey is that certain structural properties of self-experiences in relating are important motivating principles in themselves.

Experience in observing people throughout the years has taught me to respect man's profound needs for being responded to in certain particular ways. To make people respond on our own terms seems to be at the bottom of the "game" of social life. In one sense, those people could be considered healthiest who are able to make the highest number of others respond willing to them on their own terms. Yet such other-directed explanations have failed to explain the subjective preferences that people manifest in their relational choices.

Some people prefer to sit alone with the inner voices of their past relationships; repeat sequences of (compulsive) acts according to some internal patterning; never assert themselves as differing from the other's point of view; or exploit every human encounter as an opportunity for hostile rather than trusting exchanges. Some of these people lead lonely lives. Others find partners who collude with them in building up "bad" relationships. In any case, people have deep motivations for maintaining their internal or external relational commitments, because these mean very much to them. One's self obtains meaning through relationships that mean much to it. Emotional growth, on the other hand, hinges on one's capacity for relinquishing nonworkable relational commitments and substituting workable new relationships. The process of exchanging one relation-

Figure I
SIX RELATIONAL MODES

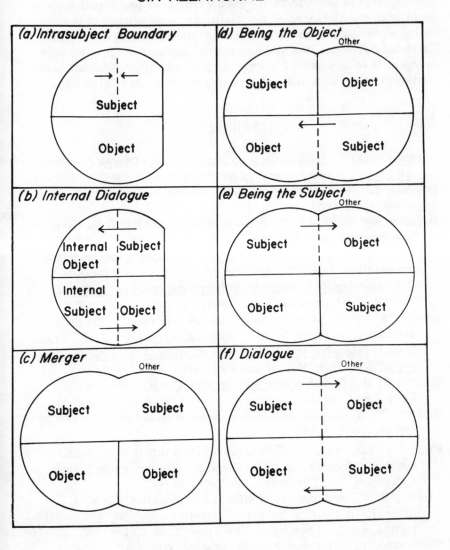

(a) Intrasubject Boundary	(d) Being the Object
Subject / Object	Other / Subject / Object / Object / Subject
(b) Internal Dialogue	(e) Being the Subject
Internal Object / Subject / Internal Subject / Object	Other / Subject / Object / Object / Subject
(c) Merger	(f) Dialogue
Subject / Subject / Object / Object / Other	Other / Subject / Object / Object / Subject

ship for another depends on complex relational need configurations
or templates in both participants.

In conclusion, I suggest that the concept of health in family
therapy ought to be fashioned according to the criteria of the modes
of relating I have tried to describe, and not according to values of
reality, genitality, effectiveness, self-actualization, or related
aims current in the individual-based writings on psychopathology.
Emotional growth hinges on the quality and possibilities of the
dialogue, realized within a context of mutually accepted autonomy.
Existential freedom is a dialectical process; it is not love through
merger. It is a capacity for symmetrical self-other delineation and
continuous new resolutions of opposing positions in relationships.

REFERENCES

Barnes, Hazel E. Humanistic existentialism; the literature of pos-
sibility. Lincoln: Univer. of Nebraska Press, 1959.
Bateson, G., et al. Toward a theory of schizophrenia. Behav. Sci.,
1956, 1, 251-264.
Boszormenyi-Nagy, I. The concept of schizophrenia from the per-
spective of family treatment. Fam. Proc., 1962, 1, 103-113.
Boszormenyi-Nagy, I. A theory of relationships: experience and
transaction. In I. Boszormenyi-Nagy & J. L. Framo (Eds.),
Intensive family therapy: theoretical and practical aspects.
New York: Harper and Row, 1965. Pp. 33-86.
Bowen, M. Family psychotherapy with schizophrenia in the hospitals
and in private practice. In I. Boszormenyi-Nagy & J. L. Framo
(Eds.), Intensive family therapy: theoretical and practical as-
pects. New York: Harper and Row, 1965. Pp. 213-243.
Cooley, C. H. Human nature and the social order. Glencoe, Ill.:
Free Press, 1956.
Erikson, E. H. Identity and the life cycle; selected papers. Psychol.
Issues, 1959, 1, No. 1.
Framo, J. L., et al. A relationship between threat in the manifest
content of dreams and active-passive behavior in psychotics.
J. abnorm. soc. Psychol., 1962, 65, 41-47.
Harlow, H. F. Development of affection in primates. In E. L.
Bliss (Ed.), Roots of behavior: Genetics, instinct, and social-
ization in animal behavior. New York: Harper, 1962. Pp. 157-166.
Heinemann, F. Existenzphilosophie lebendig oder tot? Stuttgart,
Germany: W. Kohlhammer, 1954.
Johnson, Adelaide. Sanctions for superego lacunae of adolescents.
In K. Eissler (Ed.), Searchlights on delinquency: new psycho-

analytic studies. New York: Int. Univer. Press, 1949. Pp. 225-245.

Jones, E. The life and work of Sigmund Freud. Vol. I. New York: Basic Books, 1953.

Langer, S. K. Philosophy in a new key; a study in the symbolism of reason, rite and art. Cambridge, Harvard University Press, 1942.

Rapaport, D. The theory of ego autonomy: a generalization. Bull. Menninger Clin. 1958, 22, 13-35.

Sartre, J. P. Being and nothingness; an essay on phenomenological ontology. Translated by H. E. Barnes. New York: Philosophical Library, 1956.

Szasz, T. S. Pain and pleasure; a study of bodily feelings. New York: Basic Books, 1957.

Wynne, L. C., et al. Pseudo-mutuality in the family relations of schizophrenics. Psychiatry, 1958, 21, 205-220.

A CYBERNETIC APPROACH TO FAMILY THERAPY

Warren M. Brodey, M. D.

The purpose of family therapy is this: release of fresh techniques for problem solving. In this paper, the family is conceptualized as a self-perpetuating organism with a built-in regulatory system. Family therapy is directed to altering the family's self-regulation so that it may evolve more efficient contact with its environment in terms of its purposes (Rosenbleuth et al., 1943). Moving from this point of view, one can see that the family as an organism has an environment that includes other organizational levels, e.g., the family members, the broader society, and the town.

Critical intervention in any self-perpetuating (living) process is what I define as control. Control in this sense includes small interventions sensitively timed.

Information about the control of complex systems has been accumulating under the heading cybernetics (Ashby, 1961; Pask, 1961; Weiner, 1948). Cybernetics, the science of control, has precipitated from the necessity to cope with the explosion of change that is contagiously spreading in our time. This change infiltrates the very depths of our ecology. Cybernetics grew from the need to evolve brains (control systems) to manage the complex technological muscles (power systems) that can crush us out of existence. The constraints that slow the evolution of human skills at learning need to be disturbed, else we may not survive the misuse of our new muscles.

Our existing knowledge forces us to learn still more in order to maintain the stability we need. Learning is self-reinforcing. Like all living processes it pulses into change. But each generation must process this growth through its families' child-rearing constraints, whatever they may be. As has been discussed in previous papers (Brodey, 1959, 1963, 1964, 1965), families vary enormously in their capacity to metabolize information sensed from the environment and to produce informed decisions that may lead to continuously adaptive action. Thus, family therapy allows clinical observation of the process of evolving new control (self-regulatory) skills. The therapist must learn to be responsive to the family's control system if he hopes to intervene significantly. He must be able to conceptualize the family as a system that includes both its members and society in its environment. (We are not accustomed to this approach except when considering a member of the family in terms of his internal environment of component systems—vascular, nervous, etc.—in the same way we consider a family as made up of its members.)

The ability to be responsive and to change with change is the essence of stability (Ashby, 1961). Conceptualizing behavior in terms of systems that are coherent because they are bound together by a unified communication and decision system has the advantage of allowing one to consider the family in terms of movement style: to see it in relation to the adjustments it must make in order to maintain homeostasis while evolving new variation with which to meet the changing environment. There is a timing process here that can be specified as something more than art or intuition.

Adjusting the way we conceive of a family allows the creation of a notation that includes timing, though at first in a crude form. If we use a structuring framework that is built of time, as well as energy and information we can formalize more of our therapeutic art. "The tightening circle of a family tends to spiral tighter"—but this can be no more than a poetic expression until growth process is freed from the timelessly final cause-effect convention. Beginning, middle, and end is not a useful form when change must be defined. This ancient convention still prohibits the conceptualization of illness as growing of its own accord, in its own time and rhythm. That living systems produce change without germlike external causes is not spontaneous generation—it is growth. The contagion or chain reaction of a family process in which each effort to regain stability makes the situation worse is well known. The oscillation of crisis and inactivity has a timing that every clinician knows as being more than cause-effect.

Scientific psychiatry has been tied to an antique science of states that denies the modern science of relation. No one will argue that the man sick with tuberculosis is more susceptible to more tuberculosis or to any other disease. To say that neurosis causes neurosis will still seem unscientific to many people. But here we are conceptualizing a control system and not a final cause. When families become trapped in the accelerating process of reduced communication, finding out who started the withdrawal is irrelevant to designing useful intervention.

Disease grows disease; and for those who like the word "cause" (as I do not) disease <u>causes</u> disease. These words are often spoken with a shrug when misery gone wild accelerates itself. There is a time design to the interventions of an artistic therapist. He breaks into repetitive cycling, catching the family when its boredom is "off balance." When he is expected to be helpful, he may simply exaggerate the shrug.

But shrugs and glances and fists and gut feelings shared intuitively (by physiological and body language) are inadequate for building a recorded science of man. Even the crudest external quantitation in words promotes the development of theory and leads toward a more viable knowledge. But how can one specify the living complexity of which I speak? It does not chop into the traditional pieces — good and evil, light and dark, mature and immature, ego and id — or even into the straight-line metric scalings so long considered pure. The character of living systems is nonlinear.

Where are even crude words for the moment of happening—the "now" moments of the therapist's action, not culled by memory's abstraction and made into undetailed timeless generalization, or verbatim reports, or single variable graphs that leave out living and breathing? We need a theory of growing, of working-forward process, of the process of expanding into what was unknown to expectation.

The formal language of explaining is a way of rationalizing what is already past. Psychiatrists and priests have grown rich on this explaining what is past. Impact on the present does not depend on the truth of explanation.

Explaining is of less use with a lively family. It is of more use in analyzing a family that denies its present existence in favor of explaining its own past. The family therapist needs a language of <u>now</u>, of the on-going moment of learning, of contagion, of vicious cycles mixing to form stable and unstable moments. He needs a language that points out, and helps him to set forth easily, points of control where change is facilitated by a particular matching of behaviors; where a little information, gently repeated, swings the family bit by bit toward an oscillation that carried it beyond its rut. He needs a language that does not merely connect a man's relationship to average norms by straight lines depicting objective variance from what has always been expected.

But the language of real time is still shrugs and glances. Establishing a formal language that includes events as they occur in real time is a major problem of our epoch. With the bomb at our fingertips, we are forced to make control explicit; we cannot allow history to decide.

We are so committed to our customary language—the language
we learned as we grew up—that we must look elsewhere for a base.
Other disciplines have studied moment-to-moment control without
being aware that the processes they worked on were relevant to our
own human process. It was during the last war that we learned to
program two guided missiles, each with its own electronic brain, so
that they would try to evade or catch each other. Now we map this
kind of control situation by designing two computer systems that
work at learning to evolve each other's language. Gradually our instruments allow us to move from our concept of man as a simple
energy machine to a consideration of him as a communicative machine, designed for control and operating in real time, which is
never repeated. Man has always perceived himself as if he were an
extension of his tools. For example, concepts of man's behavior as
energy-bound (such as the libido theory) grew out of the steam-
engine analogy.

Developing the capacity of two or more computers to learn to
teach each other and to adapt to environments for which they were
not specifically designed presents design problems analogous to
those of raising children in an epoch when parents cannot predict the
major environmental changes with which their children must cope.
The days of apprenticeship, when learning consisted only of learning
to repeat the performance of a previous generation, are past. Now
children must learn from their parents control skills that will apply
even in situations unthought of by those parents. The designers of
a Mars probe have the same problem. A new awareness of the science of self-evolving systems is growing.

Response-ability is a feature of this kind of control. In "Some
Family Operations and Schizophrenia" (Brodey, 1959), I have described the family that is unresponsive to the changing ecology of
the individual and of the family unit. These family organisms grow
their component parts so that they will fit with predetermined names,
roles, and abstractions—with no responsiveness to individual or
environmental growth that does not fit with expectation. This kind
of a family has limited evolutionary power. It tends to break down.
I have called it a closed-system family. The closed family is like an
automated factory that is unresponsive to unexpected change. All the
behavioral patterns are preprogrammed. This kind of assembly of
parts is not suited to a time of rapid evolution. In this factory, dials
or displays of performance are coupled directly to the levers that
make the system go. There is no play. The system cannot change
except in predetermined ways. It cannot evolve. It cannot resolve
those divergent messages (double binds) that arise out of the need

to use what was formerly irrelevance as raw material for discovery and reorganizing growth.

The destructive growth process in a closed-system family is now one of the commonest points of agreement among family therapists. Out of contact, out of control, withdrawn—these concepts are well known. But the mechanisms of contact and being in control and being related have no formal language.

Can we who study the family describe this evolutionary growing— this growing in which each person discovers the other with increasing skill at finding the unexpected and discovering the unknown? Can we describe the creative process as it begins in the family, and thereby strengthen our knowledge of child's and man's behavioral evolution? This is the challenge our human situation presents to those who study family systems.

Can the family therapist help conceptualize the ways of learning and teaching without losing the richness of common clinical experience? For example, can we describe the phenomenology of tenderness? Tenderness is not simply mirroring or joining each other's movement or speaking in each other's rhythm; it is a responsiveness—a counterpoint—that acknowledges each other's time and content variation even as they are unexpected. Tenderness acknowledges the discovery natural to living process—the touch of fingertips responding to each other's touch. And words too may touch and grow into more than each one said. The responsive family is tenderly skillful in establishing the family as useful to its members in their mediations inside and outside the family unit.

We have new tools with which to explore the process of tenderness. The movie camera, the video tape recorder, the possibility of telemetering information about responsiveness in physiological state — all present new ways of examining explicitly what we have long known to be the simple facts of responsive life. We are finding new nonlinear units for measuring complex growth patterns. No longer do we need to limit our studies to written records as if the words themselves could stand alone without the body language.

But there is the constraint that we must unlearn. The science most clinicians know is imbedded in the matrix of Aristotelian classes of things and timeless truths (or falsities). It has no formal language or relations. It denies the advances of modern mathematics—even its present struggles. When we accept the old premises unwittingly, we are constrained. Then theory of the family becomes a medical theory—a caricature of sickness. Will we have the courage to turn to the problem of enhancing growth, rather than merely correcting its failures? Or will we leave excellence to the gods lest we aspire to the moon?

Cybernetics is just beginning the construction of a language for describing complex growth systems. To some it will seem strange that growth and changing can be made the content of scientific study. In the traditional past, our tools were designed to measure end points, thresholds, and bench marks. Acute and chronic have been the clinicians' formal words for specifying change. Our language was not rich in specifying kinds of change, except as rates. This kind of measure left us without a way of describing ongoing change except by speaking of the differences between two states and by retrospective explanations, which were then translated as if they were intended motivations. The continuing forward course of actually evolving behavior has long been dismissed as beyond our measuring skill, although its operational measure is well known to the skilled clinician.

Have clinicians been intimidated by the purveyors of obsolescent measuring systems into denying that their art can be approached by science? Or are the measurement designers intimidated by our unspoken need to preserve the therapeutic art as mystery? New skill at measuring control systems without denying their complexity is now becoming possible through developments in computer technology.

In the computer, we have a new tool that allows man a new metaphorical description of himself, one that includes ongoing adaptive and complex change. We have only to learn to ask new kinds of questions and to conceptualize interactive units less rigid than inches or seconds. The new equivalence relations include similar growth shapes. The new conceptions for measurement of biological systems are being spawned in that region of mathematics called topology. To progress in the new technological environment, we have only to learn to ask the new kind of questions. To use the computer's skill, we must be able to ask questions that are relevant to our artistic and intuitive action, to the clinical sense. The creativeness of the clinical artist is no longer being denied by a restrictive science; science is changing in the direction of enrichment as the art of creating has become a scientific concern.

LEARNING TO LEARN

But where is relevant information to be found? Fundamental questions about knowledge are induced when one examines the transmission of information in a family. Each family organism has its style of growing and creating itself over time. Some families differ from the "usual" family more than others. These are easier to describe. Variant families that develop unusual techniques of growing are most important to behavioral evolution. What is grown in a particular generation is yet another issue.

As one begins to ask questions about growth process, one quickly becomes involved with whether children are being constrained in their growth by the restricted expectations that have been accepted as reality from generation to generation. Is present growth, then, a reflection of human growth potential, or do our observations reveal a commonly learned growth ritual? Most educational systems seem to operate like closed families and work to make the children fit with past roles (Bruner, 1962). It is hard to examine growth in this context. One does better to study the responsiveness of a family that is able to prosper in its growth.

Each family therapist who observes the whole family begins to be sensitive about the ways in which families teach their children to learn. There appears to be an enormous variation from family to family in these teachings. Observing the family forces the therapist to be aware that he too was taught to learn and was taught constraints that were breathed in with the knowledge from his parents' times. There is a recursive cycling of these constraints from generation to generation, as each teaches the next what to expect as human, and this somehow becomes an object of thoughtful study once one examines the family. That this kind of thinking should emerge at this time seems appropriate, for we now feel a special urgency to help our children to develop those skills which may insure their survival in a rapidly changing world.

Though the family therapist may not reach many people by the direct practice of his art, he makes available a new frame of reference from which to build toward a science of man as a control creature. Within this frame of reference, I have tried to make cybernetics something new. It is not just an attack on the past, or a renaming to be translated within the matrix of old premises.

The family therapist knows the constraint systems used for preserving family repetitions that have long been obsolescent. As a clinician, he knows the problem of helping a family unlearn its obsolescent constraints. It is time now to locate the constraint in our knowledge and to begin the restructuring we need. The information transmission between the generations in now unstable—at a switching point. The need to enrich our language for describing behavioral evolution within the family as a precursor to education is evident. Description of the family as a system for evolving children who are more or less appropriately organized for survival can serve to assist us in designing education so that it can continue this early biological education more effectively. But where can we find a point at which our fundamental knowledge is open to change? Here one approaches the problem of introducing change into the general body of knowledge. In science, one sees the same resilient use of knowledge to prevent structural change that one observes in families. As with the family, one chooses an area that has been relatively outside the conceptual frame of science, though obviously important. Timing, for example, is a territory in the scientific conceptualization of human behavior that is relatively neglected.

The timing features of a family system cannot be studied by adding up individual timings. A family, like any communicative net, must define a common time-language. This labeling system itself is relative: it moves in time. A family's timing may depend more or less on the impinging timing of its inputs at the moment. Each family has its characteristic clocking rhythms. What is defined as a moment is also a part of the family labeling system. For some families, the moment of necessity (e.g., necessary planning) is a year, and for others it is the shortest period of time that they know how to measure. The structure of the time-labeling system optimally reflects the control needs of the family. This system is more suitable for measurement than are families' opinions or explanations.

In some families, the time groupings used for decision-making ("It is the time now to decide . . .") are quite unresponsively set by what is publicly declared as the norm or average. These families, unlike others, are unable to change their timing so as to use event-packed crises sensitively and responsively in order to learn. They simply do not go into emergency mode and change the rules to accommodate to the changing tempo of a surge of happenings in the environment. For example, they do not meet the urgency or slowing of a suddenly organized adolescent with an altered developmental pace. The words and acts may be unchanged, but the action pace is unresponsive.

The expansion and contraction of usable control time during family crisis is intuitively no secret, but it has not been formalized. Well-timed crises freshen growth; therapists use the ebb and flow of critical instability. Formalizing this time process may give new understanding of growth and the growth of learning systems.

When, using the cybernetic point of view, one conceptualizes, one thinks of nonevolutionary systems as being self-limiting and artificial. As one uses these values, one begins to feel that it is exceedingly strange that we have for so long restricted the study of evolution to an examination of animal and plant species. In cybernetics, the conception of a self-organizing system includes within itself a teleology, or purpose, that is not defined in terms of its beginning. We are satisfied to consider a purpose as having no final beginning or ultimate end. Purpose is the immediate realm maintained by the self-correcting and evolving feedback system.

The study and quantification of feedback systems is one aspect of cybernetics that has become popular. It is these mechanisms that determine and maintain stable cyclings, which then simply tend to recur as the organism becomes more and more entrained to this mode of regulation. Some kinds of rhythms are hard to break out of. For example, the control system of many families is set so that a child loses contact with the information flow in the family if his growth exceeds the speed or scope conventional to the family group. He loses contact and is slowed by the family's efforts to maintain its own features. To some extent this is necessary for communication. But maintaining identity requires changing so as to hold position in relation to the changing environment. This maintaining of identity tends to regulate a continuum over time in a way that has been called "natural." The former need for parents and children to be similar in their education did not afford recognition that potentials could exist at other equilibrium levels. Growth of the family may take astonishing spurts, given a new necessity. Feedback control is not readily described by analogy to nonliving systems. Though our basal metabolism can perhaps be described in terms of a coal furnace, our capacity to change, to learn, and to be educated does not readily fit this analogy.

A given family change need not be caused by some event of equal proportion or equal meaning. The ordinary energy analogue omits the control power of small changes at unstable points or switching points. As in the building intensity of love, it is a proposal at the right time—one movement responsively coupled with another—that builds the critical field necessary for creation.

Cybernetics describes many homely and complex aspects of living systems. For example, the particular control loops each have a time duration within which they can responsively encompass change. When too neatly balanced, some control systems develop wild, over-balancing oscillations. The evolution of a family from one form of stability to another is a particularly useful characteristic for a clinician to be able to discuss openly. In some closed families, the first awareness of small change is autocatalytic, for it brings with it the expectation that change will occur again. The therapist's task is to find a way to seed growth. The expectation that change will again occur serves to focus attention on this possibility and to cultivate readiness for change. The organism's expectation then accepts events that, though ever so slightly deviant, are similar in their very difference from that which was expected. Curiosity grows. Critical intervention allows some closed families to grope out into the unknown bit by bit. This amplification is intensified as the system becomes less stable or when it is in process of transition; then intervention may dampen the process until skill in control grows further. When systems are unsettled or in process of decision, a small change that at other times would be irrelevant becomes a deciding factor. This gives power to what would otherwise have no way into the enclosure of our accepted natural reality. Often the question of the directions in which the organism will evolve is less important than the problem of its becoming sufficiently unstructured so that small change can be used to reestablish uncertainty. Only uncertainty can evolve the decisions that pattern a fresh family structure.

This process of behavioral evolution stands in contrast to the kind of direct coupling that occurs in symbiotic relationships where the freshening influence of the unknown or irrelevant or unexpected is denied. That growth suffers when this kind of control system is used has been previously reported. It is fortunate that our conception of human development and evolution is again becoming an open system. Family therapy provides an important route beyond what was dynamic in the first half of the century.

In conclusion, I must point to a question that arises for those who have become involved with family work. The new influx of observations has upset our tradition for theory, even to the extent that we must reexamine not only its content but its structure (McCulloch, 1965). We can deny the new information by renaming the old as if it were new or by renaming the new as if it were the old. But these common approaches to progress frustrate our growing awareness of the need for fresh dimensions. Even the most undogmatic thinkers are beginning to know the sense of obsolescence that comes quickly, without even the warning of a good fight.

Social science is in transition. Our augmented technology makes this evolution both necessary and possible. I am curious as to how the change will happen. Cybernetic theory serves as one source from which new concepts about the control of change are spreading. It is my prediction that the next stability will center around active augmentation of human learning skills rather than around prevention, health, or the overcoming of sickness. Study of the family prepares the way for this new growth. The evolution of augmented human control skill is necessary if we are to meet the challenge. The changing ecology requires new family skill at raising children who can enjoy the game of response and change because they have response-ability.

REFERENCES

Ashby, R. Introduction to Cybernetics. London: Chapman and Hall, 1961.

84

Brodey, W. M. Some family operations and schizophrenia. Arch. Gen. Psychiat., 1959, 1, 379-402.

Brodey, W. M. On family therapy. Family Process. 1963, 2, 281-288.

Brodey, W. M. Developmental learning and the education of the child born blind. Rev. Gen. Semantics. 1964, 22, 293-306.

Brodey, W. M. On the dynamics of narcissism. Psychoanalytic Study of the Child. New York: International Universities Press, 1965.

Bruner, J. S. On Knowing: Essays for the Left Hand. Cambridge: Harvard University Press, 1962.

Darwin, C. On the Origin of Species. Facsimile of the first edition. Cambridge: Harvard University Press, 1964.

McCulloch, W. S. Embodiments of Mind. Cambridge: MIT Press, 1965.

Pask, G. An Introduction to Cybernetics. New York: Harper and Sons, 1961.

Rosenbleuth, A., Weiner, N., and Bigelow, J. Behavior, purpose, and teleology. J. Philos. of Science, 1943, 10, 194.

Weiner, N. Cybernetics: Control and communication in the animal or machine. Cambridge: The Technology Press, 1948.

ENTROPY AND FAMILY THERAPY [1]

Speculations on Psychic Energy, Thermodynamics, and Family Interpsychic Communication

John C. Sonne, M.D.

This article represents a contribution toward linking together
concepts from the physical sciences with certain observations made
during the treatment of schizophrenogenic families. In particular,
I wish to dwell on the concept of entropy, relating it first to the
general area of psychic functioning, then proceeding to the level of
interpsychic communication. I would like to preface my speculations
with some definitions of certain thermodynamic concepts, and then
move on to conceptualize psychic energy processes occurring in
family therapy by using the language of thermodynamics and the
data obtained from experiences with the interpsychic communication
system of the schizophrenogenic family.

Fundamental to this presentation is the assumption that psychic
processes and interpsychic processes are not independent of physical
processes (i.e., chemical, biological, or physiological processes),
and that a fundamental law on the physical level is not valid unless
it also holds true for the level of psychic processes.

THE SECOND LAW OF THERMODYNAMICS

According to the second law of thermodynamics, a fundamental
law of physics derived from observations of nature, heat cannot
spontaneously flow from a cold body to a warm body. This is a fundamental fact of experience. Stated differently, all natural or spontaneous processes (that is, processes occurring without external
interference), are irreversible. Expressed still differently, it is
impossible to construct a machine functioning in cycles, which can
convert heat completely into the equivalent amount of work without
producing changes elsewhere.

In order to study these energy changes more precisely, systems
have been described as characterized by the possession of a property

[1]A preliminary draft of this paper was presented at the Sixth International
Congress of Psychotherapy, in London, August 1964.

called entropy. The word entropy comes from the Greek word for change, and is signified by the letter S. The quantity S is known as the entropy of a system in a particular state. It is not easily described directly, and so is best defined in terms of an increase of entropy of a system; this is equal to the heat taken up isothermally and reversibly, divided by the temperature at which it is absorbed. The actual entropy of a system depends only on the state of that system, and consequently dS is an exact or complete differential. It is evident, therefore, that if a system changes from state A to state B in an irreversible manner, then the change of entropy is still given by the sum of the $\frac{q}{T}$ in the formula:

$$\sum_{A \longrightarrow B} \frac{q}{T} = S_B - S_A = \Delta S$$

where q is the heat that would be absorbed in each stage if the process were carried out reversibly. Since entropy is determined by a quantity of heat divided by the temperature, it is generally expressed in calories per degree. The unit, calorie per degree, used in measurement of entropy changes is sometimes called the conventional "entropy unit," abbreviated as E. U.

Entropy is an extensive property of a system. This means that the magnitude of an extensive property is determined not only by the state of a system but also by the amount (or amounts) of substance (or substances) contained within it. This is in contrast to an intensive property, which is independent of the quantity of material concerned. All spontaneous processes are accompanied by an increase in entropy; it is possible, therefore, to regard entropy as a measure of the "randomness" or "state of chaos" in a given system, and to suppose that all natural processes lead to an increase in random distribution. Since a disordered state is more probable than one of complete order, entropy and probability are evidently related. For this purpose, Boltzmann defined the thermodynamic probability of a system as the ratio of the probability of an actual state to one having the same total energy and volume, and in which the molecules are completely ordered.

ENTROPY AND LIFE PROCESSES

The above are concepts from the field of thermodynamics, which is the study of the energy changes accompanying chemical and physical changes. The applicability of these concepts to psychological, biological, and social processes is difficult to demonstrate;

however, there has been an increasing interest in recent years, particularly on the part of the physicist, in relating these concepts to human behavior and communication. Bridgeman (1953), in an article "Reflections on Thermodynamics," spoke of the need for, and the difficulty of, doing this. After speaking of the many unanswered questions relative to the first two laws of thermodynamics, he states: "Classical thermodynamics defines the entropy only of those states of a body which can be reached by some reversible process from a standard state. Such a definition rules out on principle most of the matter of daily life, because most states can be subject to no reversible displacement whatever—any plastically deformed metal is an example, or any biological system." He speaks of quantum mechanics as paper and pencil devices of which it is meaningless to ask whether the description they afford of macroscopic phenomena is true or not. "In general, the meaning of our concepts on the microscopic level is ultimately to be sought in operations on the macroscopic level. The reason is simply that we, for whom meanings exist, operate on the macroscopic level." He proposes the as yet unfinished task of reducing the meaning of quantum mechanics to the microscopic level, and then speaks of newer concepts, including the recognition of fluxes of heat and mechanical energy. Bohr, in his book, Atomic Physics and Human Knowledge, stresses that the psychological processes of the physicist are intimately related to the question of how one may grasp both the wave theory and the quantum theory of physics. This thinking is based on Heisenberg's uncertainty principle, now widely accepted as one of the fundamental bases of modern physics: "The simultaneous determination of velocity or any related property, e.g., energy or momentum, and position is impossible."

Since theories such as these about nature come from the minds of men studying nature, could we not include man's mind as a part of nature, and apply to the study of the mind theories developed from the mind? Some of these theories are not only tools for comprehending the mind's processes, but are themselves unusually peculiar products of the mind's theory-building processes. They may be particularly important examples of concepts, which, having been made by the mind, embody the very principle they are defining. Could we not profitably relate the creation of, the grasp of, and the experiencing of certain physical theories to the interpsychic communication processes of the physicist's family, within which the mind and the theories develop?

Ostow (1949), in an essay, "Entropy Changes in Mental Activity," calls attention to the breadth of some interpretations of the thermodynamic concept of entropy, which, by virtue of these interpretations, become applicable to certain objective aspects of thought. From a consideration of Maxwell's idea that an intelligent being, called Maxwell's demon, might effect a decrease in entropy in a gaseous mixture of nitrogen and oxygen in equilibrium by selectively opening a gateway between two enclosures containing the mixture in such a manner as to retain all the nitrogen molecules on one side, and all oxygen molecules on the other, Ostow concludes that the essential activity of Maxwell's demon is selection, and that the demon suggests strongly that we may have a device for calculating the entropy changes within a living organism consequent to mental activity. He proceeds to calculate the decrease in entropy achieved when a man selects one tie from ten in his wardrobe to be 7.6×10^{-24} calories per degree.

Szasz (1955), leaning heavily on the argument of Klein (1953) against an increase in biological organization of a system being considered as equivalent to, or at least closely connected to, a decrease in the entropy of a system, arrives at a position that the concept of entropy does not have applicability to psychological processes. Szasz wonders how it could be explained that both the psychotherapist and the patient accumulate negative entropy. Several writers have questioned the applicability of thermodynamic concepts to psychological systems on the grounds that psychological systems are ordinarily considered open systems, whereas the thermodynamic laws were derived, in the main, from experience with what are ordinarily considered closed systems.

ENTROPY AS TIME'S ARROW

Entropy has been thought of as time's arrow, the idea being derived from the second law of thermodynamics when stated as: "The total amount of entropy in nature is increasing." Grunbaum (1955) has written on the relevance of entropy to an understanding of the objective passage of time, subjective sense of time, and the direction of time. He speaks of how we record the past: ". . . a record of an event being a partial effect of that event possessing a certain amount of order, like the imprint [of a foot] on the beach. And we can see why a record of information can be treated as negative entropy, or 'negentropy,' acquired at the expense of the environment of which the record is a part, as is done in recent information theory."

One may see that although the passage of time is characterized by an increase in entropy in nature, the recording of this passage of time and the increase in man's knowledge over time involve an increase in negentropy.

INFORMATION AS NEGENTROPY

As a further step toward developing my speculations, I would like to review some ideas relating entropy to information. In information theory, a piece, or a bit, of information is thought of as having negative entropy, insofar as it is thought of as organization, ordering, and disequilibrium as opposed to the equilibrium or chaos of a high entropy state (Shannon, 1948; Brillouin, 1949, 1950, 1951, 1954). Blum (1955), in "Perspectives in Evolution," speaks of the evolution of intelligence and compares the brain with the computing machine: in the human brain the negative entropy implied in an orderly thinking process may involve the expenditure of a very small amount of free energy; but the functioning of the brain is directly dependent upon the energy metabolism of the man who maintains the brain, which is considerably greater. Looking at the matter more broadly, any extensive thought process involves learning from others, and so the metabolism of many other men needs to be included in the energy balance sheet."

NEGENTROPY AND PSYCHIC, INTERPSYCHIC,
AND CULTURAL EVOLUTION

Later (1955) Blum states: "What I want to emphasize by introducing them [questions about human nature] is that beneath established human behavior there lies a particularly fluid type of evolution, which must have changed its direction often, and can again. A long range evolutionary view could lead us to reexamine much of our thinking about ourselves, our culture, and our intelligence."

In the psychic sphere, I would propose that the natural course, over time, would be for the psyche to be increasingly and perpetually undergoing a process of differentiation, reintegration, and reorganization that would involve the acquisition of ever more information; this might be thought of as involving the acquisition of ever more negative entropy. The same may be said about the refinement of form in an interpsychic communication system, for in psychic growth, finality of form will never occur, since the process is dynamic and ever-changing. This, too, could be said of an interpsychic communication system and, by extension, of a cultural system as well. Blum (1963) has pointed out that the rate of cultural evolution, occurring by means of learning and the transmission of learned ideas, started very slowly thousands of years ago, but has gained impetus exponentially over time to its present state of low probability and high negentropy. The invention of one kind of tool opens the way for further developments.

A SUB-IDEA FIELD

I would suggest that when we think of the creation of new ideas, we consider that there is such a thing as a sub-idea field, composed either of sub-idea particles, uninformation, un-ideas, or sub-idea energy. Out of this field, ideas are continuously created, from the most rudimentary to the most complex. Born (1949) believed in continuous creation, and flatly disputed the metaphysical principle that everything must have a cause. He said that it is inevitable that a monistic concept of experience has to be abandoned. "If quantum theory has any philosophical importance at all, it lies in the fact that it demonstrates . . . the necessity of dual aspects and complimentary considerations." There should be no more loose talk about the principle of psychological determinism. "Nature is ruled by laws of cause and laws of chance in a certain mixture." If we apply this thinking to thinking about thinking, we can think of a state of non-thought out of which thought would arise. The non-thought field would be another way of naming the sub-idea particle or energy field conceptualized above. As an interesting aside, Hoyle et al. (1964) speculate that quasars in outer space contribute to energy fields, called C-fields, or creation fields, in which hydrogen is created.

If a choice is made, or a form created, actually this decision is a binary event, since a choice actually involves a yes and a no. A separation or condensation involves a change in form of the thing and the ground against which the thing is defined. Development increases the form of both the positive and the negative. Put differently, if one makes a certain choice, although he cannot simultaneously make the opposite, he defines the opposite. In thermodynamic terms of entropy, both the chosen and the rejected have acquired negentropy. Put still differently, the differentiation of a thing from a non-thing results in increased negentropy of the thing and of the non-thing.

THE SCHIZOPHRENOGENIC INTERPSYCHIC COMMUNICATION SYSTEM

It is possible to conceptualize the schizophrenogenic family in terms of a matrix of socially shared psychopathology and to make observations from the frame of reference of such a defined dynamic system of interpsychic communication. It is observable that the schizophrenogenic interpsychic communication system is such that disagreements are not resolved in a creative way; decisions, selections or choices are not made, and the members do not learn from each other or teach each other. This all may be subsumed under the idea of poverty of concept formation, since new concepts are not formed in the interpsychic system, nascent concepts are negated, new concepts impinging on the family system are negated, and certain stereotyped concepts (interpsychic family myths or delusions) are perpetuated unchanged. In clinical terms, one observes a great deal of noisy, repetitive conversation, a great amount of flat or inappropriate affect, and the denial of what the therapists would ordinarily consider to be meaningful or significant associations between thoughts. Schaffer et al. (1962) have written, in an article "On the Nature and Sources of the Psychiatrist's Experience with the Family of the Schizophrenic," that it would seem that the interpsychic communication system of the schizophrenogenic family is designed to negate meaningfulness. Arguments and disagreements, which might at first appear to be approaches to creative change, are seen over time to be mainly noise, which dissipates energy and serves to perpetuate the status quo. When, in family therapy, the family way of keeping anything new from happening is threatened, a family member will often absent himself from the treatment sessions, thus keeping the interpsychic communication system protected (Sonne et al., 1962). A significant peripheral person involved in the interpsychic communication system may also function to prevent creative change (Sonne, 1965).

The very conception of an interpsychic communication system represents the invention of a tool offering opportunities for conceptualizing and possibly measuring psychic processes, including energy processes, by allowing us to examine psychic processes at a level outside the individual psyche. The schizophrenogenic interpsychic communication system described above may characterized as possessing poverty of concept formation, high noise level, and poverty of affect. Energy seems to be dissipated in ineffectual attempts to communicate new information in the system, or to be used in the repetitive replacement or reinforcement of a fragmented, chaotic, undifferentiated, disorganized state composed of nonintegrated bits of information: that is, used in the maintenance of the "family psychosis." The system is also characterized by a quality of timelessness and reversibility similar to that seen in dreams and in the unconscious, and may be thought of as a primary process system despite whatever surface appearance of order there may be. If, for the moment, we ignore such things as symbolic meaning, attempts at meaning, and spotty areas of successful communication within the system, and speak in gross, macroscopic, simple terms, we could say that the communication system appears to hopelessly waste time and energy, and to produce noise rather than music.

THE SCHIZOPHRENOGENIC INTERPSYCHIC
COMMUNICATION SYSTEM AND ENTROPY

If we apply the concept of entropy, order, and organization to the concept of the schizophrenogenic interpsychic communication system, may we speculate that the schizophrenogenic interpsychic communication system is deficient in negative entropy, which would correspond to poverty of concept formation, and has an excess of positive entropy, which would correspond to noise and disassociated, inappropriate, or flat affect? It is as if the energy system stabilizes chaos rather than differentiation and tension. In terms of probability, it exists in a state of high probability rather than in the state of low probability characteristic of life processes generally.

A further speculation would be that the interpsychic communication system of the schizophrenogenic family attempts to refute the second law of thermodynamics, stopping psychic growth, which, even though it involves the accumulation of negative entropy, contains an awareness of impending biological death and psychic dissolution. If one does not grow psychically, perhaps one might assume that one might not die, and one might pretend to psychic immortality. Psychic immortality, however, could be equated with a state of high entropy.

A denial of the second law of thermodynamics in the psychic sphere actually results in a premature and conspicuous expression of it. Fear of the equilibrium of death may cause fear of differentiation, which in turn causes premature equilibrium. By refusing to accept the passage of time, approaching biologic death, and ultimate psychic death, the family actually lives a life of "psychic death" already. A psychic system which is not growing is as if dead. It is already operating at a high entropy level. The family system appears as if it has already reached equilibrium or homeostasis. Jackson (1957) has written on the question of family homeostasis. I would postulate that only sick or disturbed families are in equilibrium or homeostasis. The concept of equilibrium or homeostasis allows no room for the concept of growth or differentiation over time. It is a concept most limited in time, probably never applicable to a creative psychic or interpsychic system. To my mind, it is impossible to conceive of a psychic, interpsychic, or cultural psychic system that would cease differentiating and changing. An interpsychic system could not remain unchanged unless strong forces were operating to stop psychic growth and replicate stereotypic concepts, which may be considered as tantamount to family myths or shared delusions.

THE FAMILY PSYCHOTHERAPIST AND NEGENTROPY

Let us consider the concept of the schizophrenogenic interpsychic communication system existing at a high entropy—high probability state in reference to the matter of family psychotherapy. The family psychotherapist exposes his psyche to the impact of this system and, conversely, the system is exposed to the impact of the therapist's psyche. Energy processes are occurring. The schizophrenogenic interpsychic communication system tends to include the psychotherapist's psyche into its high entropy disordered state; the psychotherapist attempts through his psychic work to create new concepts and negative entropy in the schizophrenogenic interpsychic communication system. The psychotherapist's psyche (which in turn is part of various other interpsychic communication systems) may be thought of as engaging in psychic work upon the schizophrenogenic interpsychic communication system to introduce order, organization, and negative entropy into the system. The therapist's affect may be thought of as a measure or manifestation of (or as closely related to) the psychic work required to communicate concepts interpsychically and to make an idea meaningful, significant, or related. Beyond the actual creation of negentropy in the schizophrenogenic interpsychic communication system, the introduction of the basic concept that psychic life involves the continuous increase of negentropy in itself becomes a tool that allows for continuing increases of negentropy, or psychic growth, in the family system without the continued contribution of the therapist.

Transitory phases of potentially creative turbulence occur during periods of impact and observation in the therapy. Such phases could be thought of as phases of increased disorganization and increased entropy of the system; they are disturbing to all participants, especially the therapist. If such a phase drifts toward equilibrium, therapy may drift to a non-defined, hopeless "dead end" with the therapist's psyche caught up in the positive entropy system and "injured." If concepts are developed in the course of therapy—and this could include a clear definition of termination—these concepts could be classified as new or absolute information, and the psyches of all participants in the experience, including the therapist's, would profit from a gain of negative entropy.

SUMMARY

This paper has attempted to conceptualize psychic energy processes in thermodynamic terms, using the interpsychic communication system of schizophrenogenic families as data. The very conception of an interpsychic communication system represents the invention of a tool offering opportunities for conceptualizing and possibly measuring psychic energy processes.

Crucial characteristics of the interpsychic communication system in schizophrenogenic families include high noise level, poverty of concept formation, and poverty of affect. The high noise level and poor concept formation, in thermodynamic terms, may represent a high entropy level, and poor affect may represent lack of psychic work.

Affect may be thought of as a measure or manifestation of, or as closely related to, the psychic work required to communicate concepts interpsychically. Concept formation, representing ordering and growth, may be thought of as occurring through conversion of psychic work into negative entropy. The concept has been proposed that a sub-idea field may exist from which ideas are continuously created.

Applying these concepts to psychotherapy, one might speculate that through his psychic work the psychotherapist creates new concepts and negative entropy in the family interpsychic communication system.

REFERENCES

Blum, H. F. Perspectives in evolution. Amer. Scient., 1955, 43, 595-610.

Blum, H. F. On the origin and evolution of human culture. Amer. Scient., 1963, 51, 32-47.

Bohr, Niels. Atomic physics and human knowledge. New York: J. Wiley, Sons, 1958.

Born, Max. Natural philosophy of cause and chance. Oxford: Clarendon Press, 1949.

Bridgman, P. W. Reflections on thermodynamics. Amer. Scient., 1953, 41, 549-555.

Brillouin, L. Life, thermodynamics, and cybernetics. Amer. Scient., 1949, 37, 554-568.

Brillouin, L. Thermodynamics and information theory. Amer. Scient., 1950, 38, 594-599.

Brillouin, L. Maxwell's demon cannon operate: information and entropy. J. appl. Phys., 1951, 22 (1), 334-343.

Brillouin, L. Information theory in uncertainty principle. J. appl. Phys., 1954, 25, 887.

Grünbaum, A. Time and entropy. Amer. Scient., 1955, 43, 550-572.

Hoyle, F., et al. On relativistic astrophysics. Astrophys. J.,
    1964, 139, 909-928.
Jackson, D. D. The question of family homeostasis. Psychiat.
    Quart. Supp., 1957, 31, 79-90.
Klein, M. J. Order, organization and entropy. Brit. J. Phil. Sci.,
    1953, 4, 158.
Ostow, M. Entropy changes in mental activity. J. nerv. ment.
    Dis., 1949, 110, 502-506.
Schaffer, L., et al. On the nature and sources of the psychiatrist's
    experience with the family of the schizophrenic. Psychiatry,
    1962, 25, 32-45.
Shannon, C. E. A mathematical theory of communication. Bell
    Syst. Tech. J., 1948, 27, 379-423 and 623-656.
Sonne, J. C., et al. The absent-member maneuver as a resistance
    in family therapy of schizophrenia. Fam. Proc., 1962, 1,
    44-62.
Sonne, J. C. The role of significant peripheral persons in allo-
    plastic resistances of schizophrenogenic families. In A. Fried-
    man, et al., Psychotherapy for the whole family; case his-
    tories, techniques, and concepts of family therapy in the home
    and clinic. New York: Springer, 1965.
Szasz, T. S. Entropy, organization and the problem of the economy
    of human relationships. Int. J. Psychoanal., 1955, 36, 289-297.

FAMILY SYSTEM AS MODEL FOR EGO SYSTEM

James L. Titchener, M. D.

This treatment of ego-family transaction has three parts. First, I shall argue for the importance of an intrapsychic point of view in the comprehension of family process and psychopathology. Second, I shall describe a family-system phase of ego development, a phase which we can usefully define and delineate. Third, I would like to show how family life influences the maturing ego through the development of a self representation and an object world as subsystems in the ego.

I had an experience while preparing this paper which lent support to my thesis and illuminated for me the problems with which I was dealing. I started gathering notes from a diversity of sources — my own research, reports of others, theoretical papers, clinical experience, and sheer fantasy. One night I gave up the job of trying to organize something communicable from this buzzing welter of raw information and ideas. I went to bed and had the following dream:

I was at a lectern in a conference like this one. I wore a morning coat and striped trousers. They were formal clothes, but the coat was threadbare, torn, and shabby. It was worn over a false shirtfront and a drooping, greasy, formal tie such as an undertaker might wear. The striped trousers were baggy at the knees. I spoke pompously and with a Teutonic accent. I said, "I am Professor Graustark. I am a doctor of philosophy, arts, literature, science, medicine, and psychiatry. Psychiatry and psychoanalysis are a lot of bunk!" There was pleased laughter and cheering from the audience, and I woke up.

Graustark is a mythical country in a fiercely romantic novel of the same name. I do not believe I have read it, but I have known the meaning of the adjective "graustarkian." In association I think of Ruritania, another mythical country in an equally ridiculous romantic novel and movie of the twenties with Ronald Coleman — the Prisoner of Zenda. Ladies and gentlemen, I can halt the flow of associations here because I see that in the story of the Prisoner, I have plunged directly into my own family dynamics! If I continued the associations you would be able to see with me the representations of self and objects in my own family, and you would recognize the processes and attitudes that contributed to ego development in the family of which I was an offspring. My dream illustrates, then, the possibility of recovering from the individual's ego the nature of his experiences with his own family processes, and it points to the value of understanding families from an intrapsychic point of view. In addition, the dream indicates the problem of the identity of the investigator in the area of family dynamics. The dream visited me in the midst of my overstraining to produce a brilliant and original piece of theorizing on the transactional relation between the ego and family systems. The Teutonic, know-it-all clown-professor speaking pompously was a vision warning me that I was about to prepare for this conference a pompous paper, a highly abstract vehicle full of Zeitgeist and jargon and far from the realities of family life. In such a paper I would betray the psychiatric and psychoanalytic profession.

Above all, the dream admonished me that, though I am now a family researcher, I was once growing up in a family, and that my theories should have correspondence with real-life events in my own family and other families I have known.

THE INTRAPSYCHIC VIEW OF FAMILY INTERACTION

The study of family process and structure, the use of family observation in diagnostic work, and the practice of family therapy do not require a departure from emphasis on understanding the intrapsychic influences on behavior. In my view, the study of family interaction and the practice of family therapy will be and is of immense value in further exploration of the inner feelings, thoughts, and modes of ego adaptation in man. Because of the phenomenon of internalization of the family experience by the offspring in a family, we can learn much about the shaping of the ego from our study of the ego-family transaction.

There are some methods and theories in the family research field that tend to put aside the concept of the unconscious from thoughts about family interaction; yet family interaction experiments and family therapy sessions, studied carefully, bring to our attention time and again the unconscious communication channels in family experience. In unconscious communication, the feeling of the sender is repressed from his own awareness and dissociated from the explicit information he is transmitting. The message is received below the repression barrier by the other member of the family: e.g., a mother's seductiveness in voice tone, posture, and movement causes manifestations of shame in her son without either of them being aware of the feeling transmitted from one to the other. This phenomenon of unconscious communication is but one example of important occurrences in the fast-moving complexity of family life that require study from the intrapsychic point of view as well as the extrapsychic.

Furthermore, the very intimacy of the relations under study in family research or therapy and the intensity of charge or cathexis in the interaction of a family have intrapsychic connotations. Like analysis of dreams, the study of the behavior of an individual in his family affords us one of our best opportunities to make inferences on intrapsychic processes and to test them. An interaction between two people—an interpersonal exchange, if you will—carefully analyzed in a session of psychotherapy, a psychoanalytic hour, or a family interview can be more illuminating on intrapsychic processes than any interaction with an ink blot or anything else.

The family experience is perhaps marginal between intrapsychic and extrapsychic processes. It is an experience from which the ego internalizes images, ideas, attitudes, representations of objects, and representations of the self in relation to significant objects. A family myth, for example (Ferreira, 1965), has a controlling influence on family interaction; but its deeper effect is upon the ego, which internalizes the myth and uses it as a guiding principle for interpreting human relations (as it has been used in the family).

The ego binds together inner life and social action (Gill and Klein, 1964). This synthetic process is most acutely fostered by the ego's transactional experience in the family. Often this synthesis of inner feelings bound with internalized representations of the family experience may be presented as a symptom, a pathological character trait, or especially as a transference attitude.

A successful attorney discovered during treatment that he had very often been overly critical of his family and colleagues. He thought his work was socially without value and unproductive, though it paid very well. He complained that he drank too much at weekend parties. These three facets of behavior vividly represented and reenacted within the patient the dynamics of the relationship between his father and mother. His mother had frankly despised his father for drinking, though he agreeably resisted changing the pattern. The patient drank and despised himself for it. Father had been a country lawyer with a small-time practice which nevertheless provided a comfortable living. The myth was that the son would be a prominent attorney with a big-city practice and powerful clients. He gained that kind of position in an impressive law firm, but was unhappy with it. His mixed attitude towards both law and drinking expressed both sides of the conflicts between his mother and father. His symptoms of hypercriticism of others and unhappiness with himself synthesized some identifications with the representation within himself of the relationship of his parents.

THE FAMILY SYSTEM PHASE IN EGO DEVELOPMENT

The interaction in the network of family relations may be characterized by the fact that it includes at least three persons (Titchener et al., 1963; Titchener and Golden, 1963). The capacity to respond to at least two others simultaneously in a triadic communication system marks the beginning of the family experience for the growing individual. Prior to the acquisition of this capacity to differentiate and integrate responses to more than one other person, the experiences with others are dyadic in form. There must be cases of arrest in development at this level of integration, and there must also be variations in the form and manner of its acquisition, for there are families that appear to be structured along dyadic lines. For example, there is the case of over-differention between parents, in which the functions are overly demarcated and distinct (discipline by father, tenderness from mother, etc.) with anxiety when the compartments break down. In such families, the child has no awareness of his own influence upon his parents. In other families, the interaction with regard to both cognitive and affective functions is almost entirely with one parent, the other parent having effect only through physical or emotional absence. The offspring in families heavily weighted toward a dyadic structure grow up without a sense of interplay of feelings in family life. Therefore, concepts of ambivalence and change and comparison of attitudes are difficult for them. I believe there is, in this case, more of a tendency toward thinking of relationships in a conditional way or with a quid pro quo style (I will do this for you if you will do that for me, and so on).

A competent businessman sought help for a marriage plagued by almost constant uproar. He was effective in the marketplace, but depressed and passive in dealing with his fearsomely controlling wife. The uproar was increasing, partly because the wife was testing the extreme limits of her power to control and partly because she had managed to provoke some signs of assertion on the part of the husband. The intensity of their interaction and their way of always circling and eyeing each other tended to exclude their young son and daughter, though dyadic interactions of one parent with the one or the other child were frequent. They did not interact in concert with the children. The man had grown up in a family in which father was usually away and faded away even when he was there. This father was hardly a memory in the patient's mind during the several years of treatment. There had been a sister, too, but the mother's preoccupation had been with demanding her son's love and attention and giving it. This man's adaptation had been developed to deal with a sometimes overpowering, sometimes wheedling, and sometimes submissive figure — the other member of a dyad. His adaptation had not developed in response to the interplay of a social system like the family.

The developmental series worked out by Erikson (1959) for the epigenesis of the ego serves best as a continuum for locating and delineating the family-system phase of development. The dyadic phase of ego epigenesis takes place during the period of developmental crisis that Erikson calls "basic trust versus basic mistrust." The degree of confidence (Benedek, 1956) shared by mother and child and, later in this same crisis, the trust between father and child versus the impairment of confidence or the amount of basic mistrust will indeed be influenced by the field of interaction provided by the family. The family system of relations does influence the dyadic parent-child relation but does not yet affect the child directly.
When and if the crisis of trust versus mistrust has been overcome or better, resolved, the next crisis is that of autonomy versus shame and doubt. Simultaneous with this crisis comes the ego's experience with the system of family relations. At this time of acquiring autonomy and a further differentiation of the self from objects, the child is ready to move from dyadic relations to triads and even more elaborate systems. The transactions between ego and family systems continue to have their peak of influence on development during the crisis of industry versus inferiority (the grammar school crisis) and until the adolescent crisis of identity versus identity diffusion has been almost entirely overcome.
The delineation of a family-system phase of development extending through three crises in ego development suggests a system for categorizing family therapies. We may borrow from Gedo's (1964) classification of psychotherapies to derive an application of a developmental concept of family interaction to family therapy. It might be useful to apply Erikson's constructs to the types of problems we formulate in families. Some families have not overcome the excess of basic mistrust over basic trust. These family units, in the way of thinking of this paper, are not yet families at all in the systemic

sense. Their adaptations and adjustments are dyadic. To treat a unit like this, one would try to help the individuals overcome fundamental jealousies and rivalries from which the basic insecurity of each family member emerges. The treatment would be very largely educative, an action-oriented training in modes of family living.

Family therapy in the more formal sense is clearly applicable to the next three categories of family organization: that is, to those dealing with the crisis of autonomy versus shame and doubt, initiative versus inferiority, and identity versus identity-diffusion. The goals and methods of treatment would be different in each case. We would expect that in all these categories the problems in the offspring would be coordinated with the main crisis affecting family organization.

Many families, perhaps a majority, who bring troubled offspring to clinic or private psychiatric help have been unable to resolve the crisis of autonomy versus shame and doubt. Each of these families, struggling chiefly with autonomy, may have had trouble with gaining basic trust and will surely be unable to attain the feeling of continuity and sameness that comes with the crystallizing of identity. This interdependency of stages is the essential meaning of the theory of ego epigenesis.

A family of seven came originally because the neuroses of the parents had led to severe marital fighting. However, the effects of the disturbance were widespread in the system, and family therapy became an adjunct to individual treatment for the parents. Waves of aggression spread through the family system repeatedly. If the parents managed to stifle a marital fight, one of the boys might attack another; sometimes when aggression was blocked in the children, a fight between the parents could be provoked. Discipline was violated, inconsistent, physical, and an almost constant subject for discussion between parents and children. Control of the childrens' actions was harsh, rigid, brittle, and full of loopholes. There was a continual alternation between demands for success in the children and mourning over failure, with short bursts of achievement by the children. If success were threatening one of the boys, for example, he would get into a fight with a teacher and be expelled from school. In sum, the family fought to protect their individual and family autonomy against constant doubt and shame. The family therapy brought out the ways they were armed against a hostile world as a family and also the ways each fought within the family system to maintain autonomy against controls by others in the system. Most strikingly, they used a counterphobic mechanism.

The boys would physically attack the father or verbally provoke the mother in order to establish their lack of fear. When the whole family was in a near-panic, one of the children, usually one of the boys, would be sent out to attack someone outside the family. A safe return from the foray was supposed to reassure the rest. The family therapist worked to gain autonomy for the family without the necessity for excessive, invasive controls, while helping them to decide upon more consistent, more possible, and more rational ones.

The family problems associated with the crisis of initiative versus inferiority and with identity versus identity-diffusion call for varying techniques of family therapy. A formulation placing the family's organization in the Erikson epigenetic series allows therapeutic planning in the treatment of family crises.

THE FAMILY, THE SELF, AND THE OBJECT WORLD

A major contribution of the family experience to ego epigenesis is the filling-out and crystallizing of object and self representations within the system ego. The acquisition of dependable endopsychic representations of the self and significant others begins before the family-system phase of development but the process is considerably enriched by the ego's transactions with the system of family relations. This way of thinking about ego and family transaction permits unification of intrapsychic and extrapsychic points of view and elucidates the hypothetical process of the ego's binding of inner feeling with social experience.

The notions of self and object representations as substructures within the system ego have been employed by many psychoanalytic investigators, but the ideas in this paper depend mainly upon the work of Jacobson (1964) and Sandler and Rosenblatt (1964). The original theses of these writers will have to be condensed and oversimplified for the purposes of this paper.

The "self" refers to the whole person of an individual, including his body and body parts, and his psychic organization with its parts. The self, a whole person, is also distinguished from the ego which is a mental agency. A self representation is an internalized accretion of images of the self, i.e., of the body self and of the mental self. An image of the self is the state of perception of the self at a particular moment. These perceptions or images are internalized and laid down within the ego to build a partly conscious, partly preconscious, partly unconscious, more or less enduring and stable, representation of the self. Secondary narcissism and secondary masochism consist of loving and hateful feelings toward facets of self-representation.

The object world, an important ego subsystem, consists of object representations of persons in the individual's environment. These representations are accumulated from varying object images and they are internalized to become more or less stable and enduring substructures within the ego.

What is the importance of these constructs in theories of human behavior and family dynamics? The process of identification can be understood in these terms. In identification (Sandler and Rosenblatt, 1964) there is a modification of a self representation (using an object representation as a model), with consequent changes in the ego. In the case of the development of the superego, an object representation acquires a "special status" having the authority of the parents. The self representation is peculiarly modifiable through identification with this special object representation. These changes in object and self representations have widespread and complicated influence upon ego functions. The stability and form of object and self representations would largely determine the nature of the sense of identity which is crucial to the adolescent crisis near the end of the family-system phase of human development.

The family's major contribution to ego epigenesis is toward a crucial organization of ego functions. This step in development depends upon modes of perceiving others in relation to the self, upon perceiving others in relation to others, and finally upon the delineation of the self and others. These accomplishments can only be completed in the network of family relations and only in a family that has at least partially resolved the issue of basic trust versus basic mistrust. The elemental feeling of jealousy must have been overcome enough to permit a higher form of relating than symbiotic, narcissistic, or dyadic forms. Then, in the more complex system of family relations, the individual can perceive himself against a backdrop of the relationships that others in the family have.

This representational world serves to inform the ego in the conduct of intimate and social relations throughout the remainder of life. The style of conducting relationships, the style of perceiving and describing others, and the style of communicating thought and feeling in the family will be internalized with this representational world and will transmit a style to the organization of the ego.

This transmittal of style to the individual can be observed in research on family interaction and can be a crucial finding in the conduct of family therapy. It would be painstaking and difficult, though feasible, to study each of the steps involved in the formation of the representational world, from the perception and intake of self and object images to observations of the influence of these on ego organization. The form, if not the underlying conflict itself, of psychopathology in an offspring is taken from the family's thinking and expressive styles.

The influence of family modes of relating, expressing, and thinking on the ego's representational world, and therefore upon ego's style and organization of behavior, is difficult to exemplify and to demonstrate in a scientific manner. Our method of family interaction experiments (Titchener and Golden, 1962) and a family relations inventory (Emerson and Titchener, 1964) have at least offered promise for this theoretical approach. Family therapy and psychoanalytic therapy also show us repeatedly how representations of family objects and family relations act to guide perception, action, and feeling for a lifetime.

SUMMARY

The argument in this paper has been threefold:

1. The intrapsychic point of view elucidates studies of family process, and studies of family process will elucidate issues in ego psychology.

2. There is a family-system phase of ego development. It may be delineated according to the Erikson series of epigenetic crises.

3. The ego-family transaction results in a crystallizing of the ego's internalized object world.

REFERENCES

Benedek, Therese F. Toward the biology of the depressive constellation. J. Amer. Psychoanal. Ass., 1956, 4, 389-427.

Emerson, R., and Titchener, J. The expanded item questionnaire. Paper read at the Ohio Valley Sociological Society, 1964.

Erikson, E. H. Identity and the life cycle; selected papers. Psychol. Issues, 1959, 1, No. 1.

Ferreira, A. J. Family myths. Read at Regional Research Conf. on Family Structure, Dynamics and Therapy. Amer. Psychiat. Ass., Galveston, Texas, Feb. 1965.

Gedo, J. Concepts for a classification of the psychotherapies. Int. J. Psychoanal., 1964, 45, 530-539.

Gill, M., & Klein, G. The structuring of drive and reality; David Rapaport's contributions to psychoanalysis and psychology. Int. J. Psychoanal., 1964, 45, 483-498.

Jacobson, Edith. The self and the object world. New York: Int. Univer. Press, 1964.

Riskin, J. Family interaction scales: a preliminary report. Arch. gen. Psychiat., 1964, 11, 484-494.

Sandler, J., & Rosenblatt, B. The concept of the representational world. Psychoanal. Stud. Child, 1962, 17, 128-145.

Titchener, J., et al. Family transaction and derivation of individuality. Fam. Proc., 1963, 2, 95-120.

Titchener, J., & Golden, M. Predictions of therapeutic themes from observation of family interaction evoked by the 'revealed differences' technique. J. nerv. ment. Dis., 1963, 136, 464-474.

THE VICTIM AND HIS SILENCERS:
SOME PATHOGENIC STRATEGIES AGAINST BEING SILENCED

Gerald H. Zuk, Ph.D.

I have suggested elsewhere that "there is a causal relation between silencing strategies and pathogenic silence and babbling which
may themselves be used as silencing strategies" (p.33, Zuk, 1965a).
Silence and babbling, and variants which would include silly smiling
and inappropriate laughter, are rather common symptoms of mental
disorders, particularly the more severe disorders such as psychosis
and schizophrenia. The immobile silence of the catatonic is classic,
as is the silly babbling and smiling of the hebephrenic.

Silence requires no definition. Babbling may be described as a
verbal melange, unrelated to the situation but idiosyncratically
meaningful to the individual. If one listens carefully, one finds that
babbling often has a definite fantasy or delusional content. The person appears to select the technique of babbling to avoid a direct confrontation of his fantasy or delusions. Silence and babbling are
equivalents in the sense that both add up to the individual's saying
nothing, though of course they are not equivalents in other important aspects.

In the study referred to above (Zuk, 1965a), two schizophrenic
young women were described, whose silence and babbling were major symptoms of illness. The writer was the young women's therapist in combined individual and family therapy, and observed, in
family therapy, the way powerful silencing strategies were directed
at them by their parents. In specific instances, the silencing seemed
to have the effect of provoking them to increased symptomatic behavior. In continued work with these young women and their families,
it became apparent how deeply held were these strategies, how much
a part of the style and functioning of the family they were, and how
resistant they were to change.

Silencing strategies are widespread repressive interpersonal
phenomena, and, in many instances, are quite socially acceptable
ways to punish individuals for perceived misdeeds. They are be-

lieved energized by at least two types of motives, one rather superficial, the other more deeply dynamic. The first motive is the wish
to obtain compliance or conformity from the person on an issue one
is supporting or to punish his lack of compliance. The second motive
is the wish to possess the person as an object for the projection of
one's own feelings of being worthless or bad, or the wish merely to
possess. The second motive is, of course, the key one in relation
to the question of pathology, for in energizing a silencing strategy,
the second motive lends a direction, intensity, and consistency that
raises silencing to the level of an effective pathological force.

Silencing strategies may be remarkably subtle; they almost always permit the silencers to deny what they are doing. Thus they
tend to generate, as another byproduct to silence and babbling in the
victim, paranoid ideation. If the victim is so bold as to challenge
his silencers, they accuse him of unreasonable suspiciousness and
gross misreading of intentions and motives. The message to the victim is: "Keep quiet, or at least spout nonsense as punishment for
your failure to comply or conform. Until you do comply—and maybe not even then—we will act toward you in a manner designed to
render you silent or nonsensical. If you complain, we will deny that
we are doing anything but at the same time suggest possible steps
you can take to bring our activities against you to a halt."

Some silencing strategies have become so regularized that popular terms have been attached to them: scapegoating is one, stere-
otyping another, and "brainwashing" still another. The gambit of
"changing the subject" is a well-recognized silencing measure directed against an issue or area of communication rather than against
a person. The "silent treatment" is directed against a person—it
is sometimes referred to as the "cold shoulder."

The writer's prior study described some silencing strategies
and explored thoughts and speculations about their relationship to
individual psychopathology, particularly pathologic silence and babbling. Relatively little attention was given to the special contribution
of the victim of these strategies to his own psychopathology, although
it was noted that the victim made discoveries about his silence which
were of as great etiological significance to his pathology as the fact
that silencing strategies had been directed against him. One such
discovery is that the victim can turn the maneuver of his silencers
against them with considerable force. It is possible for him to discover even that he can beat his silencers at their own game, although this discovery carries with it the dangerous temptation to
meet all threats and crises with intractable silence.

This paper will make some observations on the nature of the
victim's discoveries about silence, speculate about factors that may

predispose him to make such discoveries, and detail the counter-
retaliatory efforts of the silencers once they get wind of the victim's
own retaliation. Hopefully, the speculations offered here will be
consistent with the observations of behavior on which they are
based—observations essentially made in the context of psychotherapeutic work with disturbed individuals and families.

Two of the victim's counter-strategies to silencing will be described: the first in considerably more detail than the second because I suspect the first contains the elements leading to pathogenic
silence or babbling and the second does not, although the second does
carry with it implications for pathology. The first will be designated
the active, aggressive, competitive position (even though the victim
may appear in behavior to be anything but active, aggressive, or
competitive); the second will be designated the compliant, supplicatory position (even though the victim may appear quite different in
behavior).

THE ACTIVE, AGGRESSIVE, COMPETITIVE POSITION

In what follows, it shall be assumed that the silencers are deeply motivated by the wish to possess the victim as an object on which
to project feelings of being inadequate or bad, or simply as a needed
object. They may be relatively aware or unaware of this motive.
At the level of "public" motives, of course, they respond to a need
to enforce the victim's compliance on some issue, or a need to punish him for lack of compliance, so as themselves to appear conforming and compliant.

In their thinking, the silencers assume that their victim is dependent on them and frequently this assumption is justified, at least
in part. They expect that eventually the victim will comply with
their demands, such as they may be, because of his dependency on
them. In the case of parents and their children, the belief in a dependent relationship obviously has considerable biological and social
support. Prior to the onset of a silencing strategy a relationship
between the silencers and victim (parents and child) has existed in
which dependency has been a major realistic factor.

But the victim who takes the active, aggressive, competitive
stance challenges the silencers' assumption of his dependency on
them and their assumption that eventually this factor will bring
about his compliance. He sets out to undermine the assumptions by
attempting to prove to his silencers that they are at least as dependent on him as he is on them. Initially, his response to silencing may
be one of hostile negativism. He may attack his silencers verbally
or attack nonverbally by pouting or sullenness. These responses

confirm to the silencers that their method has begun to strike home. They presume that the victim is ready for the next step, which is to outline to him the course he must follow if he would have them cease their activities against him.

But the victim has just begun to fight. He indicates by silence that he will not follow the course leading to his absolution, although his silence partly confirms that he is a true victim of his silencers: that is, that he has come under some real constraint to employ silence as a sign of contention between himself and his silencers.

The silencers may shun him, may give him the "cold shoulder." Their behavior is calculated to precipitate silence in him, but then he begins to explore the options available to him in this position. He comes to recognize that in maintaining his silence vis-à-vis his silencers he has communicated to them the message that he is prepared to resist what he perceives to be the key underlying motive of their strategy—namely, the wish to immobilize him, possess him, rob him of his independence and initiative.

Some ameliorative bargaining may occur during this phase or even prior to it. The victim carefully probes the silencers to see if they will amend their terms so as to reduce the likelihood he will be robbed of his independence. He may test this possibility by taking a step or two along the path his silencers originally set down leading to absolution, in the hope that they may now be ready to revise the course and reduce the likelihood of its suspected intent. He hopes his silencers have perceived his resistance and that they may be led to reevaluate their strategy. He hopes he has established the fact that there is a mutual dependency in their relationship. He may even be so bold as to signal a readiness to terminate his relationship with his silencers, if this threat is at all within the realm of those available to him, in order to demonstrate dramatically his lack of dependence on them and, as much to the point, to expose the extent of their dependence on him.

The silencers may or may not decide to settle at this point: so much depends on how needy they are to possess the victim. An element of fury may now enter the picture, however, as a result of the counter-measures of the victim. Sensing a possible frustration of their strategy, the silencers may now amend it in a pointedly vicious way: they may now decide to change their game so that the victim is offered not one but various and inconsistent courses leading to absolution. In effect, the victim is denied absolution.

The victim continues to explore the various meanings of the silence that has in a real sense been forced on him. He learns that if he continues to maintain silence he can produce in his silencers a definite state of agitation and disorganization. He comprehends this is so because they are frustrated in their expectation that he will eventually comply with their demands. Then he makes an exciting but at the time dangerously tantalizing discovery: in the same way his silencers demanded that he be silent, at a later time they demand that he speak, that he accede verbally to their demands. Finally the victim has a concrete bit of evidence that his silencers are dependent on him—dependent on him to speak—but of course only as they would have him speak. He correctly perceives that his silencers wait eagerly for his words to signal that he is ready to negotiate his release from their trap. His words of admission are eagerly awaited to confirm the silencers in their role, for it is an important source of power and gratification for them to believe that they have played their role and played it successfully.

Meanwhile, the victim has discovered how effectively silence can be used to counter silence. He may conclude, with considerable insight and strategic sense, that he can win against his silencers simply by not losing; that is, insofar as their game is concerned, the victim effectively checks his silencers by turning his silence against them. But in winning a prolonged game with his silencers, the victim is exposed to a very serious danger: namely, the discovery of the degree to which silence can control and dominate human relationships. This discovery, coming too early in development and with too great force can be disastrous, for it can cause the individual to seek to control and dominate all his relationships, all life crises or threats, through the use of silence. Applied with a low degree of selectivity to human situations and relationships, silence can only be regarded as a pathology.

What is the cause of the pathology? Is it the leveling of a silencing strategy, motivated by a wish for possession, against the victim? Is it the victim's falling silent in response to the pressures of the silencing strategy? No. The cause is presumed to lie more in the nature of the discoveries the victim makes about silence while engaged in series of transactions with his silencers. If he concludes, quite rightly, that silence is a powerful controlling device in human relationships, if the discovery comes too early in his development and with too great force, and if his continuing life situation is such that he is chronically encouraged to use silence in coming to terms with disturbing human relationships and situations, then, in this writer's opinion, the likelihood of his developing at some time a serious pathology involving silence will be considerable.

THE COMPLIANT, SUPPLICATORY POSITION

Earlier in this paper it was stated that the active, aggressive, competitive position would be contrasted with another position that can be taken vis-à-vis silencing strategies: namely, the compliant, supplicatory position. Some attention will now be given to this latter type, although, as also stated previously, it is not believed to eventuate in a pathology of silence.

A major need of the victim who selects the compliant position is to avoid possession by his silencers. However, instead of setting out to demonstrate his independence of them and use this to force them to alter their strategy against him, the compliant victim accepts his dependency on his silencers as a fact of life. His counterstrategy is simply to prove to his silencers that he is not worth possessing totally. His object is to get his silencers to ask themselves: Well, what do we really want this fellow for?

The victim who assumes the compliant position becomes dutifully silent and contrite as soon as he notices the presence of a silencing strategy directed against him, thus accepting or at least seeming to accept the penitent role prescribed for him. He quickly seeks to discover the steps in the path the silencers have set down leading to absolution. He may even suggest steps himself as a means to get them to shorten the course. Indeed, his helpfulness to his silencers is part of his strategy to persuade them that he is not really worth having. He cleverly undermines them in their expectation of heavy resistance to their maneuvers.

In my opinion, it is unlikely that the victim who selects the compliant position will make the same profound discoveries about silence that the victim who selects the aggressive position makes. I doubt that he is as likely to get locked into a vicious struggle for control through the use of silence. But there is real danger in this position, to be sure: the victim cannot be certain that his over-easy capture will discourage his silencers' thirst for possession; he may still become the object of quite sadistic impulses. Thus pathology may also be the outcome of his position, although it may not be a pathology of silence.

DELUSIONAL, HALLUCINATORY, AND PARANOID IDEATION IN THE CONTEXT OF SILENCING STRATEGIES

In my opinion, delusional, hallucinatory, and paranoid ideation can result from taking either of the positions to silencing that have been described. The victim may accuse his silencers of plotting against him—which, after all, they are—but a common characteristic of the silencing strategy is that it permits the silencers to deny what they are doing. The silencers may say that the victim is "reading things into their behavior," that he is unduly suspicious, and so on. In this way they subtly promote the development of delusional, hallucinatory, or paranoid ideation. Even while denying their acts, however, they may be outlining to the victim the steps he must take if he is to receive absolution.

Lifton (1957) has described the development of disordered think-ing in victims of Chinese communist thought reform, which may be thought of as a very harsh and unrelenting silencing strategy strongly motivated by the wish to take possession of the victim's political ideology. The victims' past ideology was silenced by a variety of means including incarceration, physical punishment, humiliating practices, and constant threatening interrogation. The victim is shown that he can obtain absolution by signing a confession stating that he has engaged in the past in evil practices and by promising to correct past errors and adopt the "right" way of thinking. At a sign of willingness by the victim that he is complying with demands, the harsher punishments devised by jailers and interrogators are reduced.

The interrogators go to considerable lengths to obtain a con-fession from the victim, though they know it may not be genuine. They count on the psychological principle that once a verbal pattern is set down and repeated sufficiently in a rigorously controlled set-ting, that pattern will tend to ultimately establish itself in the indi-vidual and become genuine. This practice provides some confirma-tion for what has been proposed as one of the key transactions in the relationship between the victim who takes the aggressive position and his silencers: namely, that at some point the silencers are de-pendent on the victim to talk, to break his silence, to give a verbal sign that their strategy is in effect and working to some degree.

Lifton describes one case of a Catholic priest who, under the harrassment of his interrogators, had an hallucinatory episode: he had reveries that were half dreams, half hallucinations, in which he imagined things on the order of a rescue, a savior fantasy, or someone calling. He imagined his own consul, the consul from his European country, coming to the cell, walking past his cell, and not saying anything to him (p. 269).

The experience of paranoid ideation or delusional or hallucin-atory episodes was apparently not uncommon among the victims of the brand of thought reform practiced by the Chinese communists. Similar results can be observed in the case of "thought control" ex-ercised in families, for example, by parents against children. One clear example was shown this writer recently while conducting a multiple family therapy session. Present among the families were a girl in her early twenties and her parents. The girl had recently become engaged to a boy she had known for some time, but her par-ents strongly opposed her intention to marry. Both parents were allied in their opposition to the marriage, and supported each other in their attack on their daughter's decision. The girl was an intensely needed person in the maintenance of the family and of the marriage relation itself, and her threatened loss through her own marriage was a greatly feared prospect. The parents were bent on undermining her decision. The girl, it should be explained, had a history of delusional thinking, although at the time of the session her thinking was relatively orderly and realistic. Her parents, it should also be said, exhibited rather serious personality disturbances.

In the multiple family therapy session, the parents mounted a powerful undermining attack against their daughter. They questioned whether she was ready for marriage and criticized her choice of a mate. They thought she should at least put off the decision for six months. The girl replied that she did not intend to wait; she had made up her mind. The parents then proceeded, one after the other, to sow doubts as to whether she was mentally well-balanced enough to make such an important decision: after all, she was still in treatment, maybe she should delay her marriage until she was "well enough."

The verbal assaultiveness of her parents provoked the girl into making bitter comments. She accused them of plotting against her decision to marry and stated she was confused as to whether the plotting was in her best interests, as they insisted, or theirs. She stated that she was forced to become silent toward them in order to avoid their incessant barrage of questions and accusations.

In the session the parents were quite skillful at turning her statements against her, which discouraged her from commenting at all. But when she became silent, when she appeared sullen and stubborn, they then raised a question about her mental condition: was her silence a sign she was again delusional? And if she was delusional, how could she make any decision about marriage? An especially interesting aspect of this rather vicious interaction was the tendency of the daughter, following the parents' implication she was delusional, to actually say something to suggest that she was. The terrible pressures on her to act or say something insane dragged a confirmation out of her. The parents then sat back, pleasant smiles on their faces, content that they had reestablished their symbiotic bond with their daughter.

This clinical example illustrates the idea that delusional, hallucinatory, or paranoid thinking may sometimes be the outcome of silencing strategies. The parents clearly signaled their daughter to say something delusional. The girl, who had been silent—a response indicating a high degree of resistance to their silencing—decided to comply with the parental demand, as if to say to them: "All right,

I will act a little insane for your benefit; perhaps this will make you feel guilty enough to stop what you are doing. Anyway, I am feeling terribly guilty myself for showing signs of independence and I will feel easier if by acting a bit crazy I can transfer some of it on to you."

Delusional, hallucinatory or paranoid ideation can occur, it is proposed, when the victim of silencing moves away from an entrenched position of counter-silence and decides to engage in some degree of mediation with his silencers. The mediation often involves powerful guilt-arousing maneuvers on both sides, efforts to get to each other to "admit" what they have been doing to each other, efforts to label each other's maneuver as "bad," "vicious," and "premeditated." One is quite likely to hear disordered thinking from either victim or silencers at this stage of their negotiations.

It may be appropriate here to note that whole ethnic or cultural groups have developed characteristic counter-strategies against silencing that involve what might be labeled a paranoid, delusional, or hallucinatory element. For example, in commenting on the harshly repressive English rule of Ireland in the 18th century, Shannon (1963) writes:

> The Irish coped with the toils of the insensate law machine by developing the art of soft deception ("blarney"), and the disingenuous oath which is not really an oath at all. These were the acts of the imagination designed to oblige the hearer with the fiction of compliance while preserving fidelity to one's own conception of justice. They were dangerous, self-destructive arts, perhaps, but a people with no tangible resources to meet adversity must rely on inscrutable silence or the resources of wit and speech. The Irish, it seemed, were not good at cultivating silence. They preferred what Sean O'Faolain has termed "that so typically Kerry-ish form of silence, an affluence of volubility" (p. 11).

Although Meissner (1964), in his perceptive review and analysis of the literature, concluded that "patterns of interaction within the family are not specific to any type of pathology" (p.17), the premise of this writer, as established and documented in this paper, is that such patterns do exist and that they are causal to the development of specific types of pathology. One such pattern of interaction in families and other groups has been designated as the silencing strategy, which is a means to constrain a victim to be silent. The victim and his silencers engage in a struggle whose outcome can be pathological silence, babbling or laughter, or the development of delusional, hallucinatory, or paranoid ideation in the victim. Steps believed involved in such possible developments have been laid down in the paper. Special attention has been paid to the notion that the victim "discovers" the extraordinary power that accrues to the one who maintains the silent position.

In the view of pathology taken here, there are a number of implications for the practice of psychotherapy that have been presented in a more detailed manner elsewhere (Zuk, 1965b). It cannot be stated too strongly how powerful and controlling is the patient who assumes the silent position in psychotherapy or the patient who exhibits symptomatic silence or babbling. The therapist may be helpful if he patiently, persistently, and wisely refuses to limit the relationship to the question of whether the patient starts talking or stops babbling. The patient is all too ready to perceive the therapist as another silencer and to attack him as such. The therapist should guard against consciously or unconsciously invoking a silencing strategy against the patient, either as a result of his countertransference or simply because an important element of his professional skill consists in getting the patient to be silent about what he, as therapist, is not interested in.

SUMMARY

This paper describes certain pathogenic aspects of silencing strategies, which are interpersonal, repression-like, multiply motivated processes, that may be conducted by one or more persons. It focuses on the so-called victim's attempts to engage and overcome his silencers by counter-silence. The victim discovers the power of silence to control and dominate human relationships; he may then be seduced by his discovery and fall victim to a severe pathology of silence such as schizophrenic mutism or hebephrenic babbling.

This paper proposes also that silencing strategies contribute to the development of paranoid, delusional, or hallucinatory states. It offers a clinical example in support of this view. Paranoid and delusional parents were able to trigger paranoid and delusional thinking in their daughter by resorting to a silencing strategy.

Silencing of children by parents is widely used as a means of punishing noncompliance and ensuing future conformity. The motive to possess the child, to rob him of independence, may be attributed to some parents who employ particularly harsh and persistent silencing. Family therapy is a useful arena in which to observe parental silencing strategies and the counter-manipulatory efforts of the child.

REFERENCES

Lifton, R. J. Chinese communist thought reform. In B. Schaffner (Ed.), Group processes: transactions of the third conference. New York: Josiah Macy Found., 1957. Pp. 219-312.

Meissner, W. W. Thinking about the family—psychiatric aspects. Fam. Proc., 1964, 3, 1-40.

Shannon, W. V. The American Irish. New York: Macmillan, 1963.

Zuk, G. H. On the pathology of silencing strategies. Fam. Proc., 1965a, 5, 32-49.

Zuk, G. H. On silence and babbling in family psychotherapy of schizophrenics. Confin. Psychiat., 1965b, 8, 49-56.

PART III

Pythogeny in the Relationship
between the Sociocultural System
and the Family

THE COMPLEXITY OF SPOUSE SIMILARITY AND DIFFERENCE [1]

Seymour Fisher, Ph.D., and Rhoda L. Fisher, Ph.D.

INTRODUCTION

This is by way of an initial account of a study of similarities and differences among spouses whose response characteristics were tapped at a number of different levels. The study to be described involved 119 families. Of the families involved, 46 were Jewish and 73 were of Protestant background. Only families in which both the mother and father had at least a high school education were included. This was done to minimize the effects of differential educational attainment upon the various evaluation procedures employed. Originally, the project was undertaken to ascertain the parental variables that play a role in determining how a child learns to experience and evaluate his own body. But as the work has progressed, the data have permitted entrée into basic questions of similarity-difference between spouses.

The families in the project were recruited in Syracuse, New York. Financial incentives were offered to various organizations to persuade their members to participate as subjects. The cooperating organizations included church groups, scout troops, Parent Teacher Associations, and others of a similar character. It was possible to recruit a high proportion of the membership of most of the organizations approached; but there is undoubtedly some sample bias related to volunteering. When a family agreed to participate, evaluations were undertaken of the mother, the father, and at least two children. The tests administered to the parents (on a group basis) involved a variety of procedures intended to tap personality, value, and attitudinal dimensions. Included in the battery were a modification of the Parental Attitude Research Instrument (Chorost, 1960; Platt et al., 1962), suitable for administration to both mothers and

[1] This study was partially supported by USPH Grant M5761 and National Science Foundation Grant GP-1137.

fathers; the Allport-Vernon-Lindzey Study of Values; the Thurstone Temperament Scale; the Rorschach Ink Blot Test; and a task requiring recall of the physical symptoms most frequently occurring in the two youngest children in the family who served as subjects. All the children took a series of tests designed to measure their organization and evaluation of body experiences.

The median duration of the marriages of the Protestant families was 15 years; in the Jewish group, it was 14 years. Mean number of years of education was 14.4 for fathers and 13.6 for mothers in the Protestant sample, and 16.0 for fathers and 14.4 for mothers in the Jewish families. It should also be indicated that mean social class level, as defined by the Hollingshead index (Hollingshead, 1956), was 34.0 for the Protestants and 24.6 for the Jews.

SPOUSE SIMILARITIES

The nature of the similarities that exist between spouses is still an unsettled issue. Some have underscored the point of spouses being alike (Burgess and Wallin, 1953; Terman, 1938); whereas others, such as Winch (1958) and Katz et al. (1963) have tried to picture the spouse interrelationship in terms of complementarity. The notion underlying the concept of complementarity is that spouses possess trait and need patterns that supplement and contrast with each other as part of an equilibration process. Considerable controversy may be found in the literature concerning similarity versus complementarity models. Tharp (1963) and Levinger (1964) have reviewed several of the prime issues involved. It was anticipated that data from the present study would provide some clarification.

Analysis of the family data collected revealed surprisingly variable patterns of correlations between spouses. Results for each of the test procedures will be considered in turn.

PARENTAL ATTITUDE RESEARCH INSTRUMENT

The modified Parental Attitude Research Instrument (PARI), which was administered to all parents, consists of a series of 115 questions dealing with childrearing practices and beliefs. Each parent indicated on a five-point scale the degree to which he or she agreed with the various statements. There are 23 subscales, which embrace such categories as Fostering Dependency, Intrusiveness, Marital Conflict, Autonomy of the Child, and Suppression of Sex. However, factor analytic studies indicate that there are two broad factors basic to the items. One relates to how Authoritarian the expressed childrearing attitudes are; and the other concerns the emotional Warmth versus Coldness of such attitudes. Correlational analyses[2] demonstrated that for both of the factor scores the correlations between husband and wife in the Protestant as well as the Jewish samples were of little better than a chance order. This finding was indeed surprising. One expected some commonality between spouses (most of whom had had children for a decade) in their concepts of appropriate childrearing practices. There are few previous studies in the literature in which childrearing attitudes of both parents have been simultaneously measured. Even in the published studies where such measures were taken, the matter of spouse similarity was subsidiary to other issues; and so direct information concerning degree of similarity was not included.

An investigation by Baragona (1964) did use the PARI to measure Authoritarianism of childrearing views in a sample of 27 spouse pairs and found a significant positive correlation between father and mother scores. But in the same project, measures of parental acceptance of the child taken from both the fathers and mothers proved to have only a chance relationship. Dentler and Hutchinson (1961) found little consensus within husband, wife, and child groups for a series of general statements concerning proper childrearing practices. Barger (1963) also observed minimal similarities in expressed childrearing practices, as ascertained from interview data. Medinnus (1961), using a Q-sort technique, noted that parents show significant agreement in how they perceive their child's real behavior, but lack such congruence in stating their general expectations and demands with regard to the child. If one considers that the PARI inquires concerning general childrearing expectations and standards rather than the actual behavior of one's own child, it can be seen that Medinnus' results (and also others just cited) are congruent with the lack of significant relationship between spouses' PARI scores in the present study. It should be added that Medinnus' observation that parents do agree in perceptions of specific behaviors of their own children was also borne out in the present study by data involving parents' reports of physical symptoms manifested by their children. Each parent has been asked to indicate the frequency with which certain types of muscle and skin versus stomach and gut symptoms had characterized each of the two youngest children in the family. Low but significantly positive correlations were found between spouses' judgments in both the Protestant and Jewish groups.

It is interesting, too, that there is one previous study (Staples and Smith, 1954) in which it was observed that there was less sim-

---

[2] Detailed tables concerning these and other statistical analyses described in the paper may be obtained by writing to the authors.

ilarity in childrearing attitudes between young mothers and their mothers who were living with them in the same house than between young mothers and their mothers who were not living in the same house. This observation, taken in conjunction with other findings already cited, suggests that it may somehow be paradoxically true that persons closely associated in a childrearing enterprise arrive at general childrearing views which are neither similar nor opposed, but rather neutrally contiguous. Perhaps such a vaguely defined position vis-à-vis one another means that those who have intensively and collaboratively engaged in the enterprise of raising children (and who have been able to stay together in the process) have learned not to complicate their relationships by seriously trying to influence each other about general, abstract standards of childrearing. That is, they may largely confine such exchange to specific behaviors at specific times, in specific settings related to their own children. An interesting analogy to this possibility has been presented by March (1953). He observed in an analysis of interactions between husband-wife pairs that they tended to "specialize" in certain verbal political views. One might concentrate in forming opinions about labor issues; whereas the other would focus on local politics. March suggested that one function of such specialization in opinion might be the avoidance of disruptive conflict.

THURSTONE TEMPERAMENT SCALE

No correlations of significance were found between spouses in either the Protestant or Jewish samples for any of the subcategories of the Thurstone Temperament Scale. This scale is a self-report questionnaire that asks the subject to indicate his agreement or disagreement with a series of statements, as they would apply to him. The statements embrace the following dimensions:

1. Degree of speed and activity manifested in everyday movement and activity (e.g., Do you ordinarily work quickly and energetically?)

2. Amount of muscular vigor (e.g., Do you enjoy having a good physical workout?)

3. Impulsivity (e.g., Do you let yourself go and have a gay time at a party?)

4. Sociability (e.g., Do you often tell stories to entertain others?)

5. Dominance (e.g., Do you like to be the chairman of a meeting?)

6. Ability to remain calm in the face of distractions (e.g., Can you relax in a noisy room?)

7. Inclination to deal with problems in a reflective, individualistic fashion (e.g., When you have an important problem, do you prefer to think it through alone?)

The lack of significant findings for the Thurstone Temperament Scale supports most previous observations that spouses show low to zero correlations with each other on temperament or personality questionnaires (Crook, 1937; Patterson, 1946; Hoffeditz, 1934; Roff, 1950). Adams and Sarason (1963) reported only two significant positive correlations between parents out of eight involving a series of self-report anxiety measures. Blum (1959) could not find a significant relationship between spouses for a measure of personal rigidity. However, at the same time it must be acknowledged that there are reports in the literature that spouses and engaged couples show significant similarities in the intensities of certain needs (e.g., nurturance), presumably measured by the Edwards Personal Preference Schedule (Bowerman and Day, 1956; Schellenberg and Bee, 1960; Banta and Hetherington, 1963). Few, if any, of these need parameters in the Edwards Schedule are duplicated in the Thurstone Temperament Scale that was used in the present study. Also, the Edwards scales are constructed in such a fashion as to minimize the social desirability ("making a good impression") factor, which enters so prominently into most self-descriptive personality inventories. It remains to be seen whether the more positive findings obtained with the Edwards Schedule are a function of the specific dimensions measured, or of the greater control placed upon social desirability response sets.

STUDY OF VALUES

In contrast to the results with the modified PARI and the Thurstone Temperament Scale, the data emerging from the Study of Values indicated a number of significant similarities between spouses. The Study of Values was designed to tap six variables based on the Spranger concept of the basic types of persons found in Western culture. The six Spranger types are as follows: (1) the Theoretical person, who takes an abstract intellectualized attitude toward the world; (2) the Economic person, who emphasizes use and productivity; (3) the Social person, who is devoted to identification with the group; (4) the Political person, who is interested in power; (5) the Esthetic person, who places great value on beauty and creativity; and (6) the Religious person, who regards the world in terms of religiosity and the will of a Supreme Being.

In the Jewish sample, spouses were found to be significantly alike for the Social category and similar at a borderline level of statistical significance for the Economic and Religious values. Within the Protestant sample, spouses were significantly alike for the Esthetic and Religious values, and similar at a borderline level of statistical significance for the Economic category. If one considers simultaneously the results for both the Jewish and Protestant samples, one notes that the Economic and Religious values are those for which the spouses manifested most consistent similarity: that is, the spouses were most likely to have similar views with regard to the importance of economic and religious activities and issues. But even here the degree of similarity must not be exaggerated. The correlation coefficients involved cluster in the high .20's.

Looking at the past relevant literature in this area, it is difficult to find measures involving spouses that can be strictly equated to the Study of Values. But there are numerous results indicative that spouses are rather highly related in their attitudes toward such matters as war, religion, moral standards, and specific voting issues (Hartshorne et al., 1930; Roff, 1950). Gitlin (1958) has also shown modest correlations between spouses for certain interest inventory scores. Variables such as those just cited bear some similarity to the content of Study of Values categories. Apparently, husbands and wives do have some overlap in their evaluative attitudes toward prominent objects and issues in the extra-familial environment. It is puzzling that spouses should show more similarities in their attitudes toward certain issues encountered largely outside of the family than they do for intrafamily matters. Why, for example, should there be more commonality in spouses' expectations and goals with regard to religious and economic issues than appears in their expressed childrearing standards? Taking a general view, one could speculate that some of the dimensions measured by the Study of Values involve longstanding attitudes that were already well crystallized when the spouses were first becoming acquainted with each other. Therefore, those who lacked a minimum congruence in value orientation would have experienced too much conflict to enter into a marriage relationship. During the courtship period, however, crystallized childrearing attitudes would not yet exist because neither spouse would have had serious childrearing experience. Conflict about childrearing attitudes would consequently have minor selective impact upon the possibility of marriage. Only later in the relationship, when a child had been born, would childrearing attitudes become sufficiently articulated to become a potential source of disagreement.

PROJECTIVE INK BLOT RESPONSES

The complexity of spouse similarity patterns is further underscored when one considers the results pertaining to several measures derived from Rorschach ink blot responses. The Rorschach
was administered primarily to obtain a measure called the Barrier
score, which is an index of the degree to which the individual experiences his body as having definite boundaries that clearly demarcate
him from his environs (Fisher and Cleveland, 1958). This score is
based on the number of responses given in which there is an emphasis on the protective, containing, or decorative attributes of the
peripheries of percepts. Some examples of such responses follow:
cave, woman in fancy costume, mummy wrapped up, vase, animal
with striped skin. In each of these responses boundary features are
emphasized or dramatized. Multiple studies have demonstrated the
construct validity of the Barrier score (Fisher, 1963). Details concerning the score are provided because it will be referred to at a
later point apropos of other findings.

Aside from the Barrier score, a count was also made in each
protocol of the number of Human responses and the number of Movement responses. None of the other usual Rorschach determinants
were computed, because the mode of administration of the blots
was such as not to involve the conventional Inquiry.

In the Jewish sample, it was found that there was a significant
positive correlation between the Barrier scores of the spouses. The
correlations between spouses for Movement and Human were positive, but not significant. In the Protestant group, the Barrier indices of spouses were not related, but spouses did evidence significant similarity for both Human and Movement scores. Thus, for
three of the six Rorschach comparisons involving the two samples,
the spouses were significantly alike. Incidentally, the findings for
Movement are confirmatory of a study by Piotrowski (1956), in which
he reported that married couples were more likely to produce a
similar number of Rorschach Movement responses than were ran-
domly paired men and women or former spouses who had divorced
each other. Why do spouses show more similarity in something as
"out of this world" as fantasy responses to ink blots than they do in
their expressed attitudes about certain explicit objects and senti-
ments (e.g., childrearing practices, preferred ways of relating to
others)? Is it possible that the projective responses tap an underlying congruence between spouses that is like a correspondence of
basic inner needs or conflicts, but which at the level of their cir-
cuitous expression in conscious defenses and coping mechanisms
may take very diverse and even antithetical forms?

That such a possibility is a real one may be further reinforced by citing earlier work by Fisher and Mendell (1956) and Fisher and Fisher (1960). This work revolved about the administration of projective tests (Rorschach, Thematic Apperception Test) to representatives of three different generations of a series of families. It was observed that over a three-generation span members of the same family were likely to exhibit highly visible similarities in certain aspects of their projective images. For example, all members of one family might fashion unusual images relating to exhibitionism. In another family there might be a consistent expression of sexual themes; and in still another, a preoccupation with concepts expressing anxiety about hostility. Further studies have demonstrated that Rorschach protocols of three generation representatives of Jewish families could be blindly distinguished by judges from representatives of Protestant native Texas families in terms of specific Rorschach content categories. There seems to be converging evidence that fantasy productions of members of given families may share unusual similarities. This would argue for likenesses between spouses, and also between spouses and their families, which relate to unconscious wishes and expectations. But these "inner" or "core" similarities probably assume extremely complicated forms and become covered over in overt behavior.

INTER-TEST SIMILARITIES BETWEEN SPOUSES

Another line of analysis to be pursued concerns how well a spouse's score on a given variable predicts all of the scores (except the corresponding one) of the other spouse. For example, can a wife's Study of Value scores be predicted from a knowledge of her husband's Thurstone Temperament Scale or Barrier scores? Such a mode of analysis gets at the generality of spouse similarity-difference and provides an opportunity for determining which spouse attributes are best overall predictors for the other spouse characteristics.

The data revealed few relationships that held true in both the Protestant and Jewish groups. None of the husband variables consistently predicted the PARI indices for wives; the same was true for wife variables predicting husband PARI indices. Likewise, the Thurstone Temperament Scale scores for either spouse had largely chance relationship with the various scores of the other spouse. The following relationships involving the Study of Values did hold up in both samples: the husband's Study of Values Theoretical score was positively correlated with his wife's Esthetic score and negatively so with her Religious score; the husband's Economic score was negatively related to his wife's Esthetic score. Furthermore, certain spouse variables turned out, within the limits of either the Protestant or Jewish samples alone, to be unusually good predictors of the other spouse's scores. In the Protestant group, the wife's Esthetic score was positively and significantly correlated with the husband's Theoretical, Economic, Political, Barrier, Rorschach Movement, Rorschach Human, and Thurstone Reflective scores, and negatively with his Religious score. The wife's Religious score was negatively correlated with the husband's Theoretical, Esthetic, Political, and Rorschach Human scores. The husband's Rorschach Human score was positively linked with wife's Esthetic, Thurstone Dominance, and Rorschach Movement scores, but negatively so with her Religious score.

Within the Jewish sample, the wife's Theoretical score was positively and significantly correlated with husband's Esthetic score, and negatively so with his Economic, Barrier, and Rorschach Movement scores. Her Barrier score was positively correlated with husband's Economic, Thurstone Impulsive, Rorschach Movement, and Rorschach Human scores. The husband's Economic score was positively correlated with his wife's Esthetic and Barrier scores, and negatively so with her Theoretical, Esthetic, Rorschach Movement, and Rorschach Human scores. Also, his Barrier score was positively linked with his wife's PARI Authoritarian, Economic, and Political scores, and negatively so with her Theoretical and Thurstone Dominance scores.

Incidentally, educational level was analyzed, too, as a predictor of spouse attributes. It was found that the wife's educational level had few consistent correlations with the husband's various scores. However, in both the Protestant and Jewish samples, the husband's educational level was positively correlated with the wife's Theoretical score, and negatively so with her PARI Authoritarian and Economic scores.

Detailed trends in the data have been cited in order to show that there are spouse variables that have moderate generality in predicting attributes of the other spouse. It is, for example, impressive that the wife's Theoretical score in the Protestant group is related to eight different husband scores tapping a variety of response levels. Similarly, one notes that both the husband's and wife's Barrier scores in the Jewish group could predict a range of responses in the other spouse. One certainly gets an impression of interweaving connections between the levels of personal organization of spouse pairs. Spouse values are linked with spouse values; spouse values with spouse modes of fantasy production; and spouse body image characteristics with spouse personality traits. There are obviously all kinds of relationships that need to be traced and explained. This will be a difficult task, because the relationships are probably quite relative and likely to be influenced by the ethnic, religious, and educational levels of the samples being studied.

SPOUSE DIFFERENCE SCORES

An important question that arises in analyzing husband-wife congruence is whether differences between spouses in one area are predictive of differences in other areas. Does one find, for example, that those differing most in childrearing attitudes also differ most in values or self-report personality traits? How specific or generalized are the correlations between spouse difference scores over the range of variables involved in the present study?

In order to answer these questions, there was determined for each variable the difference between the husband's score and that of his wife's (i.e., husband score minus wife score). Intercorrelations among all of the difference scores were then computed in the Protestant and the Jewish samples. Rather shifting correlational patterns were uncovered. First of all, spouse differences for PARI-Authoritarianism failed in either sample to be related in more than a chance fashion to any of the other difference scores. This same chance pattern was found for the PARI Warmth difference index. The Thurstone Temperament Scale spouse difference scores likewise had only chance relationships with the other difference scores in both samples. And the same chance pattern was noted for amount of disagreement between spouses with regard to the kinds of physical symptoms typifying the two youngest children in the family.

The results for the Study of Values were, on the contrary, indicative of significant and consistent links between difference scores. In both the Protestant and Jewish groups, it was found that the larger the difference between spouse Theoretical scores, the smaller the spouse differences for the Social and the Political scores. In the Protestant sample, the Theoretical difference scores were also negatively correlated with difference scores for the Religious dimension, Rorschach Human, and (strongly so) the Barrier score.

The Economic difference scores were negatively and significantly correlated in both samples with Esthetic, Social, and Religious difference scores. The Political difference scores were negatively correlated with the Religious difference scores in both samples. Finally, it should be mentioned that in the Protestant group, the Social difference scores were significantly and negatively correlated with the Political difference scores, but positively so with the Religious difference scores. Despite some discrepancies, it is generally noteworthy how similar the patterns of relationships between the Study of Values spouse difference scores were in both samples of subjects. This, of course, indicates considerable stability in the observed patterns. It should be indicated, too, that the Barrier difference scores in both samples were positively correlated with Rorschach Movement and Rorschach Human difference scores.

If one looks at the findings in their broadest context, they suggest the interesting possibility that the greater the difference between spouses in certain attitudinal areas, the smaller are their differences in other areas. This pattern is obviously not explainable in terms of simple models of spouse similarity or difference. Rather, it would seem to require unusually complex and novel notions of complementarity. Apparently, the nature of spouse attitudinal differences and similarities cannot be realistically appraised by considering only scores for discrete variables taken one at a time. Similarity in one region may signify differences in several others, but also similarities in still others. Thus, it is intriguing that one should find that the more a husband's Economic value score exceeds that of his wife's, the smaller is the difference between them for Esthetic, Social, and Religious values. It is as if sufficient disparity between them in Economic orientation had to exist before they could attain congruence in other areas. Or, one could translate this into the concept that sufficient role disparity (specialization) is necessary in one attitudinal dimension in order to permit similarity in others. This type of complementarity would be, then, not a matter of similarity or difference, but rather both. It could mean being different in certain ways in order to be alike in other ways. This raises a question as to whether present methods for evaluating similarity theories versus complementarity theories are sufficiently sophisticated. Can the existence of complex complementarity be determined in terms of how many similarities or differences spouses display over a range of measures? Clearly, such an approach does not do justice to the concept of complementarity as a patterned network in which spouse similarity-difference for a variable may be either proportional or inverse to the amount of spouse similarity-difference shown for one or more other variables.

OVERVIEW OF FINDINGS

As the spouse scores were analyzed in different ways, shifting perspectives were provided concerning the similarities and differences between husbands and wives. It was possible to find certain straightforward spouse similarities. In both samples, husbands and wives did have related Economic and Religious values. Further, they proved to be alike for certain ink blot fantasy measures; it was pointed out that such similarities in fantasy productions among family members have been reported in other studies (e.g., Piotrowski, 1956; Fisher and Mendell, 1956). At the level of fantasy and unconscious needs, family members apparently show significant commonality. But it is difficult to detect this simple commonality to a convincing degree in the correlations between spouses for corresponding measures derived from the entire range of self-report personality and value scales used.

Scanning the data for spouse relationships that go beyond corresponding measures and which involve correlations between difference scores, it becomes clear that such relationships are of greater complexity than previously realized. There are certain spouse parameters (e.g., Study of Values-Esthetic, Rorschach scores) that are not correlated with their equivalents in the other spouse, but are significantly correlated with a whole series of nonequivalent characteristics. That is, totally unexpected links are present between spouse attitudinal and personality subsystems — and they are not really interpretable within current theory. However, the most unexpected results have been derived from studying the spouse difference scores for the various measures. When the wife's score is subtracted from the husband's for each variable and these differences are intercorrelated, unusual patterns appear. One finds no overall tendencies for the amount of difference between spouses in relation to one variable to be positively related to their amount of difference for other variables. It is true there is an example of such a tendency within the localized category of projective responses. One observes in both samples that the greater the degree to which husbands exceed their wives in number of Barrier responses, the more do they exceed them in Rorschach Human and also Movement responses, the same is true for Movement versus Human differences. However, a quite different pattern characterizes the spouse difference scores derived from the Study of Values. Consistent examples are provided in which the greater the difference between spouses for one score, the less is their difference for another; and yet the larger it is for a third. Apparently, being different in one area may mean more likeness in another or less in still another. As already mentioned, this suggests a kind of complementarity which involves both likeness and difference, and the novel possibility that similarity in one area betokens difference in another. To describe, within the context of such a model, the meshing of spouse attributes one needs to compare spouses for several variables simultaneously and to treat the differences in profile fashion. One could then attempt to set up criteria for complementarity between spouses in terms of expectations like, "If they are different for variables A and B, but alike for C and D, then . . ." The problem under consideration becomes even more complicated if one considers that for some response systems (e. g. , those tapped by projective tests) similarity rather than complementarity may be the more usual phenomenon. A total picture presents itself, in which spouses who have been married for long periods may be alike at some levels, simultaneously opposite and alike in a balanced way at other levels, and related in only a chance fashion at still further levels. This portrays an intricacy that explains why conflicting results have been so common in the literature dealing with spouse relationships. Depending upon the variables one chooses to measure, spouses will appear to be similar, different, or both. The simultaneous measure of multiple levels of response would seem necessary strategy in any attempt to develop a general concept of the nature of spouse similarity-difference.

The pessimistic view taken here of simple concepts of similarity (homogamy) or complementarity (heterogamy) has been voiced increasingly in the current literature. Many studies have reported "mixed" results rather than conformity to homogamous or heterogamous patterns (e. g. , Katz et al. , 1960). Murstein (1961) noted, after an incisive study of need similarities in newlyweds and middle-aged married couples, that (p. 196) "the heterogeneity-homogamy dichotomy seems a gross simplification of the actual marital situation . . . . The assumption seems far more plausible thus, that for adequate marital adjustment some needs require complementary needs in the marital partner, while others necessitate homogamous need patterns. "

The results of the present study clearly support this view.

REFERENCES

Adams, Elsie B. , & Sarason, I. G. Relation between anxiety in children and their parents. Child Develop. , 1963, 34, 237-246.

Banta, T. J. , & Hetherington, M. Relations between needs of friends and fiances. J. abnorm. soc. Psychol. , 1963, 66, 401-404.

Baragona, Rosalie. The relationship between certain parental attitudes and selected personality characteristics in nursery school children. Unpublished doctoral dissertation, Rutgers State University, 1964.

Barger, Patricia M. Parental dominance and conflict-relationship to personal history variables and child control techniques. Unpublished doctoral dissertation, Northwestern University, 1963.

Blum, A. The relationship between rigidity-flexibility in children and their parents. Child Develop., 1959, 30, 297-304.

Bowerman, C. E., & Day, Barbara R. A test of the theory of complementary needs as applied to couples during courtship. Amer. sociol. Rev., 1956, 21, 602-605.

Burgess, E. W., & Wallin, P. Engagement and marriage. Philadelphia: Lippincott, 1953.

Chorost, S. B. Parental childrearing attitudes and their correlates in adolescent aggression. Unpublished doctoral dissertation, University of Texas, 1960.

Crook, M. N. Intra-family relationships in personality test performance. Psychol. Rec., 1937, 1, 479-502.

Dentler, R. A., & Hutchinson, J. G. Socioeconomic versus family membership status as sources of family attitude consensus. Child Develop., 1961, 32, 249-254.

Fisher, S. A further appraisal of the body boundary concept. J. consult. Psychol., 1963, 27, 62-74.

Fisher, S., & Cleveland, S. E. Body image and personality. Princeton: Van Nostrand, 1958.

Fisher, S., & Fisher, Rhoda L. A projective test analysis of ethnic subculture themes in families. J. project. Tech., 1960, 24, 366-369.

Fisher, S., & Mendell, D. The communication of neurotic patterns over two and three generations. Psychiatry, 1956, 19, 41-46.

Gitlin, S. A study of the interrelationships of parents' measured interest patterns and those of their children. Unpublished doctoral dissertation, Temple University, 1958.

Hartshorne, H., et al. Studies in the organization of character. New York: Macmillan, 1930.

Hoffeditz, E. L. Family resemblances in personality traits. J. soc. Psychol., 1934, 5, 214-227.

Hollingshead, A. B., & Redlich, F. Social class and mental illness; a community study. New York: Wiley, 1958.

Katz, I., et al. Need satisfaction and Edwards PPS scores in married couples. J. consult. Psychol., 1960, 24, 205-208.

Katz, I., et al. Effect of one type of need complementarity on marriage partners' conformity to one another's judgments. J. abnorm. soc. Psychol., 1963, 67, 8-14.

Levinger, G. Note on need complementarity in marriage. Psychol. Bull., 1964, 61, 153-157.

March, J. G. Husband-wife interaction over political issues. Publ. Opin. Quart., 1953, 17, 461-470.

Medinnus, G. R. Q-sort descriptions of five-year-old children by their parents. Child Develop., 1961, 32, 473-489.

Murstein, B. I. The complementary need hypothesis in newlyweds and middle-aged married couples. J. abnorm. soc. Psychol., 1961, 63, 194-197.

Patterson, C. H. The relationship of Bernreuter scores to parent behavior, child behavior, urban-rural residence, and other background factors in 100 normal adult parents. J. soc. Psychol. 1946, 24, 3-49.

Piotrowski, Z. A., & Dudek, Stephanie Z. Research on human movement response in the Rorschach examinations of marital partners. In V. W. Eisenstein (Ed.), Neurotic interaction in marriage. New York: Basic Books, 1956. Pp. 192-207.

Platt, H., et al. Comparison of childrearing attitudes of mothers and fathers of emotionally disturbed adolescents. Child Develop., 1962, 33, 117-122.

Roff, M. Intra-family resemblances in personality characteristics. J. Psychol., 1950, 30, 199-227.

Schellenberg, J. A., & Bee, L. S. A re-examination of the theory of complementary needs in mate selection. Marriage Fam. Living, 1960, 22, 227-232.

Staples, Ruth, & Smith, June W. Attitudes of grandmothers and mothers toward child rearing practices. Child Develop., 1954, 25, 91-97.

Terman, L. M. Psychological factors in marital happiness. New York: McGraw-Hill, 1938.

Tharp, R. G. Psychological patterning in marriage. Psychol. Bull., 1963, 60, 97-117.

Winch, R. F. Mate selection; a study of complementary needs. New York: Harper, 1958.

SOCIAL AND CULTURAL INFLUENCES
ON THE PSYCHOPATHOLOGY OF FAMILY GROUPS

Marvin K. Opler, Ph.D.

The natural setting of human behavior is, of course, human society. There cultural groups such as the family are traditional. Despite the label of "family," anthropologists know that this unit of social organization varies notoriously in size, in extent of kinship, in locale, and in functional relationships both within the unit and with other social units. Its economy, its degree of autonomy from other elements in social structure, its religion or pattern of beliefs, even its modes of marital and sexual regulation and its recreational forms are matters that are not self-defined nor internally arrived at by some process of reasoning. Anyone who doubts this may compare the current American family with its progenitor of a hundred years ago in size, locale, functions and beliefs, sexual customs, recreational modes, or even relative dependence on external economic agencies.

Just as families may change in form and function over time, so the individuals making up family groups—the component elements of family process—themselves go through a life course or life history, which anthropologists refer to as "life cycle." In this course, they successively occupy different social roles, or even several roles simultaneously. Behavioral impairments in life functioning (psychopathology) can be found, of course, in the individuals making up families, but they exist more broadly, from the epidemiological point of view, in whole communities, in social classes, or in nations, cultural groups, and ethnic subcultures. Indeed, the chief finding of social psychiatry to date is that neither the forms nor the amounts of psychopathology are distributed in populations at random. Rather, the different types of psychopathology vary in amount with cultural group. They can be mapped according to social and cultural characteristics of human populations, or more accurately, according to social and cultural stress systems which induce the pathology.

It is precisely at this point, however, that family processes of particular types become important. Family functioning deserves

careful scrutiny, for cultural stress systems influencing psychopathology become visible at such nodal points as the family, the adolescent youth group, the places where social isolates and deviants
convene, and in other institutional frameworks. The analogy to a
node is helpful since in organic pathology systemic disorders may
be expressed not only in organic aberrancies but also through related pathology in structure and function. It is true that psychopathology can come to reside in families, so that social welfare has its
term "multi-problem families"; psychiatry also very commonly
comes to regard such families as affecting individual psychogenic
disorders by reason of repetitive experiences in distorted settings.
But psychopathology lives on, in addition, in those individuals who
have been cut off from family settings for one reason or another. In
social psychiatry, therefore, one begins with studies of persons in
social communities —usually combinations of class and cultural factors—but one must inevitably reach back into family matrices to un-
cover traces of pathology. For patients isolated in hospitals or in
other institutional frameworks, either families or family surrogates
are still relevant.

We referred above to "family processes" in the plural because
cultures, and therefore cultural stress systems, are not a mould or
template producing a uniform product. While, epidemiologically, a
certain kind of product may become prevalent, it is never one hundred per cent. As with most other ills—including those which are
organic in etiology—psychogenic disorders do not affect a total population. Statistical incidence or prevalence of a mental disorder refers always to its actual amount, either in newly developing cases
or in cases continuing unabated; a highly stressful cultural system
may still contain individuals and whole families which are symptom-
free. Nevertheless, the same may be said of the ravages of small-
pox epidemics or of bubonic plague, in their time. Far more research effort should be devoted to studying in depth the extremes
in psychopathology and in mental health from the same cultural settings, especially where the epidemiological rates are high, so that
psychiatry might learn more about its own subfield of "immunolog-
ical processes."

It is clear that our terms "family process" and "psychopathology" are mediated by a concept of cultural stress system. By
"stress," in the context of this discussion, no one today can mean
psychological stress, pure and simple. Since Cannon, since Selye,
since Freud, and especially since the emergence of modern psychosomatic medicine, too much is known about physiological concomi-
tants of emotional states to limit psychophysiologic stress to some
abstract psychological parameter. First of all, we maintain that

the organism (and its reactive mechanisms, including the limbic system and central nervous system) is constantly responding—sometimes in an adverse manner for its own survival—to conditions under which it exists. Yet respond it must. Second, as humans we are responsive, even acutely or subtly so, to human signs and symbols. Symbols swell enormously the whole gamut of our own meanings and the meanings of others, and it is here that culture enters into our reactive mechanisms with enormous force and scope. Third, the focus on psychophysiological connections, real though they are, should not lead us into thinking erroneously that the reactive apparatus is merely patterned by culture in its impingement upon the individual anew in each instance and for the instant only.

Wolberg's famous posthypnotic experiments with three patients, each of whom responded in his characteristic mode of personality, should indicate that patterns of imbalance and balance exist in individuals as they do in cultures. In brief, the patient who characteristically used conversion symptoms did not even see the negatively charged object (in this case, simply candy) though it was in full view; the second, with anxiety neurosis, reacted with sweating and faintness at the mere sight of it; while the third, a psychosomatically ill patient, ate the candy and initiated promptly the channel of reverse peristalsis and vomiting. When one considers the difference among cultures in the epidemiological rates of conversion hysterias or of anxiety neuroses, and then considers the alleged increases in psychosomatic disorders in our modern civilizations, it is clear that hysterias were once a more common pattern of psychopathology, which today takes the alternative forms of widespread anxieties and psychosomatic reactions. This is one way of phrasing the fact that both culture and psychopathology have changed.

The manner in which this change has occurred involves family functioning. We shall have little to say in this essay concerning the alleged increase in various kinds of psychosomatic ailments, except to note that conceptions of illness today tolerate the somatic reactions but, for the most part, heap scorn and even blame upon mere hysterical emotional outlets. Such impairments were once treated par excellence by the shaman and curing cult in a manner that laid the blame elsewhere and in ceremonies that involved some degree of family participation and concern for the patient. Since Breuer and Freud, however, psychiatry has made the concern a matter of direct interest for patient and practitioner primarily by removing supernatural or pseudo-scientific causation in favor of medically attested psychogenic origins of hysterical maneuvers. The secondary gains accruing to mysterious impairments, the compensations of immobility and handicap, the psychological concern of family or of physician—all are now transferred instead to the scientifically attestable ulcer, skin disorder, asthmatic attack, or blood sugar imbalance, where wish and impulse can now evoke concern, and for which doctors may now prescribe. No doubt the paradigm for one psychosomatic reaction form is discrete and different from another, so that even psychiatric and psychogenic attacks on the disturbance would vary with each ailment. What we are commenting upon here is merely the total epidemiology of somatic reaction forms as a class. It would seem that the relative isolation and autonomy of the individual in modern cultures is paralleled by the relative isolation of the organism; at one time the organism disguised wish and impulse by hidden and mysterious impairments wholly mental, but these are now passé and are acceptable only if actual organ injury has occurred.

Present-day discussions of adaptive paradigms in the family describe sexual identity with the parent of the same sex, maternal failures due to narcissism in the mother, splitting of ego and superego by confusions in introjects demanded by each parent separately, and failures in family socialization processes. The difficulty with the paradigms is the wholly unitary form of family assumed to exist. Or if families are differentiated, this is done entirely in terms of psychological type, such as obsessive parents rearing rigid children, or sociopaths producing delinquents. Unfortunately, epidemiological fluctuations show greater rise and fall, more diverse ethnic patterns, and greater class variations than a purely psychogenic theory can accommodate. We suspect that missing from this type of account are massive areas of cognitive meanings, cultural values, and even affective styles in kinds of family. Concepts of psychological stress, or emotion and stress, have been criticized by phenomenologists as leaving cognitive approach, outlook, and meaning out of the formulation. Psychological stress deals with negatively toned emotions such as fear and anxiety, hostility and anger, depression, guilt and shame, and so forth, both in terms of antecedent conditions and processes, and their possible measurement. Cognitive styles affect all of these parameters and qualitatively tone all of these emotions. In an experiment reported by Stanley Schachter and Jerome L. Singer (1962), visceral responses and emotional ones were found to relate to such environmental factors as the human cognitive meanings transmitted in the interpersonal transaction. The theory of the "double-bind" in promoting schizophrenic reactions is, similarly, a theory of cognitive and emotional conflict in essence.

Experiments in cognition are broader in scope, and perhaps more difficult to arrange in a lifelike manner, than most work in laboratory experimental psychology. But cultures are, in themselves, laboratories of human cognitive meanings. We have claimed (Opler, 1956) that humans have enough spare adjustive and adaptive "machinery" and that cultural laboratories were often more appropriate to this complexity. Put otherwise, human cognitive processes of the cultural type are rarely caught within the cross-sectional laboratory conditions of most contrived experiments. For these reasons, cultural environing contexts or social categories in the conditions of existence of groups of people are convenient rubrics and should be used to select samples for study. In our own work with a team of psychologists (Opler & Singer, 1956), we found that samples of Italian and Irish schizophrenics showed striking and statistically significant differences according to ten central variables in the illness. Obviously, behavioral sciences need not eliminate conditions and contexts of human existence in favor of the vague hope that laboratories and white coats may magically produce scientific properties.

This matter can be put another way. In most experimental strategy of the psychologist, the designer of the experiment assumes he is dealing accurately with humanity—with Man with a capital M. For years, such experimentalists, thinking of their laboratories as the analogue of the physicists' and chemists', devoted considerable care and attention to questions of statistical reliability and significance, to checks with control groups, and in a casual sort of way, to the matter of the validity of the experiment itself. However, this did not prevent them from building up a peculiar excrescence on the landscape of their science, namely, a sort of science based on college student samples taken mainly from those enrolled in Introductory Psychology! Even in more sophisticated experiments of the Schachter-Singer sort, the environmental cues of the questionnaire kind (where, in this instance, the questionnaire used becomes more and more personal and insulting), we can note that the stimulus conditions are really of a particular subcultural variety. Sophisticated experimentalists nowadays bewail the fact that variegated physiological display seems to accompany all behavior in the laboratory, including behavior in emotional and stressful situations. In their haste to control matters better, the experimentalists dealing with rats, now assuming they are dealing with Rodent with a capital R, today are careful to avoid contamination of "subjects," or the intrusive nonexperimental environmental effects on the animals! They are proceeding in the belief that science makes its strides solely on the basis of quantified observations, a claim made most dubious by studies in the sociology and the history of knowledge. One could hardly account for Einsteinian relativity, Pauling's theory of the chemical bond, Darwin's perceptions during his voyage on the <u>Beagle</u>, Morgan's discoveries of kinship patterns, Freud's system (built on approximately a dozen cases), Pavlov's ingenious experiments, or a score of other works of genius, by recourse to this amazing claim.

The pendulum has swung in experimental psychology, and both the theories of ego defense and theories of psychological stress are illustrated on levels of cognition (see Lazarus and Alfert, 1964, and Speisman et al., 1964). In both experiments, it was demonstrated that different cognitive preparations for the same stimuli resulted in different physiological responses. The cognitive level of meanings and symbolic interaction in humans is the very level on which anthropologists and sociologists begin their inquiries, and it is for this reason that their sciences demonstrate the importance of social and cultural contexts that have rendered useless obiter dicta about Man with a capital M. In social and cultural behavioral science, knowledge has accumulated concerning the conditions under which cultures operate. These are the settings in which human beings adapt, strive, cope, and develop.

For an anthropologist working in the field of social psychiatry, the problem of psychological stress or psychopathology among groups in society resolves itself into the question of what social and cultural conditions or backgrounds, or what types of human experiences in such known contexts, produce maladaptive or sick behavior. In the same settings, how is the family implicated in the furtherance of psychopathology?

Our first case, or example, concerns the Southern Ute Indians of Colorado, a southern tribal branch including descendants of three aboriginal bands. Of the three bands of this tribe, two are located on an eastern sector of the modern reservation, near the towns of Ignacio and Durango in southwestern Colorado. Their agency was for years known as the Consolidated Ute Agency or Reservation, and it is cut through by white land holdings devoted to agricultural pursuits, which were sold during extensive periods of land sales. The two eastern bands inhabiting this agricultural locale have been swept, over decades, into rapid acculturation. To the west, a single band inhabits a desert terrain surrounding Ute Mountain, where they have maintained Ute customs in defiance of surrounding white culture.

We have reported the differences between rapid acculturation of the eastern bands and the slower pace of acculturation of the one western band elsewhere (see Opler in Linton, 1940). Briefly, social organization and tribal beliefs underwent greater attrition among eastern bands. The process of differentiation began over a century and a quarter ago with three bands having practically identical cultures. The two on the eastern sector (Consolidated Ute Reservation) began a history of rapid accommodation to surrounding white culture, while the third band attempted to maintain the old culture in mobile camps that moved up the mountains in spring and summer and returned to the plains below in the fall. To be sure, constrained conditions of reservation life affected these Ute Mountain families (Weminutc Band) with their subagency at Towaoc. Nevertheless, the differentiation between more rapid acculturative change in the east and slower acculturation with greater maintenance of cultural norms in the west became apparent, with greater amounts of social pathology in eastern bands, despite their slightly better economic position. The consequences in family breakdown, in alcoholism, in suicide rates, and in worsening forms of psychopathology were apparent after a hundred years of this process when we studied Southern Ute bands in the initial breakdown phases of the 1930 decade. At that time, the mild conversion hysterias (a major form of Ute Indian psychopathology) were still being cured by Ute shamanistic methods of dream analysis. Today, family breakdown, alcoholism, suicide, and greater rates of psychotic pathology would have to be recorded. Among the Southern Ute bands in the 1930 decade, one could note the cultural breakdown occasioning psychological problems of stress in rapid acculturation, and cultural methods like nativistic religious cults developed to buttress and bolster up the old culture. The western band, by delaying economic involvement in white culture, was more successful in resolving conflicts occasioned by rapid acculturation.

A second case or example likewise concerns differentials in the development of psychopathology. We conducted research for five years, the period of 1938-1943, at the Morningside Clinic and Hospital, then located in Portland, Oregon. At this time, the Morningside Hospital was the only federal institution for Northwest Coast Indians and Alaskan Indians, Eskimos, and whites anywhere in the United States or its territories. Patterns of Culture (Benedict, 1934) had devoted a lengthy chapter to Indians of the Northwest coast, to Kwakiutls, Tlingits, and Tsimshians, who had cultures that seemed aberrant or abnormal from our western European and American perspective (just as ours would seem curiously aberrant from the standpoint of these cultures). The doctrine was one of unabashed cultural relativism. It held (quite correctly, we thought) that culture deeply affects the psychology of a people. But we felt also that it was wholly incorrect to assume that the relativity is absolute, or, as Benedict held, that the abnormals of one culture could fit normatively into another culture somewhere else. Assuming an effect of culture on the psychology of peoples, our real problem was now the nature of such cultural relativism. Was it, indeed, absolute? Could the "abnormal" fit in normatively elsewhere? As a cultural evolutionist, we completely doubt that cultural relativism is absolute. As a social psychiatrist, we do not believe that well and ill psychological functioning depends simply on transfer from a less appropriate cultural context to one more appropriate, but rather that illness grows in one context, and that the context, as well as the individual, must be modified.

We therefore prefer the analogy of Einsteinian physical relativity, which might be paraphrased: The human and cultural universe (or context) is bounded by its own conditions of existence, but it is unbounded in its possibilities for development. It is finite and predictable for all types of human problems, but if human problems are accurately analyzed—if both the individual and his cultural position are taken into account—then again the possibilities for development are infinite. The binding conditions (much like equations of mass and energy) are always those concrete conditions of the culture or subculture impinging upon the individual, and even the combinations of class position and ethnic group background in modern times determine the concrete conditions of existence under which one copes and strives and hopes and aspires. This is the meaning of "finite, but unbounded." While Benedict would hold that anything can happen in the realm of human or cultural psychology, we believe in limitations imposed by stages of cultural evolution. However, such stages are not immutable or unchanging, as evolution itself implies.

On the other hand, while some stress the causative force of infantile disciplines such as nursing, weaning, toilet training, and baby-swaddling, we charge that these are just as likely to be derived from cultural conditions of existence, and are too rigidly limited to determine personality in cultures. There were formerly other theories of the effects of such factors on adult personality, which now seem to have waned in importance in personality theory in psychology. In anthropology and anthropological psychiatry, Kardiner, Linton, Gorer, among others, at one time derived not only adult personality but whole cultural adaptations from infant disciplines. E. H. Erikson, in an early theory of both personality and culture, used a zonal conditioning theory of a putatively Freudian sort in his book, Childhood and Society, to state that cultures emanate from infant disciplines centered in such zones as oral, anal, and so on. Unfortunately a recent revision of this book does not correct such assumptions as the derivation of Sioux culture from cradleboard swaddling, and from long nursing or late weaning wherein teeth erupt and previously nurturant mothers reject their teething and still-nursing children. We have pointed out in reviews of Erikson's Childhood and Society that Ute children were cradled in exactly the same sort of swaddling cradleboard and were nursed even longer than Sioux children, into tooth-eruption stages, but that the cultural correlates that Erikson hastily derives, namely, a disposition to wander over the plains (due to cradleboard restrictions and inhibitions and occasional cruelty directed towards rejecting females, of course) were lacking entirely for the Ute. Because they were a Great Basin tribe, Utes did not follow buffalo over the plains; like other Basin peoples, they are essentially unwarlike, and are devotees of sexual egalitarian rights. Studied further, beyond the much too facile zonal theory, child training and infantile disciplines are important, not as causes of cultural forms and practices, but as reflections of broader social and economic styles developed in cultures and their subcultural varieties.

To continue with the Einsteinian analogy: the modern physicist or astrophysicist makes corrections in his observations or in his ordering of data according to the limitations of his position. Analogously, the question is not whether "anything can happen" in human psychology, but rather what does happen and why it happens. Obviously, child-rearing practices do not initiate culture historically, but they reflect it; they are themselves mitigated in their effects by a lengthy catalogue of other cultural practices in the experience and history of a people. This is why the culture and the psychology of a people, the mental pathology and illness epidemiology they may suffer, and even mental-illness typologies, fall into related categories according to cultural evolution. The illness epidemiology and typology fall into regular patterns because psychological stress and mental disorders are epiphenomenal to culture and to the conditions of existence imposed upon given cultures and subcultural varieties.

Morningside Hospital in Oregon, with its Kwakiutl Indians, Tsimshians, and Tlingits, with its Alaskan Eskimos and Athabaskan Indians, and with its frontier whites from what was then the Territory of Alaska, did not exhibit "abnormals" who would be normatively acceptable elsewhere in some other culture, nor were the mental-illness typologies those of a single panhuman sort—say, that exemplified by the diagnostic nomenclature and system of the American Psychiatric Association. Rather, the illnesses varied with the group of origin and reflected conditions of existence in each group's culture. For the purposes of this discussion, it is fair to add that only problematic families were represented. There were families broken by death, divorce, and separation, and those rendered more problematic by disease. Studies that focus on divorce, or on the so-called broken home, may derive samples from a variety of social and cultural background conditions, and thereby fail to define a broad pathogenic family matrix in favor of an overemphasis upon a single factor; other studies fail to denote or even consider when, in the individual's life cycle, the pathogenic factor was experienced. On occasion, we found that disease or economic pressure, an absent (even if not estranged) parent, marital conflicts unaccompanied by legal divorce—even a physical handicap in an Eskimo male which made marriage improbable—could be devastating in effect and increase the hazards of a germinating pathology. It follows that family pathologies reflected into individual cases, but still, at the same time, cultural belief, values, and sanctions interwove with family psychopathology.

Proofs of general propositions of this type do not ordinarily emanate from single experiments as they do in the physical sciences. In Culture, Psychiatry and Human Values (Opler, 1956) we sought to preserve the kernel of truth in cultural relativity (if not absolute cultural relativity) by calling our system a relational system linking culture and its value systems, on the one hand, with conditions affecting psychopathology, on the other hand. In the physical world, finite but unbounded, the relativistic positions of observers are important. The experiment attacks a part of physical phenomena, ranging from atomic physics to astrophysics, thus accounting for uniformities where these exist. The design for experiment can indeed, then, be tailored to the requirements of the special phenomena being investigated. We do not wish to simplify such matters. As everyone knows, one demonstration of Einstein's theory required, or awaited, a solar eclipse to determine that light in vast spatial reaches traveled a curved rather than a straight trajectory.

In the behavioral sciences, human experiments, demonstrations, and descriptions may also have broader or narrower parameters; but because of cultural differences in the experiences of people, a relational system tends to require additive proofs, demonstrations and descriptions. No matter how evolutionary the general phenomena of culture, psychological anthropology is still interested in the Ute, the Kwakiutl, the Irish, and the Italian as special cases. That is to say, while general cultural evolution may be viewed as unitary or as involving mankind as a whole in a kind of macroevolutionary process, microevolutionary variations and even exceptions may be instructive for special purposes in the short run. Indeed, the short run of specific cultural conditions (often seen as an historical rather than an evolutionary sequence) is the level that impinges on the individual life cycle, with its possibilities for mental health or for psychopathology. Thus, in social psychiatry, we have found it convenient to write about both macroevolutionary processes and microevolution at the same time. The Ute Indian acculturation and historical divergence of band groups is, of course, microevolutionary, as are cultural breakdown processes among Kwakiutl, Tlingit, Tsimshian, northern Athabaskans, Eskimos and frontier whites. Yet a relational theory can deal both with cultural evolutionary sequences, such as those involving Paiute and Ute, Hopi and Aztec cultures, all of which concern cognate or historically related peoples, and with microevolutionary variations such as Ute bands. In one essay (Opler, in Dole and Carneiro, 1960), we stated that cultural factors are placed in developmental sequence through evolutionary principles, and that these aid in setting up comparative categories among or between the cultures as a way of understanding past sequences or considering future possibilities. Such principles allow one to generate hypotheses about kinds of psychologies of people in art or creativity, or otherwise in such pathological dimensions as the kinds and the epidemiology of mental disorders, or the types of therapy and organization of the healing arts, all of which are, in last analysis, evolutionary phenomena. On a microevolutionary level of analysis of the specific forms of psychopathology, the healing arts, and epidemiology, special theories of relativity are needed that, through minute comparisons, throw such elements as family process into high relief. The format of such study begins with cultural type, but it proceeds down through a continuum of typical stresses in the life cycle to samples distinguished by such subcultural phenomena as class and ethnicity, age and sex groups, contrasts of normative and disturbed lines of development, and the like.

At Morningside Hospital in Oregon, we had opportunity to study psychotics from Benedict's Northwest Coast cultures, who, of course, could not gear into or normatively fit any culture anywhere. Illness is maladaptive to the human condition as well as to the cultural condition. Cultures cannot merely be ranged in an endless arc of "possibilities," to use Benedict's term, nor does each culture, as she stated, select from the arc of possibilities some segment by a process she termed "psychological selectivity." The error lies in presuming that the process of culture-building begins with "psychological selectivity": for what determines such selections if not culture in the first instance? The reasoning is obviously circular, but it selects a dependent variable (psychology, in this instance) as a prime mover. Quite the contrary: in Morningside Hospital patients, illness histories and developments, as well as the form and content of psychopathology, differed from one cultural group to the next. Nevertheless, there were general typologies according to types of family culture. Patients who had not experienced positively meaningful family life or cultural life went through hysteriform early stages of illness into psychotic, confusional, and delusional states. The white population had more of its share of fearful catatonias

than one sees in hospital populations today. Kwakiutls might have
some paranoid delusions, but unlike those in our society, delusions
were fluid rather than systematized and related very little to sexual
content. The hunchback Eskimo, neglected and an outcast in his own
society, had little green men to help him on the hunt, but such guard-
ian spirit conceptions merged easily with generous amounts of normative cultural materials and were hardly noncultural paranoid or
idiosyncratic compensations. While one observed Freudian mechanisms of defense at work in individuals, their self- and social concepts, which they defended against assumed threats, were not necessarily the self- and social conceptual materials found in our culture.
Nor were the threats of an order that we might, because of our cultural conditions of existence, consider threatening to ego adaptation.
Thus, one found maladjustments directly traceable to specific kinds
of stressful cultural condition for particularized human existences.

There are those who argue that behavioral sciences should have
far more broad generalizations, but we believe that they have never
perceived nor understood cultural or subcultural specificity. But-
tressing this myopia in cultural matters are the endless formulae
we have for educating medical students. "They should learn how to
deal with death," said one young professor. But death, like life, has
many disguises. "They should discover what the illness means to
the patient," he continued. But there are many divergent cultural
conceptions of illness. At any rate, the scaffold from which one
perceives these varieties of cultural conditions is evolutionary. For
this reason, Morningside Hospital patients could not be understood
through the single historical product of American Psychiatric Association nomenclature, for the patients did not have, in any sense,
the same kinds of illness, even when psychotic, that could be found
in the nearest state hospital. While etiology of illness was similar
within groups from case to case, it was variable among the groups.

In Culture, Psychiatry and Human Values, we discussed such
regional variations in illness as reactions to stress of different
types. Take, as an obvious example, the series of psychotic de-
rangements known as latah, running amok (known in Malaysia, Micronesia and Mongolia), and imu (among the Ainu of Hokkaido).
These, and Arctic Hysteria, so-called (which occurs in northeastern
Siberia under conditions of rapid acculturation), are not psychoses
in the current Western European or American sense of guilt-ridden
depressive states, nor schizophrenias with paranoid reaction. Rather, they remind one of former accounts of psychoses in European
uneducated peasant societies. In latah, imu, and Arctic Hysteria,
for example, there are echolalias, often with obscene punning involved. A startle reaction, as in the Giles de la Tourette syndrome,

in the form of a sudden statement to the patient (or, in Southeast Asia, the simple act of touching him) is enough to set the reaction in motion. Echopraxia can be induced by showing the subject any action, whether easily imitated or not. In northeastern Siberia, sailors touching at ports where acculturated Chukchi with so-called Arctic Hysteria lived would torture these victims of echopraxia by doing physically taxing things such as running uphill with a knife or a slender fish in their mouths. The Chukchi victim, no matter how aged and infirm, would attempt the same act. In Hokkaido, imu victims, usually women, were utilized at banquets for similar amusements. A sudden cry or an act of grabbing might induce stereotyped prancing, or else echolalias and echopraxias. Variations of simple imitation are the simple negativism such as doing the opposite action, or, in speech forms, saying the opposite thing or blurting out obscene puns. (In latah, the puns are made on the words used in polite conversation). Such confusions blend into the hostile and dangerous "mad dog runs" of running amok, where the victim leaves a trail of maimed and dead in his wake until he is himself slain.

There are, of course, some differences to be noted, in that latah, imu, and Arctic Hysteria are most often female disorders, while running amok is a male syndrome. The excited confusional states and catathymic outbursts reported for parts of Africa (and noted as being open to equally sudden remissions) are transitory psychoses of types not usual in our culture. But still these are psychotic states in the sense of profound, if transitory, disturbances in thinking, in affect, and—especially in these cultural settings demanding of activity—in action. The episodic nature of these seizures, the periods of remission, the age and sex epidemiology involved, all indicate that in the cultures we are discussing the stress systems vary from our own. Further, the rates of such psychotic ills seem less than in our modern, urbanized cultures. M. E. Spiro (in Opler, 1959), reporting on the island of Ifaluk in Micronesia with a complete illness sample and census, noted extremely low rates of psychosis in general. Just as illness rates have, in the better and more complete studies of nonliterate cultures, been found to be surprisingly low, so the modes of therapy have often been found to be unusually sophisticated. We have already commented on the Ute Indian usage of dream analysis for the treatment of conversion hysterias, and their shamans' tendencies to involve families in therapeutic practices. In Nigeria, where affectively volatile confusional states are found, native curing cults use rauwolfia serpentina or reserpine tranquilizer along with restraint of the patient. The powerful sedative agent and physical restraint by shackling during a period of heavy dosage is intended to make the patient accessible to psychotherapy. The drug is peculiarly well-adapted to the kind of short-lived psychotic disturbance, or "seizure," which affects the patient episodically. The family, often coming from a great distance for the treatment, becomes involved in the therapeutic process, and may minister to the patient's needs while he is in residence near the practitioner. Also, practitioners may be called to patients to administer "home treatment."

In either case, be it analogous to "walk-in clinic" or "home treatment," the family is involved in the curative procedures, so that "family therapy" may be added to the list. Group therapy is also utilized, as is after-care and follow-up of cases through participation in curing cult activities. There is a nice fit between the characteristic ailment and the powerful folk-medicine sedation, between catathymic outburst and temporary restraint, between confusional state and family orientation, between cultural values and curing cult activities involving after-care, and between group norms and group psychotherapy. No one looking at the confusional outbursts, the Nigerian concept of curse or bewitchment, or the startle reaction in other episodic psychotic states of the type of latah, imu, and Arctic Hysteria, or the outburst phenomena in either running amok or the so-called catathymic outburst, can fail to note similarities in the above series, and, at the same time, important divergencies from our own schizophrenias with paranoid reaction, greater fixity of delusions, and greater defensiveness in depth.

The suggestion is that human culture is man's mode of adaptation to environment, and that his illnesses of psychogenic source are monuments in each instance to man's relative degree of success or failure in making such adaptations or adjustments. Similarly, the healing arts in their mode of organization reveal important aspects in the ethics and values of the culture.

Robert K. Merton (1957), in his writing on manifest and latent functions, pointed out that the unity of a social system must be empirically determined. He added that, to do this, no item in the system can be automatically considered functional in the system. In other words, some are functional, others nonfunctional or dysfunctional. At the very least, these distinctions stress what anthropologists frequently test out in studies of cultures. If one knows the total pattern of a sociocultural system as it operates, with humans behaving in it, one can assess particular aspects such as the family. Second, one can denote cultural stresses within the system. Sex and Repression in Savage Society (Malinowski, 1951) is such an attempt at a paradigm of stress, in this case in Trobriand Island society. There the family, as we think of it, is clearly dysfunctional, though it exists, while avunculate, clan, and economic reciprocities between sister and brother have a more unequivocal importance. No one has attempted a similar paradigm, exactly, for the kinds of family existing in the United States, though we know that the extended family, for example, is more functional among Italian first and second generations than it is in nuclear English family types, among German-Americans, and so on. Yet Freud, Fromm, and countless others have attempted a psychological paradigm of the effects of family functioning. Why is there this timidness about analyzing family types directly for analytic purposes? Either, as we have charged above, the type is made panhuman, which it is definitely not, or the psychoanalytic persuasion is to ignore family typology entirely, something we are sure Freud himself would have deplored.

Let us begin below with a point that goes beyond Merton's classification, and which is, as a matter of fact, clearly a panhuman attribute regardless of family type. We refer to the importance of early learning for humans, no matter what the family constellation or its special characteristics may be. Using this concept, but in a manner far different from the Freudian assumption of a universal Oedipal arrangement, we can combine modern methods of anthropology and social psychiatry.

Our final cases derive from modern American society in the United States, and relate to ethnic groups studied over a period of years. The subcultural groups were each known in their history and setting, and additionally acculturative stress could be analyzed in a number of ways. Obviously, the methods used are those of studying individuals and families in their "natural" development, or microevolution. In addition, in both studies, much was known about local epidemiology. When one studies individuals and their families against a background of the local culture as a whole, one is erecting a scaffold from which to view careful etiological analysis of such samples. The controlled conditions of such an experiment, as it were, are to be found in the sheer amount of knowledge of what is happening in the community and in the families that make it up; here one can develop a playback, or feedback technique, between psychiatric or psychological knowledge of the actual patterns of behavior and knowledge of the stresses acting upon the group.

As we said above, some theory of weights or weighting is utilized to replace a crudely unreasoned distributive system. For instance, we assumed that the doctrine of "early learning" in subcultural family settings sometimes exerts extreme stress through repetitive events producing psychopathology. At the same time, we felt that psychopathology, as it emerged, could not be imitative, but instead must be mediated by psychodynamic happenings. The latter are mediated in a fuller and clearer view by systems of defense which are discrete or different for different subcultural groups, and which arise from the pre-existing sociocultural patterns and values in the group. For years, in social and behavioral sciences, the term "social dynamics" has been used with a variety of vague connotations. We propose here to give it special meaning, for psychodynamic events are backgrounded, we find, by sociodynamic ones. We therefore define sociodynamic as those events which, as a class, can interpenetrate with and influence psychodynamic processes. Social psychiatry has long needed such a term, for it deals constantly with social and cultural factors influencing psychopathology. At any rate, this view of process which begins with quantitatively large and qualitatively potent elements in the psychology of social and cultural groups is more scientific in our lexicon than a distributive stringing out of unweighted, disparate factors like the constitutional, the biogenic, the psychogenic and the cultural.

The first case in this ethnic group category concerns the Japanese-Americans uprooted from the West Coast, from Washington, Oregon, and California, during World War II. They were studied by me for three years as Chief of Community Analysis (chief social science analyst), with a hired staff of sixteen community analysts, in the War Relocation Authority, United States Department of the Interior. The major studies to which we allude were part of an intensive ongoing community analysis of the Tule Lake Center, the most problematic setting of all, in northern California. The time was 1943-1946, followed by a shorter period of writing up data for a volume called Impounded People (Spicer et al., 1946). Several chapters in this government publication apply to the Tule Lake Center; a further chapter, about psychogenic disorders (which were typical), appears in Clinical Studies in Culture Conflict (Seward, 1958).

Let us begin, briefly, with some general facts about epidemiology. The Center contained approximately 18,000 persons, men, women and children, who had suddenly been forced out of their West Coast homes following Pearl Harbor, and who, after a series of governmentally-defined moves (sometimes six or more), had arrived at the Tule Lake Relocation Center. In the course of our study, this Center was made the government Segregation Center for Japanese-Americans, so that in addition to all the moves and the original uprooting, there were thousands leaving and thousands arriving during its three-year history. In the town of 18,000, because so many aspects of living were completely controlled, with central hospital, block mess halls, conditions of employment and welfare, property control, and legal offices functioning for the town as a whole, we could study all aspects of center life, including recreational clubs, like the one for senryu poetry writing; sports groups, like those concerned with judo, sumo, and baseball; vocationally oriented groups, like those for dress- and suit-making; or conditions of labor, say, on the project farm, mess hall department, or even garbage crews. In addition, rumors and center attitudes towards a variety of governmental programs and decisions could be sampled. As a research unit, producing on the average two studies per week, larger or smaller in scope, we could describe mental health epidemiology including cases known to hospital and courts, but also cases hidden in the Center—those known to welfare offices, or those somewhat disguised by aberrant health or religious cult membership. Concurrently, if we studied economics for the town population, we were in the privileged position of knowing about every single item of funds coming in to all the people of Tule Lake, and all expenditures, whether through community cooperative stores, mail order, or taxes, and legally known payments going out. We therefore learned who was losing ground economically (the average picture during "relocation," unfortunately), and to what extent, and could graph this loss according to population segments. Similarly, mental health problems, suicides, divorces, and social pathology like gambling and prostitution were no strangers in our statistical mapping. We studied rumors—for instance, the well-founded one that the Cooperative was involved in individual family economic losses, or that Japanese-American professionals (like the community hospital "Center Resident" doctors) were losing tens of thousands of dollars per year. We could study the economic plight of Dr. H., who "outside" had run a surgical and medical clinic in Fresno, and was a Fellow of the American Board of Surgeons: he now imported his surgical implements from his closed clinic, continued his subscriptions to 19 professional journals, and, in the Center Hospital surgery where he worked for the standard professional salary of War Relocation Authority ($19 per month), took orders from a nonsurgeon, the Caucasian Chief Medical Officer. Equally, in cases of mental pathology, individual cases could be studied in depth. Acute breakdowns increased after long periods of center tensions, when rumors, community pressures and unrest, the divisive movements of cliques, and pressure-group duress and persuasion were most strongly felt. Such tensions were often found dramatized not only in publicly proclaimed social movements, but inside family confines, where a first-generation (Issei) father, his second-generation (Nisei) wife or son, and a Japanese-educated (Kibei) younger sibling might be chief actors in the drama.

The facts of epidemiology and its fluctuations with conditions of life in Center history are therefore more completely known than in most studies of most towns. The "controlled laboratory conditions" of a uniform cultural group of 18,000 divided only by generation level and acculturation processes, and at the same time unified by being confined in one square mile of manproof fenced-in area, are probably unique.

A further leveling force was that of having suffered the same indignities and economic losses. Although classes and educational backgrounds varied considerably, public toilets, mess halls, showers, and the fixed Center salaries ($19 monthly for professionals, $16 for semiprofessionals, and $12 for laborers) gave a monotonous unity to life in small tarpaper operations-barracks apartments decorated with similar appurtenances and amenities snatched from woodpiles or dug from the Pleistocene lake bottom on which the Center stood.

Since most forms of pathology are complex phenomena, let us focus only on one of intrinsic interest in Japanese epidemiology in Japan or in the United States. Just as our studies of poetry production would gather all examples written in a given period of time, subjecting them to content analysis, stylistic and thematic study, and so forth, so the categories of terminal suicide, attempted suicide (gestural, mild, and serious), or suicidal ruminations could be studied with considerable completeness. As with other forms of mental pathology, suicide threat, attempt, and terminal act increased epidemiologically in the periods of greatest Center tension. While rumors might be sampled in blocks and wards, for suicide every case of neurotic or psychotic type could be utilized. The Community Analysis staff was able to make predictions not only of Center upheavals and demonstrations, but of a Center political murder (even though we did not know then, nor do we know now, who committed the crime). One son of the victim was on our Community Analysis staff, as staff artist, at the time. At any rate, predictions of suicide attempt rates could be made if one analyzed Center tensions as a constant background.

Those who have read Suicide and Scandinavia (Hendin, 1964), know that high rates of suicide in Sweden and Denmark contrast with low suicide rates for Norway. We know, further, that suicide rates seem to be increasing in the United States, particularly in younger age groups, so that in the age group, 15-19 years of age, suicide ranks third, following accidents and cancer, as a cause of death. In the Tule Lake Center, we did studies of age and status groups, including the Issei (the first-generation immigrant group, born abroad, and, by U.S. law, not eligible for citizenship), the Nisei (second-generation, and citizens by virtue of having been born in the United States), and the Kibei. The latter, of the same generation level and citizenship status as their Nisei siblings, were a curious population category by reason of having been sent to grandparental or elder sibling homes abroad for education. While Kibei varied in the age sent or the length of time spent abroad, they formed a large segment of the population, and were the subject of many of our studies, chiefly psychological, in the Center. The early training and education received abroad often meant that they experienced separation anxieties if, at the time of separation, they were young enough; the return, to an uncomfortable and minority status among their Nisei siblings and the latters' friends in the bobbysocks set of California towns, often spelled what seemed to some a "double rejection"—first with parents and second with peer group. The culture conflict they exemplified by having a foot in each culture was intensified by the fact that Kibei, often spoiled by grandparents and older uncles and aunts, and experiencing some contact with modern Japan, were none too respectful of old-fashioned Issei ways—an attitude tempered further by years of living in the United States. While the Center was, perhaps, a kid-glove version of a concentration camp, it added to feelings of nonacceptance, rejection, or even discrimination, so that Kibei proved to be the most pathogenic group in the population, and, in particular, the group most prone to suicidal behavior. Three years of concentration camp existence and periods of mounting tension and governmental error (Eugene V. Rostow, former dean of the Yale Law School, first called this "America's worst wartime mistake") are registered sensitively in both higher rates of Kibei breakdown and in higher suicide rates for this group.

Analyses of Japanese culture by a wide variety of scholars have stressed the early spoiling, the early dependency training, the cherishing of male children, and the possible narcissistic and magical thinking in some. For the culture, in general, there are later problems in the realm of assertiveness in the post-adolescent phases of the life cycle. The same paradigm is characteristic of Hendin's analyses for Sweden and Denmark, and he raises in addition the parental modes of punishment by threat of magical control, which he finds present in Swedish and Danish child-rearing practices, but wholly absent in the matter-of-fact and realistic approaches to punishment and threat among Norwegians.

In Japan, where religiously sanctioned ritual suicide (seppuku) was once practiced, and where suicide rates are generally believed to be high, magical manipulation of others, problems in the balance of dependency and assertiveness, and introjections of "rejection" and separation anxieties are probably chief characteristics. The Kibei at Tule Lake Center were most open to these hazards. However, our description would be sorely lacking if we did not add that concerns about being ejected from the Center (the War Relocation Authority program encouraged children to separate from parents and to find jobs in the eastern United States) intensified discussions of the differences between Nisei and Kibei children and the double senses of rejection and of separation that were always playing upon Kibei minds. Those psychodynamically better off were keen scholars, bent on bettering their education or their skills during the Center sojourn. Some among them had the keenest sense of the social and political forces at play in World War II. But the meeting point of psychodynamic vulnerability and sociodynamic crises produced in Kibei as a statistical set the largest problems in the realm of dependency and assertion, in magically manipulative tactics, and in throttled hostility at their untenable position, so that this group was marked by higher suicidal rates in threat, attempt, and terminal categories than any other Center population segment.

This predictable epidemiology, based on psychiatric and also cultural or familistic knowledge, may be tested also in the age and sex specific studies of Okinawan suicide developed by Thomas Maretzki, or in Japanese youth studies by Mamoru Iga, both of whom plan to publish their studies in the International Journal of Social Psychiatry. In our study of the Kibei, or in Hendin's work, or in these later studies, epidemiological work and knowledge of the stress points in cultures, acting upon family systems, constitute the method for studying the resulting psychopathology.

Our final case is a collaborative study developed with the assistance of Dr. Eugene B. Piedmont, a former colleague. It illustrates another way to work methodically in the direction of greater psychodynamic knowledge of groups after beginning, first of all, with the generalized and more normative picture of the larger cultural context. This study grew out of the author's work in the Midtown Manhattan Mental Health project, where for ten years combinations of class and ethnic group samples were studied for their forms of schizophrenia. In Midtown, each cultural group was first studied, as in the Tule Lake Center, through a wide variety of community studies. A generalized questionnaire was next prepared (and translated where necessary) for use with a random sample of community group representatives in which social classes and ethnic groups, as subtypes, were properly evidenced. These were only two phases of research in the Midtown Manhattan Mental Health Study, to which a census of all persons in treatment (at a given time) was added. Obviously, a community generalized questionnaire, a

social work and practitioner's census, and antecedant community
studies are not psychodynamic or sociodynamic studies of individuals and of families.

A third phase of research was therefore developed in which, by
questionnaire ratings of psychiatrists, those ill (marked or moder-
ately ill) and those symptom-free or relatively well were now selected for each major ethnic group component and, where possible,
for class differentia as well. The individual was now studied in his
family setting by a member of an anthropological team. Later, a
trained clinical psychologist gave him a battery of five psychological
tests in the home. The tests, including Rorschach, T.A.T., Sen-
tence Completion, Bender-Gestalt, and House-Tree-Person draw-
ings, were analyzed by psychologists separately from the questionnaire and anthropological data, which were thought of as complementary. A series of studies by ethnicity therefore resulted for the
more populous ethnic groups of Midtown: Italian, Irish, German,
Puerto Rican, Czech, Slovakian, Hungarian, and, of course, Anglo-
American. To develop these studies further by considering the psychopathology in extremes, samples were drawn also in hospital settings of Midtown ethnic groups, male and female, with diagnosed
schizophrenias. A number of these studies have been published and
some, concerning Italian and Irish, have been replicated.

While German and various Slavic language group studies, for
instance Czech and Slovak, were developed in the Midtown Manhattan
Research, we decided to continue various studies, for example,
Irish, Italian, German, and Polish, in the community facilities and
teaching hospitals connected with our School of Medicine in Buffalo,
New York. Here follows a description of a German and Polish study
in schizophrenias, developed with Dr. E. B. Piedmont. This particular study is illustrated in only the sketchiest outlines. This is
simply an example on second and third generation levels rather than
on predominantly first and second generation levels, as in the Midtown studies; otherwise, the studies are similar. Samples are controlled for class, age, chronicity, educational level and sex, utilizing nonorganic cases, and, wherever possible in the interethnic
samples, religion. Left starkly as independent variables are the
cluster of sex group and ethnicity. The dependent or resultant variables are the items in psychopathology given in the accompanying
table. Obviously, family typology is an intervening variable as are
the contrasting psychodynamic factors. Let us indicate what the
table connotes.

Samples of German-American and Polish-American descent
are among the highest numerically in Buffalo public institutions. It
is not that these persons with different cultural backgrounds — like

TABLE 1

COMPARISON OF GERMAN AND POLISH SCHIZOPHRENICS

PARAMETERS	DICHOTOMY OR DIFFERENTIATION		CHI-SQUARE
	German	Polish	
1. Anxiety & Hostility	Hostile	Anxious	$X^2 =$ 8.87 P < .01
2A. Emotional Expressivity	Absent	Present	$X^2 =$ 6.94 P < .01
2B. Modes of Emotional Expressivity	Sado-Masochistic	Acquisitive-Dependent	$X^2 =$ 6.88 P < .01
3. Orality	Passive-Aggressive	Passive-Dependent	$X^2 =$ 9.64 P < .01
4. Sexual Identity	Mis-Identity	Non-Identity	$X^2 =$ 9.19 P < .01
5. Tendency toward Alcoholism	Absent	Present	$X^2 =$ 5.08 P < .05
6. Relations with Authority	Passive-Aggressive	Passive-Dependent	$X^2 =$ 19.28 P < .001
7. Somatic & Hypochondriacal Features	Absent & Aggressive	Present & Dependent	$X^2 =$ 11.38 P < .001
8. Delusional System	Present	Absent	$X^2 =$ 5.125 P < .05
9. Overall Psychopathological Pattern	Paranoid	Catatonic	$X^2 =$ 6.79 P < .01

the Italians and the Irish—perceive identical situations in somewhat different ways, but rather that both sociodynamic and psychodynamic processes vary. While the author had studied German and Polish cultural background previously in Midtown research, Dr. Piedmont was encouraged to study separately such classics as The Polish Peasant in Europe and America (Thomas and Znaniecki, 1958), and whatever historical, biographical, and archival materials related to the large Polish community of Buffalo. Initial interviews with patients were held by the author and then continued by Dr. Piedmont. Differences in Midtown and Buffalo studies included the facts that Midtown samples were followed for a two-year period, and that the total battery of 13 psychological tests for Midtown could not be duplicated in Buffalo because fewer clinical psychologists were available. Nevertheless, the tabulated contrast variables are interesting.

With regard to the tabulated contrast, statistically significant by chi-square analysis, the 30 German and 30 Polish patients, all diagnosed as schizophrenics, were different as groups from one another, and different again from the Irish-Italian contrasts found

earlier. Yet to make the contrasts meaningful in the present instance, family types must be pictured.

If one begins with immigrant family types, the reference point
is usually social organization as it has been derived from Old World
peasant community models and changed in the New World. The Polish family is one in which maternal controls are often primary, by
virtue of women managing household budgets, frequently inheriting
property or holding dowries, and, as a matter of fact, contributing
heavily to farm work. In the old country, males were, of course,
valued as hard workers, skillful managers, and shrewd manipulators
of family holdings; but it must be remembered that inheritance was
not regulated by rules such as primogeniture, and in the immigrants'
villages, or in small towns, poverty was a main spur to immigration
itself. In western New York, the Polish male usually found employment in heavy industries such as steel manufacturing, and wages
fixed by major companies (punctuated by temporary layoffs or
longer periods of unemployment) became the source of family pro-
visioning.

Upperclass Polish historical values of the gentry such as valor,
honor, and courage—never very meaningful in peasant society to
begin with—had less meaning in a setting of sporadic wage labor.
The values of shrewdness, planfulness, maintenance of a hospitable
home, budgeting, and saving were all the more female prerogatives,
as were child-rearing, home discipline, and religious adherence.
In the emotional climate of the home, the fathers were more marginal and had fewer sanctions than any paterfamilias, however
humble, in the old country. In poorly constructed or more problematic families in the new setting, maternal controls were not only
paramount in the home, but often constituted attempts at overcon-
trol, spoiling of favorite sons through overprotective techniques,
introjections of fear or loss, or promoting symbiotic anxieties and
dependency on the maternal figure, all as compensations for maternal needs. We have labeled this phenomenon "anxious behavior"
in the male sample of Polish schizophrenics. It was exemplified in
various psychodynamic ways, but, to cite a single case, there was
the boy kept from school till eight years of age and assiduously
protected by his mother from a horse-phobia (like Freud's case of
Hans); from the moment his father died until well into adolescence,
he was plagued with a functional torticollis.

The typical German family type is too well known to require
extensive description, but suffice to say that paternal authority,
though more remote in daytime hours, was nevertheless a constant
threat through mother authority-surrogates. Male hostility to father
figures, tempered by passive-aggressive attitudes toward mothers,

was again expressed psychodynamically, though both attitudes were little disguised in various other relationships with authority.

The second factor of emotional expressivity also varied in each group of patients. The German families tended to see emotional expression as irrational, as being opposed to such authority models as we have sketched, and consequently as dangerous to Germanic notions of order, hierarchy, and propriety. In contrast with Polish patients, for whom these constrictions were absent, the German male sample had histories in which defensive tactics of rationalization, rigidity, obsession, and emotional control were obviously overused and had worn thin. The Polish sample interviews and histories were laden with events having clear emotional connotations; while emotional content might be naively misconstrued and distorted as to underlying meanings, they were patients at least inured to high emotional valence. Initial rapport in conversations with each sample required knowledge of these emotive and rational styles.

In the third place, the oral complex in schizophrenias likewise had a different quality for each sample. Both a dependent oral relationship and specific dependencies on mothers characterized the Polish patients. German patients, on the contrary, were critical of female figures in the family, according to rationalized Germanic cultural notions of male superiority. In actual German life histories, aggressive and hostile attitudes were vented upon mothers, wives, and female siblings.

The fourth contrast in our series, according to psychological instruments and the anthropological study of cases, was, as in the Midtown Manhattan studies of Irish and Italian cases, a major point of differentiation. The orthodox Freudian notion of homosexual conflict is derived from Freud's description of the Schreber case, which, in the classic form, is actually one of homosexual trends actively defended against with the result of sexual misidentification. The German sample fitted this model most closely. This was the point at which paranoid reactions (actually compensations, in effect) strongly appeared. The Polish model, by statistical contrast, was a pallid nonidentification and confusion as to sexual attributes.

While German male patients, as a sample group, refused to identify with male figures in the family, there were hostile elements in the rationalized attitudes towards females as well, and, of course, projective compensations to cope with feelings of inadequacy. Delusional content in the misidentification was also frequently developed, along with paranoid attitudes towards females. The outcome was a distorted, if rationalized, sexual identity. By and large, the Polish patient did not distort sexual characteristics, but instead seemed powerless to enact them or fully experience them. Rather than distortions, there were massive doubts of mature male characteristics, which, of course, were guilt-provoking in view of Polish ideal cultural values stressing male valor, honor, and courage. The Polish patient who was a tail-gunner in the air force in World War II would indicate his anxiety reactions during flight missions; the erstwhile alcoholic would state how he "needed" this to help him forget his fears; and the torticollis victim would dwell on his visits to chiropractors as footnotes to accounts of male inadequacy. Yet homosexual panics, delusional persecutions, and aggressive overtones were never part of such complaints. The sixth factor, periods of alcoholism, was utilized in Polish sample cases to quiet fears, bolster identity or find escape; it was not a factor in the German sample. Similarly, German patients were passively resistant to authority, critical and aggressive in their comments about actual authority, and full of platitudes about the need for hierarchy. Polish patients, by contrast, were wholly compliant in actual relations with authority, a matter which they regarded as fateful and entirely beyond their control. The same fateful attitude pervaded aspects of their somatic and hypochondriacal complaints, some of these having distinct hysterical features. The German sample did not utilize hypochondriacal crutches, but at the same time they were apt to wear themselves out physically by misdirected striving and coping behavior.

We come, finally, to the matter of delusional formation. As suggested above, full-blown delusional formation marked the German sample alone, and the delusions themselves had rigid ideological rationalization. Yet by contrast to the German, the Polish sample seemed almost rational or reasonable; struggles with feelings of inadequacy or the almost realistically assessed defeats in life careers were more the features of free-floating anxiety than in the grandiose German group with which the Polish contrasted so markedly.

The final variable we have evaluated is a composite of the foregoing ones; yet, in summary, it challenges the process of applying diagnostic labels (like schizophrenia) without carefully considering the connections of psychodynamic and sociodynamic processes. We do not mean that Polish second and third generation patients are identifiable as catatonics in each instance, or that German samples will uniformly reveal schizophrenias with paranoid reaction. Yet despite diagnostic labels applied to these 60 patients (all were called schizophrenic), a significant diagnostic differentiation was missed. While hospital personnel would recognize that a given patient of Polish extraction was anxious, pallidly asexual, inadequate by his own standards, and sometimes frozen in his fears, the diagnostic label of catatonia was rarely applied in the records simply because cata-

158

tonics are rarer today in urban societies than was once the case. Similarly, the German patient who was angry, subtly aggressive, delusional, and with rigid and fixed rationalizations, was not often regarded as one who had learned to base his defenses on paranoid distortions and maneuvers.

REFERENCES

Benedict, Ruth. Patterns of culture. New York: Houghton, 1934.

Hendin, H. Suicide and Scandinavia. New York: Grune and Stratton, 1964.

Lazarus, R., & Alfert, E. Shortcircuiting of threat by experimentally altering cognitive appraisal. J. abnorm. soc. Psychol., 1964, 69, 195-205.

Malinowski, B. Sex and repression in savage society. New York: Humanities, 1951.

Merton, R. K. Social theory and social structure. Glencoe, Ill.: Free Press, 1957.

Opler, M. K. The Southern Ute of Colorado. In R. Linton (Ed.), Acculturation in seven American Indian tribes. New York: Appleton, Century, Crofts, 1940. Pp. 119-206.

Opler, M. K. Culture, psychiatry and human values. Springfield, Ill.: Thomas, 1956.

Opler, M. K., & Singer, J. L. Ethnic differences in behavior and psychopathology. Int. J. soc. Psychiat., 1956, 2, (1), 11-23.

Opler, M. K. Cultural evolution and the psychology of peoples. In G. Dole and R. Carneiro (Eds.), Essays in the science of culture. New York: T. Y. Crowell Co., 1960. Pp. 354-379.

Schachter, S., & Singer, J. L. Cognitive, social and psychological determinants of emotional state. Psychol. Rev., 1962, 69, 379-399.

Seward, Georgene J. Clinical studies in culture conflict. New York: Ronald Press, 1958.

Speisman, J., et al. Experimental reduction of stress based on ego-defense theory. J. abnorm. soc. Psychol., 1964, 68, 367-380.

Spicer, E. H., et al. Impounded people. United States Government Printing Office, and U.S. Dept. of Interior, War Relocation Authority, Community Analysis Section. Washington, D.C.: 1946.

Spiro, M. E. Cultural heritage, personal tensions, and mental illness in a South Sea culture. In M. K. Opler (Ed.), Culture and mental health. New York: Macmillan, 1959. Pp. 141-171.

Thomas, W. I., & Znaniecki, F. The Polish peasant in Europe and America. New York: Dover, 1958.

THE SOCIOCULTURAL ASPECTS OF CHILDHOOD SCHIZOPHRENIA:

A Discussion with Special Emphasis on Methodology

Victor D. Sanua, Ph. D.

Ekstein et al. (1958) published an extensive review of the literature on childhood schizophrenia, in which they noted that during the period between 1946 and 1956, 515 articles had appeared in the literature on childhood schizophrenia, as compared with the 54 articles that had appeared in the previous decade. An analysis of these articles reveals that approximately 65 percent of them were concerned with problems of etiology, symptomatology and diagnosis, approximately 20 percent with psychotherapy, 18 percent with residential or hospital treatment, and about 4 percent with somatic treatment. Between 1957 and 1963, 227 references on childhood schizophrenia appeared in the Index Medicus.

Preparing an evaluation of such studies constitutes a tremendous task. Our purpose here is to discuss methodological issues, research strategies, and the problems inherent in studying parent-child relationships and parent-child interaction as an etiological factor in schizophrenia. In 1961, the present writer prepared an extensive review of the literature on research conducted with adult schizophrenics, with particular emphasis on the different methods used in studying parent-child interaction during childhood. The review also covered studies comparing mothers of schizophrenics with mothers of non-schizophrenics through psychological tests, interviews, and other approaches. In the concluding paragraph to this article (Sanua, 1961) the writer stated:

"Although the evidence of the importance of family factors in the background of schizophrenics is quite compelling, the patterns of the home environment need to be more clearly defined. . . . It has been emphasized that designs in future research should deal with such variables as social class, ethnicity, or religious affiliation; age, sex, diagnostic categories, influence of the father as well as the mother, and others" (p. 265).

159

The present survey of articles on childhood schizophrenia leads the writer to believe that a similar conclusion is applicable in this area of research. While some meager attempts of well-designed studies controlling for the patient's background have been conducted with adult schizophrenics, such designs, conducted with schizophrenic children, are even more sparse. Those who believe in the psychogenic etiology of schizophrenia have concentrated on studying the interaction between young schizophrenics and their parents. It would appear that familiarity with studies of normal children would provide the investigator with sophisticated methods of research beyond the usual clinical interview, and would provide a basis for comparison between parents of normal children and parents of disturbed children.

Child training procedures have received a great deal of attention from anthropologists and sociologists. The literature on child rearing and its influence on personality is quite extensive, and investigators of childhood schizophrenia should become familiar with it.

Adler (1945) wrote that she was unaware of any comprehensive study examining the influence of different economic levels upon the development and the prognosis of neuroses and behavior problems among children. The same statement could be made in 1964. Adler did not conduct any empirical studies, but relied on her clinical experience. In discussing eating difficulties among children, Adler stated that this symptom could only arise in families where there was an overemphasis on food. She maintains that in hardly any family "where hungry eyes watch the child with the hope that he may leave some portion of its serving, do eating difficulties develop." Adler hypothesized that when a child experiences difficulty in obtaining adequate food and has been competing with a younger brother for his mother's attention, symptoms other than feeding problems appear: for example, fainting spells, bed-wetting, and others. She reports that Jewish children have feeding difficulties and suffer little enuresis but Italian children have no feeding difficulties and frequently suffer from enuresis. As to outcome, Adler suggests that lower-class children with behavior problems tend to become delinquents and, later on in life, criminals, while children from the upper classes who have behavior problems follow a different course—prevented from joining the ranks of criminals, they become social parasites or "playboys," who remain "socially acceptable" in view of the fact that they remain protected by their economic status.

While social class variables have been taken into consideration during the last few years, particularly in areas pertaining to psychotherapy (Sanua, 1964), the present writer has not been able to locate any study on childhood schizophrenia that tries to relate cultural or socioeconomic background of the child with manifestations of schizophrenic behavior.

EARLIER STUDIES IN CHILDHOOD SCHIZOPHRENIA

A presentation of some major studies of severe disorders of children and schizophrenia that were conducted in the early forties is presented below. Various present-day theories on the etiology of childhood schizophrenia have emerged from these studies.

Kanner (1960) reported on his experiences in Baltimore with "autistic children" who come from "cold, refrigerated parents," while Bender (1956) in New York obtained different manifestations of childhood schizophrenia in various forms such as pseudodefective, pseudoneurotic, and pseudopsychopathic, all of which are brought about by organic and genetic causes.

While Kanner originally explained "infantile autism" as an expression of constitutional abnormality, he now emphasizes its functional aspects. He finds fault with Bender's general diffusiveness concerning her definition of childhood schizophrenia, and is rather surprised to find that Bender, on the basis of her definition, was able to distinguish only 850 case records over two decades. Kanner states that on the basis of limited criteria he was able to diagnose an average of eight cases per year. Kanner also finds fault with investigators who have a tendency to disclaim any serious attempt at diagnostic differentiation such as the formulations made by Szurek (1956) and Rank (1949). He is not impressed with those who proceed with the psychogenic denominator of disturbances of "ego functioning" in an effort to explain all types of severe childhood disorders, in spite of the need for differential diagnosis. Kanner maintains that, due to this diffuseness, there are two antithetical trends: one insists on a somatic basis and the other advocates psychogenicity. The looseness of the term, "childhood schizophrenia," or any other term, has made it very difficult to obtain reliable data about incidence, etiology, and results of therapy.

According to Kanner, lack of diagnostic differentiation is tantamount to the retention of "brain disease" as a category, similar to the analogy of mental deficiency as a common background for phenylketonuria, gargoylism, familial oligoencephalopathy, and so on. Reflecting on the research of organic factors in childhood schizophrenia, Kanner (1960) states:

"Much etiologic research has been directed towards endogenous factors . . . . Electroencephalographic studies have yielded no uniform pattern. Evidence of endocrine dysfunctions is scattered and, when present, does not answer unequivocally the question of cause and effect relationship. . . . Even from a purely statistical point of view, the correlation of childhood schizophrenia with parental attitudes is far higher and more consistent than its correlation with heredity, configuration of the body, metabolic disorders, or any other factor " (pp. 744-47).

According to Kanner, while Bender attributes childhood schizophrenia to a fundamental pathological process of a diffuse encephalopathy, she has not offered any confirming anatomical evidence. Bender herself (1947) acknowledged that the gross neurological findings characteristic of the more highly structured nervous system of the adult were not present among her groups of children. Instead, she relied on "soft neurological signs," which are seen in the control of facial musculature and voice, in motility patterns, and in responses to certain postural reflexes.

Before joining the Children's Division at Bellevue Hospital, Bender (1958a) was primarily interested in neurology, brain pathology, and the functioning of the brain through its motility and its perceptual experiences, as described in Gestalt psychological development of these functions into personality and behavior. Later, in association with her husband Paul Schilder, an outstanding neuropsychiatrist and psychoanalyst, Bender applied concepts of psychoanalysis and ego development, and studied the interrelationship between the neurological functions and psychological experience. This led to her later emphasis on the body image concepts, the understanding of anxiety, neurotic defense mechanism, and so on, in explaining the symptomatology of the schizophrenic child. In referring to Kanner's "cold parent," Bender indicates that this term must apply to a special group, since in a large metropolitan hospital like Bellevue she did not encounter such parents. No attempt was made to conduct a further analysis to compare the background of patients seen at Bellevue with those seen at John Hopkins Children's Hospital and to relate it to a particular disorder of the child involved. However, Bender was able to classify schizophrenic manifestations into three types: pseudoneurotic, pseudodefective, and pseudopsychopathic.

Bender's bibliography is quite extensive (1953a, 1953b, 1954, 1955, 1956, 1958a, 1958b, 1962) and includes some detailed background information about the patients. However, only one of her more recent research studies will be reviewed here.

Bender and Grugett (1956) selected at random case histories of 30 schizophrenic children, as well as a control group consisting of

30 children suffering non-schizophrenic illnesses, but representing other severe deviancies, who had been hospitalized at Bellevue. Half of her experimental sample was Jewish. Bender indicated that this high frequency of Jewish patients in her sample was due to the fact that the Jewish community has developed an especially advanced social agency structure, which encourages its members to seek social and medical help at the earliest sign of need. However, the parents' concern for the child tended to yield extensive material for case histories, which may have enhanced their chance for inclusion in this type of study. If case histories were selected because of their completeness and thoroughness, it could hardly constitute a random sample as indicated by the investigators.

The control group, on the other hand, was composed of neglected children who were referred to the clinic by various social agencies and were predominantly Negro, Irish, and Puerto Rican. The investigators reported that 16 of the parents of the schizophrenic patients complained of such problems as eating, sleeping, toilet training, and language and object relationship, and 11 parents mentioned symptoms of emotionality and excessive fears, continuous anxieties, and regressive features. On the other hand, the authors indicated that the problem with the children in the control group originated as a reaction to actual deprivation and parental neglect, and that they had a poor orientation for social learning. The investigators found that while in the majority of the cases (75%) the emotional climate of the non-schizophrenic was deficient, this same emotional climate applied to only 27 percent of the schizophrenic children. However, in spite of such a "favorable" background among families of schizophrenics, 14 of the mothers and 12 of the fathers were themselves diagnosed as schizophrenic. We fail to see how the home environment was found to be unfavorable in only 27 percent of the cases when so many parents, in a sample of 30 cases, were diagnosed as schizophrenics. On the basis of these findings Bender and Grugett wrote the following:

> "Evidence concerning the emotional climate of the environment, however, suggests strongly that neurotic and asocial behavior developed in essentially normal children specifically from distorted relationship and severe affectional deprivation. This uniformity of background was not found among the schizophrenic children, although distorted family relationships were found in some instances" (p. 141).

To those who are familiar with research designs, the weak relationship between the data, as presented in these articles, and conclusions drawn from the data by the investigators, would be quite apparent. It is our opinion that Bender's rigid definition of schizophrenia, which is found in almost every one of her articles and which is often used by other investigators as well as by students preparing their Ph. D. dissertations, has unduly influenced the field. No endeavor was made in her studies to differentiate lower-class from middle-class schizophrenics, and Jewish, Catholic, Protestant, Negro, and Puerto Rican patients were all lumped together. In spite of various symptomatic manifestations, all of these patients were diagnosed as suffering from a "maturational lag."

It has already been indicated that Bender has found three types of childhood schizophrenia; the psychopathic type in particular, which is rarely found in other treatment centers, seems to be of special interest. Bellevue Hospital is a city hospital and courts are likely to refer disturbed children there. It is not known whether pseudopsychopathic children are found in greater numbers among Protestants, Catholics, Jews, Negroes, or Puerto Ricans. We could hypothesize that the psychopathic type of schizophrenia would be more prevalent among broken-up families of the lower socioeconomic classes, where physical abuse is more common. The child "who melts into people" is more likely to come from families who tend to overprotect their children.

Although Bender (1958b) has hinted at the influence of social background in childhood schizophrenia, she is one of the few major psychiatrists who have supported the idea of schizophrenia in children being due to prenatal or embryological dysfunction. The following comments were made by Bruch (1959), in emphasizing the limitations of Bender's work:

"Dr. Bender's work is the most outstanding in the field, and it has given important impetus to many other workers. Hers is the most important single conceptual formulation, and there is no doubt about the excellence of her clinical observations and the influence she has had in awakening widespread interest in the whole problem. Objections have been raised regarding the way in which (her) criteria are applied. The statements about an individual child are too sweeping and too general. As time went on, the diagnosis was made too easily" (p. 8).

In one of the earliest studies on childhood schizophrenia, Despert (1938) collected data on 29 children, predominantly boys who had been admitted to the New York State Psychiatric Institute. She found that 19 of them had "aggressive, over-anxious, and over-solicitous mothers, while the fathers played a subdued role." How-

ever, 19 of the mothers were Jewish, and since there was no control group, it would be difficult to evaluate the differences between
the kinds of over-solicitousness that might constitute a pathogenic
influence on the child's development. Despert added a comment of
caution that indicated that she was aware of the problem, but did
not elaborate on it.

In another study by Despert (1951), the author reported that 46
mothers of 33 boys and 13 girls (all under the age of 12), like neurotic mothers, could not give a clear picture of their children, rejected treatment for themselves, and only superficially participated
in the therapeutic process. Despert found that 85 percent of these
children were either the only child in the family or the first-born
child. Two significant characteristics were found in these mothers:
(1) emotional detachment—it appears that the mother's attitude
toward sex, her frigidity and abhorrence of bodily contact prevented
her from achieving a warm contact with the child; (2) overintellectu-
alization—mothers applied excessive pressure on their growing children to achieve feats that were beyond their age level of maturation
and interest. We may assume that these children belonged to middle
or upper classes. Here again, as in the previous study, little was
mentioned about the social class and religious background of the
sample. While the previous study emphasized over-solicitousness,
the more recent one has found lack of warmth and over-intellectuali-
zation as the two major and significant characteristics of mothers
of schizophrenics. These mothers also rejected psychotherapy.

It is our opinion, however, that Despert was not discussing
the same type of mother in both studies. It could be assumed that
the mothers came from different sociocultural backgrounds. In 1938,
Despert was connected with the Psychiatric Institute in New York,
while in 1951 she was with the Payne Whitney Clinic, which caters
to different types of patients, probably to a predominance of middle-
class patients.

To compound the issue, Mahler (1952), in New York, with a
predominantly Jewish population, added another group in her reports on "symbiotic children," which Despert and Sherwin (1958)
do not find helpful to clinical understanding nor to effective diagnosis.
Rank (1949), in Boston, introduced the concept of the "atypical
child," and Bergman and Escalona (1949), in Topeka, Kansas, postu-
lated the presence of primitive constitutional pre-ego factors that
make these patients very sensitive to sensory stimulation. A premature formation of the ego breaks down under trauma and causes
the psychosis.

The variable of social class or ethnicity of the subjects as a
possible influence on the manifestations of their severe disorders

was not considered in any of these studies. Kanner (1949), however, found that the parents of "autistic children," besides being "cold," tend to have outstanding ability but are not original thinkers. His own conviction in this respect leads him to state: "My research for autistic children of unsophisticated parents has remained unsuccessful to date" (p. 421).

RECENT STUDIES ON CHILDHOOD SCHIZOPHRENIA

Kaufman et al. (1959), were able to delineate four types of mothers and fathers of schizophrenic children. They were diagnosed as pseudoneurotic, somatic, pseudodelinquent, and psychotic, with the classification depending on their manifest defense structure. This classification was based on their study of 40 parents of schizophrenic children in an outpatient clinic, and on 40 parents of schizophrenic children in a state mental hospital. The investigators found that the occupational range of the parents was from college professor to unskilled laborer. Proportionately more pseudoneurotic and somatic parents came to the outpatient clinic, while the pseudodelinquent and the psychotic type predominated at the inpatient setting. This is an interesting finding, in view of Kanner's and Eisenberg's finding that the rate of psychosis is low among parents of autistic children seen at the outpatient clinic of John Hopkins Hospital. There is little indication in the article of the sociocultural differences between the two hospital populations. It may be assumed that pseudoneurotic and somatic type parents would have autistic children, while the pseudodelinquent and psychotic parents would have pseudopsychopathic schizophrenic children.

A different and more complex approach to the study of family environment of schizophrenic children was conducted by Behrens and Goldfarb (1958) at the Henry Ittleson Center for Child Research. Their study represented an attempt to develop, through an extensive battery of rating scales, an appraisal that would differentiate families with schizophrenic children from families with non-schizophrenic children. Observations were made in the homes of 20 disturbed children, predominantly schizophrenic, and also in the homes of families with normal children. The purpose was to determine how the family interacts in its own milieu. The families were predominantly Jewish, of lower-middle class, with both parents living. The investigators reported that an atmosphere of confusion and disorganization characterized the homes of the disturbed children. Among these less adequate families they found:

"The child was handled with an exaggerated degree of tentativeness, often accompanied by overinvolvement in the child's activities. The mother, in particular, gave the impression that she felt any misstep would result in an uncontrollable situation, and seemed harassed in her effort to comply with the demands of the child and to keep things on an even keel" (p. 310).

This description is somewhat different from the one noted by other investigators of the "cold, refrigerated mother." However, it should be recalled that the differences may be due to the fact that Behren's and Goldfarb's sample was predominantly Jewish.

Goldfarb (1961) maintains that the type of patients seen at the Ittelson Clinic in New York conforms to the description given by Bender; several children fall into the category of "autistic," and some others could be classified as "symbiotic." Goldfarb separated his schizophrenic children into two groups: those in whom organicity was suspected and those characterized by psychological dysfunction. He, however, rejects both the extreme notion that schizophrenia is an illness of an organic origin and the idea that it is of psychological origin.

While practically all the studies stress the inadequacies of the mother, Eisenberg (1957) wrote a paper emphasizing the inadequacies of the father. He reported that many fathers of autistic children are themselves responsible for impairing the fulfillment of a normal paternal role. These fathers tend to be obsessive, detached, humorless, perfectionists, and occupied with detailed minutiae. They have children, not because of their need for them, but because they consider them a part of the formal pattern of marriage, which is an obligation one assumes. Eisenberg suggests that there is a need to reconsider the popular formulation that the mother's anxieties affect the psychopathology of the schizophrenic child.

Sarvis & Garcia (1961) provide a detailed account of the etiological variables in autism. Based on their experience with 80 autistic patients, the investigators enumerate four types of causative factors: (1) family dynamics specifically promoting autism, such as an unconscious need of the parents, or a "refrigerated" mother; (2) family psychodynamics enabling autism to occur, such as depression of mother; (3) circumstances such as the father being away; (4) assault on the child.

A study of 25 psychotic children by Cameron (1958) in England found that the family background showed definite ill health among the parents, rigid training methods, and restrictive and punitive measures on the part of the cold and impersonal parents. Moreover, a premature and overstimulating intellectualism and drive for education was found. In half of the cases, a traumatic incident, which occurred between the ages of 2 and 4, was related to the final illness.

Szurek (1956) and Boatman and Szurek (1960), who contend that very severe mental disorders of children are entirely psychogenic, reported their experience with approximately 100 children. According to these investigators, children who are the most withdrawn are brought in by mothers who exhibit the exact same traits. The child's reaction is a tremendously magnified mirror image of the mother's attitudes. The investigators found it to be most difficult to conduct psychotherapy with this group in view of the mother's conviction that the schizophrenic illness of their children had an organic basis.

Following 15 years of experience with severe psychotic disorders of children, the investigators conclude the following:

"The etiology of psychotic disorders of childhood are entirely psychogenic . . . In our extensive physical and psychological examinations of all children we have found no signs of any one dysfunction of physiology or maturation or pattern of dysfunctions which seem characteristic of those schizophrenic children we have seen . . . On the basis of such observations we feel we have seen few, if any, schizophrenic children who showed maturational lags or spurts which were wholly determined by physiological or genetic somatic factors" (Boatman & Szurek, 1960, pp. 401-402).

The foregoing represent important studies in childhood schizophrenia. The basic technique used by all of these investigators in evaluating the patients was the interview. More up-to-date techniques of psychology, sociology and anthropology could have provided a better evaluation of the unfavorable environmental forces that could be associated with childhood schizophrenia. Frank (1964) recently discussed the multidisciplinary thinking and the orchestration of all relevant disciplines and professions needed in research in mental illness. No one is competent to deal with this problem alone.

It would be worthwhile to mention at this point an interesting article by Clark (1961), in which she offers some hypotheses on the mother's role in the development of language in the schizophrenic child and in the manifestations of his symptoms, autistic or symbiotic, which provide new and fresher avenues of research. During the course of her experience with schizophrenic children, Clark was amazed at the differences that exist between mothers whose children have no speaking ability and those whose children speak in a distorted manner. The investigator reported that some mothers prefer using "the reality principle," that is, verbal language rather than physical contact and gestures, when the child is immune to verbal communication. Consequently, the child becomes increasingly withdrawn and uncommunicative even on a nonverbal level. A child exhibiting such characteristics and behavior is brought to a clinic and presents the picture of the autistic child described by Kanner. A second group of mothers, being over-dependent on "the pleasure principle," appear to withdraw from actual life following the births of their children, and to live through the children. They favor prolonged physical contact with the child and prevent him from forming attachments to other adults. The child develops language ability but language remains individualized and distorted. It is impossible to integrate such a child into the community; he presents a picture of the symbiotic child as described by Mahler. The normal mother makes the shift from nonverbal to verbal communication at the appropriate time and according to the needs and ability of the child. It is interesting to note that such observations were made in Canada, where the Anglo-Saxon and French culture coexist. It is possible to speculate that mothers of cultural backgrounds or social classes whose child-rearing mores encourage strict and rigid parental attitudes, and which frown on the expression of warmth, would tend to have more autistic children. In cultural or social groups where the prevailing mores encourage overprotection and infantilizing of the children, symbiotic children would be more prevalent. We could, therefore, speculate that since New York is primarily inhabited by Jews, Italians, Negroes, and Puerto Ricans, among whom the chances of finding "refrigerated parents" are rather slim, the possibilities of finding a large number of autistic children are reduced. On the other hand, autistic children may be found with greater frequency in parts of the country dominated by Protestant mores, where the expression of warmth is less intensive and less likely to be displayed (Barrabee & Von Mering, 1953).

Fester (1961) uses the concepts of learning theory to explain the behavioral defects of autistic children. He points out that the child who is receiving minimal care from a parent will be less affected by a sudden shift in environment than a child who is closely affected and controlled by the parents. In other words, if the child receives little reinforcement over a long period of time, he is less likely to respond to stimulation. It would seem, according to Fester, that a study of the actual parental and child performance and their specific effect on each other would constitute a more fruitful area of research than an analysis of such global characteristics as dependency, hostility, or somatization. Is it possible that the autistic child receives no reinforcement, the symbiotic child too much reinforcement, and the pseudoneurotic schizophrenic child reinforcement which is inconsistent?

A recent study by Heilbrun (1961), while not dealing with childhood schizophrenia, is illustrative of a well-controlled investigation of mothers of adult schizophrenics. Heilbrun is somewhat surprised at the lack of control for the social class variable in spite of the general findings reporting that schizophrenia is more prevalent among the lower socioeconomic classes. He hypothesized that mothers of schizophrenics may differ in authoritarian tendencies, but found no differences between mothers of schizophrenics and normal children when social class was not controlled by objective measures. However, he found that upper-class mothers of schizophrenics were more authoritarian than upper-class mothers of normal children, while lower-class mothers of schizophrenics were less authoritarian than lower-class mothers of normal children.

Heilbrun's findings have implications for the etiology of mental deviancy. A highly rigid upper-class mother and an inconsistent lower-class mother may possibly represent pathogenic conditions in the mother-child relationship. On the basis of these data, it is not surprising to find inconsistency among the findings reported by the various investigators, since each investigator may have studied different groups of subjects. It might be speculated that the schizophrenic manifestation itself, autistic, symbiotic, pseudoneurotic, or pseudopsychopathic, may be related to social class and ethnicity. Recently the present writer obtained some data on Japanese schizophrenics and found that 15 percent were considered paranoid—a much lower percentage than is ordinarily found in mental hospitals in the Western part of the world. This corroborates Caudill's (1959) observations in Japanese hospitals.

To illustrate further the role of culture, three papers are discussed below:

Findings of data collected in child guidance clinics in Lisbon and in India illustrate the difficulties involved in comparing incidence or even symptomatology in two different countries such as Portugal and India. Fontes and Schneeberger (1958) identified only four schizophrenic children out of 8,300 seen at their clinic in Lisbon. On the other hand, Gupta (1950), in India, reports that almost a third of the severely disturbed children were considered schizophrenic. It would be difficult to attribute this disparity between findings in these two countries solely to differences in diagnostic criteria.

Robinson (1961), having reviewed the literature on childhood schizophrenia, reports that early infantile autism is the earliest form of psychotic disturbance in children and he assumes that the symbiotic psychosis emerges after a period of more or less adequate ego development. In spite of this conclusion, he states: "Neither have we, as yet been able to observe children whose behavioral pattern differs sufficiently from that described by Kanner to be listed under another diagnosis. We have concluded that children conforming to Mahler's description are rare" (p. 544). It should be noted, however, that Robinson is director of a child guidance clinic in Wilkes-Barre, Pennsylvania, which probably has a different type of population from that found in, say, similar New York institutions.

Of all the studies reviewed, none is more thorough than the investigation conducted by Singer & Wynne (1963) of parents of different types of deviant children, including autistic children. Both the Rorschach and the Thematic Apperception Test were administered to ten pairs of parents of autistic children, parents of twenty neurotic children (10 acting-out and 10 withdrawn), and parents of ten schizophrenics who became overtly ill in later adolescence. While other investigators analyzed the individual Rorschach as a unit, this study was concerned with the results obtained when both parents' tests were examined in relation to each other and were considered together as "compounding, confusing, or correcting the impact of each parent as an individual."

DISCUSSION

Since so many published studies do not present any information with regard to patients' background, the present writer sent letters to a selected group of five psychiatrists who had published articles on childhood schizophrenia, requesting information pertaining to the socio-cultural-religious background of their patients. Three of the letters were answered. The following are quotations from replies:

"At this time, we do not have a breakdown of ethno-religious-national background of the patients in this group. It might be that something of this sort might be available at a later date, and we shall be most happy to send it to you at that time."

"It would be unwise for me to give even an impression and I would consider even a closer perusal invalid because approximately two-thirds of my child patients are of Jewish faith, and the proportion of schizophrenic patients would be colored by this factor. As you know, such a proportion is not representative of the population at large. A valid evaluation must take into consideration the general population indices for comparison with the particular psychiatrist's population. As a matter of fact, I do not know how you will get around that certain aspect of the ethno-religious-national background, unless your study is based on a less selective group such as would be found in a general clinic or hospital. . . . "

In the first instance, it would seem that the sociocultural background had never been considered, but that it is expected that future consideration will be given to this variable. The response from the second correspondent demonstrates that the purpose of my request was misinterpreted, since my intention was not to obtain normative data on childhood schizophrenia but to try to relate the symptomatology to sociocultural backgrounds of the patients of this correspondent. Incidentally, this psychiatrist has written a number of articles describing symptomatology.

In the doctoral dissertation recently completed by Korn (1963), under the direction of the author, Negro and Puerto Rican children who had been diagnosed as schizophrenics were studied. The following represents the description of the symptomatology:

"The dominant characteristics of the premorbid symptoms of schizophrenic behavior were extremely poor impulse control, low frustration tolerance, impaired reality testing, and homicidal tendencies. Negro and Puerto Rican children generally showed similar symptoms. Six of the Puerto Rican and four of the Negro children had set fires. Among the Negro children, extreme antisocial, aggressive behavior occurred slightly more often. Stealing, fighting, hyperrestlessness, and unmanageable behavior were noted frequently. The Puerto Rican children showed a slightly higher tendency to mutism, bizarreness, inappropriate affect, and poor reality testing" (p. 75).

Korn indicated that in approximately sixty cases selected among Puerto Rican and Negro schizophrenic children, none could be described as autistic or symbiotic. It would seem that the predominant symptomatology was aggressiveness and bizarre behavior. All seemed to have acquired speech.

One interesting type of cross-cultural study would require as judges psychiatrists who trained in the United States but practice in other countries. This would constitute one way of solving the problem of differences in diagnostic criteria used by psychiatrists trained in different countries and cultures. The author wrote to an Argentinian psychiatrist who had spent three years in the United States in fulfillment of his required professional residency (which he spent in a well-known child psychiatric clinic), and who has since returned to his own country, where he has been in practice for the

past six years. In his response to a letter inquiring whether he saw
any autistic children in Argentina, he wrote the following:

> "I was able to see here and in Kansas City the schizophrenic
> mother-child dyad, the symbiotic type of problem, and the
> three types described by L. Bender, plus the autistic child.
> However, this last entity is not frequent in this country. I have
> no statistics to prove what I am saying, and I am only giving you
> an impression of my clinical experience. The more common
> cases I saw were the symbiotic type. From a symptomatologic
> point of view, what we do see here is the most disorganized
> type of behavior, with lack of affectivity and a great deal of
> acting and movements, bizarre, purposeless, and wildly ag-
> gressive at times. . . ."

> "The typical withdrawn child as described by Kanner is a rarity
> among the patients I saw. Usually here they show, as I said,
> a very disorganized type of behavior making sometimes difficult
> the differential diagnosis between feeblemindedness and schizo-
> phrenia."

Recently the writer conducted an as yet unpublished analysis of
case records of thirty-two schizophrenic children who had been admitted to the Psychiatric Institute of New York. The sample consisted
of sixteen Jewish patients, nine Protestants, and nine Catholics, all
white.

Of the sixteen Jewish children, one had been clearly identified
as autistic while all the others had acquired speech. The single case
of the autistic child came from a family where the father had a
Ph.D. in biology and is well-known in his profession. During one of
his interviews, the father described his child as being a good example of the autistic child described by Kanner. Data in this case
record reveal the father to have the characteristics of the "refrigerated parent" as described by Kanner, based on his constant aloofness from his family.

Of the nine Protestant patients, four were identified as autistic
children who came from upper-class homes where the fathers were
engaged in professional occupations. The five other children in this
group came from lower-class homes. Among the nine Catholics,
only one child was identified as autistic — the father in this case was
an accountant. The other children in this group came from lower-
class families and the fathers were laborers.

It is this writer's opinion that a major reason for the polemics
and inconsistencies reported on childhood schizophrenia is the fact

174

that, in most instances, all types of schizophrenic children are lumped into one group, à la Bender. This has tended to discourage the search for differential diagnoses and endeavors to relate specific manifestations to specific noxious environments. Furthermore, many past studies have relied primarily on the interview technique, which has inherent limitations. What is needed is a concerted approach by investigators from different disciplines.

REFERENCES

Adler, Alexandra. Influence of the social level on psychiatric symptomatology of childhood difficulties, in Sociological foundations of the psychiatric disorders of childhood. Proceedings of the 12th Institute of the Child Research Clinic of the Woods Schools with the collaboration of the School of Medicine, Duke University, Durham, N.C., 1945.

Barrabee, P., & Von Mering, O. Ethnic variations in mental stress in families with psychotic children. Soc. Probl., 1953, 1, 48-53.

Behrens, Marjorie L., & Goldfarb, W. A study of patterns of interaction of families of schizophrenic children in residential treatment. Amer. J. Orthopsychiat., 1958, 28, 300-312.

Bender, Lauretta. Childhood schizophrenia: clinical study of one hundred schizophrenic children. Amer. J. Orthopsychiat., 1947, 17, 40-56.

Bender, Lauretta. Aggression, hostility and anxiety in children. Springfield, Ill.: Thomas, 1953a.

Bender, Lauretta. Childhood schizophrenia. Psychiat. Quart., 1953b, 27, 663-681.

Bender, Lauretta. A dynamic psychopathology of childhood. Springfield, Ill.: Thomas, 1954.

Bender, Lauretta. Twenty years of research on schizophrenic children with special reference to those under six years of age. In G. Caplan (Ed.), Emotional problems of early childhood. New York: Basic Books, 1955. Pp. 503-515.

Bender, Lauretta. Schizophrenia in childhood—its recognition, description and treatment. Amer. J. Orthopsychiat., 1956, 26, 499-506.

Bender, Lauretta. Child development—causal factors in mental illness and health. Neuropsychiatry, 1958a, 4, 173-188.

Bender, Lauretta. Genesis in schizophrenia during childhood. Z. Kinderpsychiat., 1958b, 25, 101-107.

Bender, Lauretta. Developmental neuropsychiatry: the future in child psychiatry. In P. Hoch & J. Zubin (Eds.), The future of psychiatry. New York: Grune & Stratton, 1962. Pp. 200-215.

Bender, Lauretta, & Grugett, A. E. A study of certain epidemiological factors in a group of children with childhood schizophrenia. Amer. J. Orthopsychiat., 1956, 26, 131-145.

Bergman, P., & Escalona, Sibylle K. Unusual sensitivities in very young children. Psychoanal. Stud. Child, 1949, 3/4, 333-352.

Boatman, Maleta J., & Szurek, S. A. A clinical study of childhood schizophrenia. In D. D. Jackson (Ed.), The etiology of schizophrenia. New York: Basic Books, 1960. Pp. 389-440.

Bruch, Hilde. The various developments in the approach to childhood schizophrenia. Acta Psychiat. Neurol. Scand., Suppl. 130, 1959, 34, 5-48.

Cameron, K. A group of twenty-five psychotic children. Z. Kinderpsychiat., 1958, 25, 117-122.

Caudill, W. Observations on the cultural context of Japanese psychiatry. In M. K. Opler (Ed.), Culture and mental health: cross-cultural studies. New York: Macmillan, 1959, Pp. 213-242.

Clark, G. Reflection on the role of the mother in the development of language in the schizophrenic child. Canad. psychiat. Ass. J., 1961, 6, 252-256.

Despert, J. Louise. Schizophrenia in children. Psychiat. Quart., 1938, 12, 366-377.

Despert, J. Louise. Some considerations relating to the genesis of autistic behavior in children. Amer. J. Orthopsychiat., 1951, 21, 335-350.

Despert, J. Louise, & Sherwin, A. C. Further examination of diagnostic criteria in schizophrenic illness and psychoses of infancy and early childhood. Amer. J. Psychiat., 1958, 114, 784-790.

Eisenberg, L. The fathers of autistic children. Amer. J. Orthopsychiat., 1957, 27, 715-724.

Ekstein, R., et al. Childhood schizophrenia and allied conditions. In L. Bellak (Ed.), Schizophrenia: a review of the syndrome. New York: Logos Press, 1958. Pp. 555-693.

Ferster, C. B. Positive reinforcement and behavioral deficits of autistic children. Child Develop., 1961, 32, 437-456.

Fontes, V. Schizophrénie infantile. Z. Kinderpsychiat., 1958, 25, 183-190.

Frank, L. K. The emergence of social psychiatry in the United States. Paper read at the First Int. Cong. of Soc. Psychiat., London, August 1964.

Goldfarb, W. Childhood schizophrenia. Published for the Commonwealth Fund. Cambridge, Mass.: Harvard Univer. Press, 1961.

Gupta, Das, J. C. Report from India. Nerv. Child, 1950, 8, 490-507.

Heilbrun, A. B., Jr. Maternal authoritarianism, social class and filial schizophrenia. J. gen. Psychol., 1961, 65, 235-241.

Kanner, L. Problems of nosology and psychodynamics of early infantile autism. Amer. J. Orthopsychiat., 1949, 19, 416-426.

Kanner, L. Child psychiatry. (3rd ed.), Springfield, Ill.: C.C. Thomas, 1957.

Kaufman, I., et al. Parents of schizophrenic children: Workshop 1958. Four types of defense in mothers and fathers of schizophrenic children. Amer. J. Orthopsychiat., 1959, 29, 460-472.

Korn, Shirley. Family dynamics and childhood schizophrenia: a comparison of the family backgrounds of two low socioeconomic minority groups, one with schizophrenic children, the other with rheumatic fever children. Doctoral dissertation, Yeshiva Univer., Grad. School of Educ., 1963.

Mahler, Margaret S. On child psychosis and schizophrenia: autistic and symbiotic infantile psychoses. Psychoanal. Stud. Child, 1952, 7, 286-305.

Rank, Beata. Adaptation of the psychoanalytic technique for the treatment of young children with atypical development. Amer. J. Orthopsychiat., 1949, 19, 130-139.

Robinson, J. F. The psychoses of early childhood. Amer. J. Orthopsychiat., 1961, 31, 536-550.

Sanua, V. D. Sociocultural factors in families of schizophrenics: a review of the literature. Psychiatry, 1961, 24, 246-265.

Sanua, V. D. Sociocultural aspects of therapy and treatment in mental illness: a review of the literature. Paper read at the Sixth Int. Cong. of Psychother., London, August 1964.

Sarvis, Mary A., & Garcia, Blanche. Etiological variables in autism. Psychiatry, 1961, 24, 307-317.

Singer, Margaret T., & Wynne, L. C. Differentiating characteristics of parents of childhood schizophrenics, childhood neurotics and young adult schizophrenics. Amer. J. Psychiat., 1963, 120, 234-243.

Szurek, S. A. Childhood schizophrenia. Symposium, 1956. 4. Psychotic episodes and psychotic maldevelopment. Amer. J. Orthopsychiat., 1956, 26, 519-543.

PART IV

Family and Marriage
Therapy

COMMUNICATING VALUES IN FAMILY THERAPY[1]

Robert MacGregor, Ph.D.

At a workshop on "Perspectives in family therapy," in 1964, there seemed to be general concern that family therapists may be erring in the direction of advocating to families the value system of the American middle-class family. In part, this is a concern about psychotherapy in general, and studies indeed have shown that therapists may unwittingly transmit their own values to their patients. The present paper proposes that with certain types of families, including many that are economically middle class, the transmitting of values that express the family relations and child-rearing practices of the middle class is a useful part of team family psychotherapy.

Of course, no evocative, analytic, or other depth therapy seeks to indoctrinate—except for some procedural values. The desirability of self-knowledge, acceptance, and love are often assumed in addition to some very specific values that have to do with the treatment contract, e.g., appointments must be kept, bills paid, dreams reported, and the therapist may not be assaulted. Self-knowledge on the part of therapists or vigilance on the part of teammates are generally agreed to be useful in keeping the unwitting indoctrination of the patient to a minimum. Additionally, there are those who feel that some of the humanitarian values associated with psychotherapy may have a beneficent effect on some patients.

As psychotherapists, we may go too far in our concern for unique individuality and the right of the patient to his own value system. Psychotherapists are called on not to monitor the uniqueness of adjustment but that part of people's lives which is neither like all others nor like no others, but which is more similar to some than to others. Before we can treat we acknowledge this similarity by diagnosis, classifying the patient tentatively with some large group

[1] This paper was prepared as part of the project "Middle class delinquency: a study of families," supported in part by NIMH Grant OM 988, and was presented at the American Orthopsychiatric Association Annual Meeting, a workshop chaired by Dr. Norman Paul and entitled "Perspectives in family therapy," March 1964.

of others (Pasamanick, 1963). While the ultimate in psychiatric diagnosis includes the way in which a pattern common to many is expressed in an individual, the part of the diagnosis that scientifically calls for strategy has been validated in observations of other individuals and groups. Strategies of therapists are attuned to the interruption of unrewarding recurring patterns which hamper self-realization. The freeing of unique individuality may be a product of the therapy rather than the reason that growth processes have been resumed, just as the return of recollections from early childhood are evidence—not the cause—of the freedom from neurosis. Family therapy is not a single set of procedures but a context for treating a variety of problems that may or may not include the value system of the family.

In particular, when diagnoses may be stated in terms of a family-wide arrest in development, treatment strategies appropriate to the developmental level of that arrest may be inferred. In many instances, the arrest in development is such that the family falls short of the ability to transmit to its members the value system and repertoire of social roles necessary to growth in the society from which that family has partially isolated itself. The function of a therapeutic team in such instances, somewhat like that of the chorus in Greek drama, may be to represent those conventional roles and values, while also enjoying the kind of entree into the family's relatively closed system that will allow the family members to function temporarily in a more open system, while they gain in experience with roles that society rewards.

Let me now give an example wherein it seemed useful to advocate a system of values. When working with families in which the father fails to exercise a leadership function in the home and allows his wife to become excessively dependent on a child for emotional expression, the multiple impact therapy team not only advocated the more conventional roles, but also demonstrated comfort with leadership by the way in which a male therapist exercised authority with the team-family situation. Sometimes, the paternal attitude was also shown by the way a therapist dealt with a team member in trainee status. Implicitly the behavior said: "This is the way we guide our youth." Acceptance of responsibility by a therapist, and at times, role-induction pressure on a team member to take the leadership role, was apparent in the behavior of the basic team members.

A third of the 62 cases we reported in <u>Multiple Impact Therapy with Families</u> (MacGregor et al., 1964) were such families. We classified them according to the problem presented by the child as:

"families presenting childish functioning in an adolescent, " and referred to the psychopathic youths as "autocrats. "

It is worth considering that perhaps the value system of the middle-class family survives so well because as a product of the adaptive mechanism of a living system it reflects the survival requirements for humans in society. It seems to be a norm from which upper-class and lower-class living is measured. It places, for example, a value on competition. In the upper class, competition is expressed in games, while monopoly is the real game. In the lower class, collusion displaces competition so much that the alliances between parts of the system threaten the welfare of the family as a system. Mental health seems associated with the ability to become known and hence to enjoy competition. In competition between peers, one becomes known and his true measure is taken. In the psychiatric illness of the middle class, the sensivity to competitive measure is most painful. The remoteness of the upper class from clear standards of measure often make it very difficult for a therapist to have an important voice in the patient's system.

In the lower class there is less readiness to accept rules of the game, since one cannot trust his competitor to follow the rules. Indeed, he knows that he himself cannot afford the luxury of gentlemen's rules. Not trusting himself, he cannot trust peers. Nevertheless, the way of life is subjectively felt as inferior to those with the capital—the waiting power—to delay immediate gratification for the larger measure of security necessary to the enjoyment of competition. We are beginning to notice in our clinical work that fostering a neurotic-competitive situation in a family presenting the kind of collusion that yields a psychopath—or in our terminology, a youth arrested at the childish level—can facilitate the resumption of growth processes. Collusion then gives way to the competition and compromise more typical of the juvenile developmental era, a situation more accessible to treatment.

Ned McL. and the H. family were brought to Galveston by the probation officer from a city 250 miles away. Our project includes a close working arrangement with that city whereby families with delinquent youth and the casework-trained probation officers participate with the clinic team in a two-day diagnostic procedure derived from the Multiple Impact Therapy program.

The nominal patient has no real friends and participates with other youngsters only in delinquent acts. He seems unable to accept regulations from anyone. Ned McL. is a 15-year-old ninth grade student of average intelligence who had been charged with four instances of theft, auto theft, and runaway. He appeared calm and arrogant. A show of affect could only be elicited when in an individual session, the doctor implied that he was being used by his agemates, rather than really participating. His complaints were only that the school principal, teachers, and his mother griped at him and unfairly expected too much of him.

The father, Mr. H., married Fred's mother when the patient was four years old. Mr. H. had been hospitalized for tuberculosis for some years after World War II and his employment as a city fireman seemed to be a vindication of his manhood—not so much because of the nature of the activity, but because he had had to pass a physical exam to qualify. On the job he was astonishingly cool. It was the stand-by nature of his work that he enjoyed. He expressed contempt for those who were impatient for the fire alarm to ring. When off duty, he went to a domino parlor to gamble before going home.

Mr. H. had further protected his inferiority by marrying an experienced wife already occupied with children. A therapeutic handle to a neurotic aspect of family difficulties was provided by his overreacting to wife's nagging of the boy, as though it were his own mother nagging him. Like his own father, he retreated from his wife and encouraged his son not to respect her "hollering." In this way and by indulgences, he attempted to buy his son's loyalty away from his wife. The son, however, never had to grant him any seniority with the mother and, in part because the man had allowed her to continue in her emotional dependency on the lad, the youth was oblivious to any authority.

The mother's clearest complaint was that when she approached the height of any passion, be it frustration over inability to control the boy or a response to a challenge from her husband, he withdrew to the domino parlor. She was a rather attractive, trim, neat, voluble blonde who presented herself as intimidated, exploited, and disenchanted. The mutually consuming relationship with her son lost its charm as he became more demanding and more obviously not a child in the eye of others. She wearied of having to gain her emotional release from family crises, and there was disenchantment too with her husband, who appeared at times to be more her child's playmate than the master of the home.

Therapeutically, we worked with the youth toward his recognizing his own fear of discovering himself through experiencing his own limitations. We viewed with obvious alarm his belief that he could not stand to take "no" for an answer. This was also approached by an attempt to gain father's recognition that the mother had been so dependent on the child that she could not enforce a "no" answer. Then we were able to help him realize that it was within his power to communicate an appreciation of strength in the lad through reassuring his son that he can stand regulation. We were also able to show his wife that her self-respect lagged for want of really trying to win her man away from his stereotyped way of life. While he could begin to see that her only route to becoming bearable lay in his viewing her as an important resource in his life, it took a crisis, in which it appeared that Ned would not be returned to their custody unless their mutual fears of tenderness were resolved sufficiently, to motivate the husband to the necessary leadership to bring his family back to the team. The change in the son when the father accepted this more conventional role was substantiated. It was a movement from one oblivious to authority to the more neurotic role of a son afraid but yearning to identify with a father who now cast a somewhat clearer image. The relation to authority generally changed in the neurotic direction of proneness to please and appease, a more treatable situation common to middle-class neurosis.

The technique is not so much that of advocating a value system as that of helping a man express his strength in a way that enables his wife and son to appreciate him more. A first step is to show the father that he is already much more influential in the child's life than he suspects. The message then is that positive attempts to influence the child in ways that give identifiable expression to the father as a person are safer than self-inflicted efforts to minimize his own influence. The father, who heretofore suspected himself of being at best a noxious influence in the child's life, is strengthened by the evidence that the therapists trust his influence. The father in this type of family seems to lack knowledge (in the content area) of what it is like to be a father. Our therapists have at times mentioned experiences with their own children and parents to such fathers. Being thus finally accepted into the cult of fatherhood is like the long overdue initiation rite that these men need before being able to welcome sons into the cult of manhood. This modeling of a conventional father role stands in contrast to the view that holds that the family therapist, by exposure of his own values and leadership, necessarily weakens the position of the parent as a model.

It is not the purpose here to dwell on technique, but to admit to and advocate the desirability of influencing the family toward more conventional middle-class values. It is not a question of how family therapy is to be done, but a matter of pursuing a treatment program drawn from an adequate diagnosis of the family's way of functioning. When the family's preferred roles and values reflect the illness, then the roles and the value system are subject to overhaul. Adjustment within the value system of the patient, while often the route of expediency, is not generally the goal of psychotherapy.

In the Wiltwyck School's use of team family therapy techniques (Rabinowitz, 1963) there was perhaps more consciously an effort to "infect" lower-class families with the middle-class family pattern. These families were difficult to understand in a human family sense. Generations of impoverished and broken home circumstances seemed to produce another culture, described by some as "the culture of the poor." In order to bring therapists and psychological influences into range of these people it seemed necessary to teach the families some of the attitudes and behavior the team understood as evidence of providing a family-like environment. Their first effort was to provide them with a consciousness of being a family. Such efforts included communicating an executive function in the home to the parents and teaching pleasure in the individualizing of children: for example, by recognizing a child's birthday with singing. Middle-class values were transmitted, perhaps, but they facilitated growth from a less human situation.

Behind this controversy may be the specific charge that the family-oriented therapists, because of their own middle-class and Freudian bias, really want the family romance to come out "right"—want the father to be the boss in the family, want the mother to enjoy her executive and homemaking functions, and want the children to want to grow up and do likewise. Betty Friedan, in her popular book The Feminine Mystique, has also usefully criticized this view. While there must be individual family solutions for the division of functions, the middle-class family values, like a statistically determined central tendency, provide a useful model for comparison.

The values of the family therapist have more to do with the vitality of living systems. As a therapist, his value system favors growth. Families foster growth when all members derive growth benefits; they also process information and supplies from their environment. The therapist deals with problems that interfere with growth benefits for family members. Such problems are most often symptoms which indicate that the family, in functioning to ward off what was perceived as a noxious influence, has become a relatively closed system in which activity is reverberating and expending energy while admission of information and supplies is diminishing. In the family that yields an adolescent arrested at a pre-adolescent level of development (one of the "rebels," as contrasted with the "autocrats" in our project's terminology), the son may be forced to function repetitively in a rebellious role because his father's role in certain home activities is serving, not as an aid to the growth function but as a substitute in activity for a feeling of fraudulence in his profession. Father's pompousness may be sponsored by mother's need to use his visible success to make up for presumed deficiencies in her earlier social life. The therapists address themselves eventually to such distorted self-perceptions which lead each family member to control, limit, or distort the admission of information and supplies. When these shared defensive operations are verified together in a context of respect, the normal interchange of influence between family members and with environment is restored, and enjoyment of competitive behavior reappears. (Note that the understanding of the immediate problem includes its current systematic distortion, the history of individuals, and the value system in terms of which the family evaluates respectability.)

The writer was able to show that the illness of obsessive-compulsive patients is clearly mirrored in the hierarchy of their values (MacGregor, 1954). Using R. K. White's "Value Analysis," a method of quantifying the verbal content of typescripts, he identified, from the intercorrelations of 32 patterns of four types, a separate factor made up entirely of these obsessive patients who had also been identified as "self-righteous moralists" (Margolin, 1952; Rosenthal et al., 1954) by an interaction process analysis method (behavioral criteria). The task of therapy with these patients was clearly different from that for patients with contrasting systems of values. For them, "right makes might," while for the hysterical patient, more oriented to fear than power, "might makes right."

In our research on families in diagnosis and treatment, we found it useful to differentiate them and our methods on the basis of the developmental level that gave them most difficulty in the identified patient. The idea that there may be one particular method in family therapy that has superiority may come from the fact that much of the pioneering has been done by research teams working with families yielding a particular level of developmental arrest—notably the infantile level associated with schizophrenia.

A second source of push toward uniformity of method comes from systematic theory itself. Embodied in existentialism, general systems theory, and psychoanalysis are general notions of the cause and treatment of human suffering. Further clinical experience has generally resulted in finding a number of strategies within the general methods appropriate to differently diagnosed but not unique patterns of malfunctioning. In the transcript of the 1963 workshop on "Perspectives in Family Therapy," there appears a caution from Lidz against pursuing conjoint family methods without regard to the type of family situation. He refers to settings in which we should not violate the generation boundaries in families that have already been seriously violated and expect the child to be a member of a group when the parents are discussing problems of their own, such as intimate details of sexual relationship. As did Wynne, he so includes examples where the blind pursuit of a method permitted the parents to use the session for a devastating attack on the nominal patient. There seemed to be consensus that family therapy sessions are sometimes situations in which family members may be unusually vulnerable and that the experts who lead them there have a special obligation to use their diagnostic acumen aggressively to protect their patients. Passivity and reliance on a general method can be an abdication of responsibility when the therapist researcher conducts a family into environs to which its defenses may be ill-suited.

In this paper, we have proposed that at times it is a useful therapeutic procedure to attempt to change a family's system of values. We have illustrated the way in which this decision, like others in therapy, can follow from adequate family diagnosis. We have shown that the value system can be poorly communicated or can itself reflect pathology. We have defended the advocating of conventional middle-class values with a particular type of case, and have related it to the therapeutic maneuver of fostering the development of neurotic conflicts as a way of rendering the psychopath accessible to treatment. Some attempt was made to differentiate these procedures from unwitting culture conflict between therapist and patient.

REFERENCES

MacGregor, R. A factorial study of verbal content associated with several types of group behavior. Unpublished doctoral dissertation, Univer. of Michigan, 1954.

MacGregor, R., et al. Multiple impact therapy with families. New York: McGraw-Hill, 1964.

Margolin, J. B. The use of an interaction matrix to validate patterns of group behavior. Hum. Relat., 1952, 5, 407-416.

Pasamanick, B. On the neglect of diagnosis. Amer. J. Orthopsychiat., 1963, 33, 397-398.

Rabinowitz, Clara. Multiple-delinquency-producing families; the use of theory to identify dynamics and specify therapy. Paper read at Amer. Psychol. Ass. Annual Meeting, Philadelphia, August 1963.

Rosenthal, D., et al. The self-righteous moralist in early meetings of therapeutic groups. Psychiatry, 1954, 17, 215-223.

THE ROLE OF MOURNING AND EMPATHY
IN CONJOINT MARITAL THERAPY

Norman L. Paul, M.D.

Conjoint marital therapy, a variant of family group therapy, is
a psychotherapeutic setting designed to treat both the marital partners and the transactional interface between them, i.e., the marriage. This term contrasts with such terms as marital counseling,
marital casework, and marital treatment, which often refer to the
practice of the marital partners being seen alone and/or together
by either the same or different therapists. Though the family is conceived of as the basic unit for treatment, such a point of view tends
to exclude sharper focus, and to define the various marital incom-
patibilities that can be more precisely delineated in the conjoint
marital setting. Conjoint marital therapy presupposes that the
couple represents a unit with its own properties, including conflicts
and needs, in contrast to another unit, the family, where the couple
function in the roles of parents. In my practice, conjoint marital
therapy is frequently used in conjunction with conjoint family therapy and individual psychotherapy for either a spouse or a given
child. Most studies of conjoint marital therapy (see Grotjahn, 1960;
also Watson, 1963) emphasize communication distortion and related
role conflict between the partners. Though a wide variety of issues
are regarded as relevant for working through in this setting, emotional responses to loss by death or desertion have not generally
been deemed critical factors contributing to the marital impasse.
This paper focuses on the role of loss, incompleted mourning, and
empathy as these relate to intense, long-standing marital incompatibility in a neurotic couple.

The type of conjoint marital therapy referred to here derives
from a composite of different points of view. Fundamental consideration is given to the crucial importance of experience, and the need
for corrective communication and development of empathy between
the marital partners. Combined with this are derivatives of dynamic
and genetic understanding stimulated in large part by Freud and

186

translated into interpersonal spheres by Sullivan. Additional features of this focus include the importance of explaining clearly, at the beginning of the therapeutic relationship with the couple, that a concrete goal is that of termination of treatment. Between the beginning and ending of therapy, each marital partner participates in the experience of becoming aware of the impact of the self on the other. By tracing out unresolved fixation points in the development of each, as these have influenced the self and the marriage, each acquires a perspective of the relevance of past experiences to the present. Exposure of affects related to disappointments, frustrations, and internal pain antedating the marriage, which sensitized each to project and displace on to the other, is designed to generate reciprocating empathic responses. Each has the opportunity, with the therapist's direction, to sort out how much and in what ways the past is not past.

The major concrete goal of this treatment is termination associated with the emergence of increased reality-testing of the self and the other, more secure ego boundaries, and improved object relations. More honest affective communication, with each partner able to bear increasing levels of disquieting affect expressed by the self or the other, is an important related goal. Particular emphasis has been placed on assisting each marital partner in becoming more aware of historical sources tending to promote different kinds of symbiotic fusion and related marital disharmony. [1]

Effective termination of treatment is more likely to be achieved if improved marital relations have been realized in treatment, and if the marital partners can each learn, in treatment, the skills of mourning, so that each is prepared to lose the therapist. Edelson (1963), in a thoughtful review of the problem of termination of intensive psychotherapy, elaborated on the problem of terminating so that the gains and areas of emotional growth can continue rather than be vengefully discarded following separation from the therapist. He enlarged on the idea that the patient's ability to master the pain of separation and loss of the therapist is related to the therapist's level of empathic responsiveness to his patient. Extrapolating from this, the focus on termination of conjoint marital therapy is designed to prepare the couple to lose the therapist, and at the same time to promote continued development of newly maturing reciprocal re-

---

[1]As here used, "symbiosis" refers to a primitive relationship, variable in scope and intensity, existing between two persons. It manifests the following characteristics: each experiences the other as essential to survival, with any suggestion of separation being equated with death or desertion of the self or of the other; self and other, in the areas of symbiotic involvement, appear fused; reciprocating patterns of helplessness and omnipotent rescuing of the helpless constitute the primary interpersonal pattern.

lationships between them. Ralph Greenson (1964), in a recent unpublished manuscript on the process of working through, equated
this process with the process of mourning.

Mourning is defined as the psychological process that is set in
motion by the loss of a loved object, and which, when completed, is
associated with the relinquishing of that object. How a person mourns
will, in large substance, be related to how he has been prepared for
this experience by his primary objects. One factor of importance,
then, would be the manner in which they mourned their own losses
while he was growing up; another would be their attitudes toward
death and mourning in the event parental losses antedated a child's
birth.

The hypothesis underlying the focus on loss, tears, and incomplete mourning is that many couples demonstrate a symbiotic fixity
in role relationships that includes characteristic inappropriate reactions to one another. Such fixity, though present for many years,
appears to be rooted in maladaptive responses to both real and
imagined object-and part-object-loss. Furthermore, it appears that
such losses and associated sense of deprivation lead to deposits of
such affects as sorrow, anger, grief, guilt, bitterness, despair,
and regret. These affects, timeless as experienced internally, appear to dictate a restitutive response characterized by the emergence of a perceptual set leading to mate selection. It is as if the
prospective mate seeks, in the mate to be selected, both what he
had and didn't have in his object relations. These background elements in both partners generate a style of marital harmony and incompatibility. It appears that both factors conspire to promote
periodic marital crises.[2] The oscillating marital homeostasis is
associated with a denial of, or a warding off of, real or imagined
losses, disappointments, or major changes that require sanctions
for and support of a greater sense of separation between the spouses.

The above hypothesis led to the development of an experimental
technique consisting of the induction of a belated mourning reaction
referred to as "operational mourning."[3] Through repeated directed
inquiry about recollectable responses to loss, the therapist invites
the exposure and expression of intense feelings in the member involved. The feelings stimulated in the other by such expressed
grief are then solicited by the therapist. The therapist's ability to

---

[2] In many couples, increased levels of marital harmony can trigger crises. It
appears here that a spouse may have unrecognized guilt about possessing a marital
relationship his parents did not have.

[3] "Operational" has been used to designate the experiential feature, and un-
derscores the vital importance of the exposure of a variety of hitherto hidden
affects.

empathize with the subject reviewing and exposing his intense inner feelings about his losses is a critical factor dictating the spouse's ability to resonate empathetically with the belated mourner.

Empathy (see the study by Chessick, 1965, and the book by Katz, 1963), a cornerstone dimension in the treatment focus here, has thus far eluded adequate definition both of its existence and the process whereby it comes to be perceived. It seems obvious that such a very complex affective transaction and state cannot adequately be defined in words. Basically it refers to the ability of one person to identify with another in terms of the other's inner emotional experience; then, to feel the other's feelings in oneself so that the empathizer and his subject recognize that both have felt kindred feelings. Empathy in any psychotherapy includes oscillation between subjective involvement and objective, detached awareness, and reflection of the same. Basically, it appears that two types of psychotherapeutic empathy exist!

(1) Empathy on an associative level, in which a therapist or patient responds associatively to the verbal thought content of the other. This associative empathy is generally expressed in the treatment of neurotic patients. Furthermore, it is representative of the kind of material presented for review at scientific meetings.

(2) Empathy on an affective level, wherein the therapist responds affectively to the emotional overtones of the associative verbal stream of the patient. This affective empathy cannot be fabricated, insofar as its presence in the therapist can only be determined on the basis of the response in the patient. As such, its existence in the therapist is difficult to assess. It is a crucial ingredient in the psychotherapy of the schizophrenic patient, whose response to others is based on what he affectively perceives in the inner self of the therapist. It includes an affective regression on the part of the therapist to a timeless feeling state which Loewald (1960) feels analysts generally tend to avoid from an underlying fear that they "may not find the way back to higher organization." Loewald outlines an avoidance pattern that is shared by therapist, patient, and non-patient more often than we may care to recognize.

As described below, the use of an affective empathic resonance with a husband provides an entree into his inner world, revealing affects hitherto hidden to him, and related to an almost forgotten experience of loss. These feelings now exposed, both the husband and his wife begin to acquire a sense of the history of some painful affects in the husband and their relevance to the marital impasse.

This focus, which attempts to generate a reciprocating empathic responsiveness in a couple via conjoint marital therapy, has so far been used with twelve couples. These couples have been seen together with the wife's family of origin, and, alternately, with the husband's family of origin. Frequently the children have been seen with the parents as marital disharmony was resolved, so as to demolish parental illusion that the children have been unaware of parental crises. In addition, such adjunctive meetings permit the children to express their inner distress about the disturbing emotional climate in which they find themselves immersed. Diagnostically, two of the twelve families examined include at least one borderline psychotic. The other ten contain variable types of character disorders, such as alcoholism, prolonged sexual infidelity, neurotic disturbances, and psychosomatic illnesses such as spastic colitis, duodenal ulcer, and migraine headache. All these couples have children. Spouses in this sample range in age from 24 to 47. The impression thus far has been that couples who have not had prior individual-focused therapy or counseling are more responsive to this approach, insofar as the achievement of a satisfactory resolution of problems associated with marital mutuality is concerned. (More detailed account of this experience, with follow-up, will be reported later.)

In presenting the following case illustration, we are on the horns of a dilemma. The process of treatment, whether individual psychotherapy, conjoint marital therapy, or family group therapy, is fundamentally one rooted in affective transactions that transcend linguistic usage. This point of view is in keeping with the findings of George Engel (1963) who, in his efforts to develop an adequate classification of the phenomenology of affects, acknowledged the inadequacy of language in dealing with affects, stating: "We still recognize, not only that in nature affects do not exist in pure, unalloyed forms but also that to deal with affects in written, verbal, or conceptual terms is fundamentally inconsistent with their nature and can succeed only at the expense of their oversimplification and impoverishment."

We are handicapped in not having suitable procedures to reproduce in print the intensity and vividness of both the affective experience of grief and its resonating impact on the other partner. The following excerpts from a taped conjoint marital meeting do offer, nevertheless, some clues to the situation.

The first case is that of the Lewises. Mr. and Mrs. Lewis were referred to me for conjoint marital therapy by a colleague who also advised concurrent individual psychotherapy for each. Mr. and Mrs. Lewis are both thirty-nine years old and have been married for twenty years. They have six children. The specific crisis arose when Mr. Lewis planned to divorce his wife in order to marry Charlotte, a twenty-one-year-old girl living in a large, distant city. Charlotte was described as both "wonderful" and "full of understanding." Mrs. Lewis panicked when she learned of her husband's plans, and initiated contact with a psychiatrist-friend. He referred them to another psychiatrist, who sent them to me. They were seen together a total of eleven sessions over a two-and-a-half-year period. Mrs. Lewis was seen three times alone, and Mr. Lewis once alone. Mr. and Mrs. Lewis were seen with four of their children twice. Their oldest daughter was seen once alone.

Mr. Lewis is a heavy-set man, bald, with a deep voice and a commanding, dramatic salesman's manner. He expresses great pride that he once lost fifty pounds by exercising his will. A self-made man, he is the owner of a successful international export company, having built this business up in the past twelve years. He is Jewish, of very poor parents, who are still living. His parents were unmarried until he was twelve years old. At that time, he persuaded his father to marry his mother; for this his father has never forgiven him. Mrs. Lewis, generally intense in manner, is attractive and well-groomed; she is Protestant, and comes from a wealthy social background. Both her parents committed suicide: her mother when she was sixteen, and her father six years ago, when she was thirty-three. Mr. and Mrs. Lewis practice no religion, priding themselves on being humanists. They met during the war and were married after a brief courtship. They were disowned by their respective families. After eight months, he went overseas and was not heard from for most of the two years he spent in Asia, where he lived with an older woman whom he promised to marry when she declared herself to be pregnant. After returning unexpectedly to the United States, he told his wife about this affair; she, in a hyper-understanding way, suggested they adopt the child. Shortly thereafter Mr. Lewis learned that the other woman had had a miscarriage, thus resolving this problem.

The Lewises have had an increasingly stormy relationship over the past seventeen years, which appears to have been aggravated by the successive appearance of more children on the scene. A crisis occurred nine years ago, when Mr. Lewis was intent on divorce; at the same time, his wife agreed to remain with him. Each has been very concerned about being rejected and criticized by the other. Curiously, the only area they agreed on at the time of referral was that the children had developed well in all areas without suffering from the noisy, almost continuous turmoil. Sexual conflict, and concerns about adultery and divorce had been in the air since Mrs. Lewis's first pregnancy.

The couple had been seen together three times before the meeting reproduced here. Tension was high during these sessions, with Mr. Lewis finalizing his plans to marry Charlotte. In the first meeting, Mr. Lewis stated that he and his wife were "very close" and "very dependent," with a "symbiotic conflict." He likened their situation to one in which "You're locked in water, you know; you're trying to save each other and kind of cling to each other." Though he acknowledged that many aspects of his marriage were good, he couldn't put up with what he perceived to be his wife's attitude toward him: she saw him as "always wrong," while she was always "sweet and pure."

Mrs. Lewis made a suicidal gesture before our second meeting, taking at least twenty unprescribed tranquilizers, which did not create any profound unconsciousness. This attempt closely simulated the successful suicidal attempt of her mother, complete with a note pinned to her nightgown. It alarmed her husband, who denied vehemently in the second session what she accused him of—namely, that he had told her in a fit of anger that he hoped she would commit suicide as her parents had done. Focus was then directed to her recollections of and feelings about her mother's suicide by an overdose of morphine. She vividly reviewed her anguish and distress, weeping as she did so and affecting her husband so much that both wanted to return for a third meeting. The pattern of intense sado-masochistic relating, with particular emphasis on the other's great lying ability, could be neutralized pro tempore by directed review of their respective pasts. The willingness of both to continue to meet in joint meeting represented the wish, however meagre and whatever the source, to continue their relationship and, perhaps, to resolve their problems. These meetings were regarded as a last-ditch attempt to see if anything could be done to rectify the destructive and distressing marital situation. Mr. Lewis maintained that his wife was a wonderful person and mother—a perfect person, in fact—and that he would recommend her highly to any other man.

The third meeting was an emergent one, in which Mr. Lewis was concerned about whether his wife would attempt suicide during his projected business trip to another country for a week. Mrs. Lewis seemed in good control, and two issues were clarified: (1) the mutual fear of the other's anger, and (2) Mr. Lewis's feeling that his wife was intent on destroying him. He related this for the first time to his fear of women and his lack of familiarity with women other than his mother and three older sisters prior to his marriage. Mr. Lewis finally acknowledged his guilt and helplessness about being involved with Charlotte. I indicated my availability to Mrs. Lewis during her husband's business trip if she felt panicked. Reluctantly, he decided to come for one final meeting.

During the eleven days between the third and fourth joint meetings, the situation at home stabilized somewhat; Mrs. Lewis did not call to see me. Mrs. Lewis reported, at the beginning of the fourth

meeting, that she felt that her husband was trying to understand her
more and didn't view her as a horrible person; as she was saying
this, Mr. Lewis was looking at his newspaper, after indicating that
this was to be our last meeting. He then acknowledged that he was
feeling better and a bit more peaceful, principally because he had
been away, adding that some insights developed during the meetings
were helpful, though disturbing. The topic then turned to sex and
Mr. Lewis spoke of himself as having been a love-baby, conceived
in passion. When inquiry was made as to whether he had ever discussed his sexual life as a youngster with his wife, he stated that
he did, referring briefly to both homosexual and masturbatory experiences during early adolescence that were associated with both
pleasure and guilt. His wife corroborated this. Mr. Lewis then
focused on his recognized protective feelings toward his mother
when she was unmarried. He stated that both he and his father were
"trapped" in marriage. He began to see parallels between past
events and his present marital crisis.

Therapist: How often did you ask your father to marry your mother?

Mr. ·L. (blandly): Oh, quite often.

Therapist: Beginning at what age?

Mr. L.: Oh, probably when I was about nine.

Therapist: And how would he greet you?

Mr. L.: He would be very indulgent. He would be . . . we, we, my
father and I, when we get along very well, we can have very friendly
pleasant relationships, I mean, at times.

Therapist: Again I draw the parallel between you and your wife; you
get along when you have pleasant relationships.

Mr. L.: But I mean . . . for example, I'd say, I've usually . . . in
fact I think this has been one of the reasons I was successful in my
own work, is that I've always had to persuade . . . I mean, I was a
kid, my parents were older. They were foreigners in this country.
They couldn't speak English. I was sort of the educator, the critic,
the persuader.

Therapist: You were assuming leadership in some ways in the home?

Mr. L.: Oh . . .

Mrs. L. (eagerly): Oh, yes.

Mr. L. (with pride): I led that family from the time I was probably five years old, and in many, many ways. I really marshaled the family's direction in many ways. And they appreciated it. They were very proud of me for this. I mean, then . . . but I would say to my father sometimes when we were alone, I would say: "Pop, you know it would be nice if you married Mom; after all, she is a woman, and she, she'd feel better if she were married." Incidentally, my mother would sometimes mention this to me.

Therapist: That she'd like to be married?

Mr. L. (with increasing excitement): Yes. I mean she would mention it. See, I don't know how I ever got the impression that I was illegitimate, because no one ever said it to me. It's a funny thing. Now, speaking of hearing things—no one ever told me that.

Therapist: Did you ever see any documents?

Mr. L.: No, that's a funny thing. It's a funny thing. I just knew. I don't know.

Therapist: Do you believe in the supernatural?

Mr. L.: No, but something must have told me.

Therapist: A vapor in the air, sort of.

Mr. L. (mellow with warmth): No, no, but I think maybe my mother must have said, I remember, I know what, I was with my mother and aunt and one of the things I think has influenced me a lot, my Aunt Emma was a most wonderful person. Oh, she was . . .

Therapist: Her sister?

Mr. L.: Yes, my mother's sister.

Therapist: Older?

Mr. L.: Younger, and we were, we would go on vacation, not vacation but we'd go visit my Aunt Emma in North Carolina, and I would be in bed with the two women as a boy.

Mrs. L.: Yes, you told me that you used to overhear the two women talking.

Mr. L.: And they were talking. They wouldn't see each other for a year and they talked for all night.

Therapist: You'd sleep where, on the end or between?

Mr. L.: I'd sleep on the end.

Therapist: At what age would this occur?

Mr. L.: Oh, I must have been eight, seven. And they would talk all night about men, and all night they'd be, the sisters having a real personal, intimate relationship, and. . .

Therapist: What?

Mr. L. (with embarassment): A personal and intimate relationship, discussing men and discussing life with men, and the problems of men, and every so often I'd just wake up and hear . . . men are so and so, men are so and so.

Therapist: Did that make you feel sort of positive about growing up to be a man?

Mr. L. (momentarily bewildered): Make me feel positive? Well, I don't know about that.

Therapist: What do you think?

Mr. L.: I don't know. My mother would always criticize my father. You know, she'd say, she'd always be very critical at some times. Then she'd be nice at other times. My Aunt Emma was wonderful, though. There was a remarkable woman. (Voice softened) She died when she was a young woman. She was a remarkable person.

Therapist: When did she die?

Mr. L.: She was thirty-five.

Therapist: And you were how old?

Mr. L.: I was about, oh, ten or eleven. She was a remarkable, nice person.

Therapist: And how did you feel when she died?

Mr. L. (with mounting emotion): Oh, I felt sadder about my Aunt Emma's death than anybody.

Therapist: How sad?

Mr. L. (with tears in eyes): Miserable, miserable.

Therapist: What do you remember?

Mr. L. (sobbing): I feel terrible.

Therapist: Do you feel that you still miss her?

Mr. L.: Oh, I do. She was so nice. She was so nice. (Sobbing)

Mrs. L.: She had, she did all the things, you know, for him, you know, when he was a little boy, that little kids need that he didn't get at home. You know, she had animals around the house and things, you know; his parents never understood things like that.

Mr. L.: She's really the woman I've been looking for, really. She was so nice. She was a beautiful woman. She was so kind.

Therapist: She was single?

Mr. L.: No, she was married. She had a family. She had her children, and uh, but she was always understanding.

Therapist: Do you ever see her family?

Mr. L.: No. Never had any really close relationship with her family.

Therapist: Since she died.

Mr. L. (pensive): Since she died. She was a remarkable, kind person.

Therapist: Do you know where she's buried?

Mr. L.: Yes, Charlotte, North Carolina. I've never been to her grave.

Therapist: Never?

Mr. L.: No. You see, I don't know why I've never been to her grave, but I haven't been to anybody's grave. She's the only person I ever, the only close person that's ever died in our family, you know.

Therapist: Do you feel that she's the only one that you really loved that way?

(Mr. Lewis has outburst of bitter weeping, then silence)

Mr. L.: I've always loved her. She was very kind to me.

Therapist: She loved you?

Mr. L.: Yes, she did (heightened sobbing). I don't know what I'm crying about.

Therapist: You know what you're crying about.

Mr. L.: I don't know.

Therapist: You don't? You still miss her.

Mr. L. (sobbing brokenly): She was so nice. It wasn't anything she did, especially, it was just. . . she was always so nice. She always, she was always so sweet, and so kind, and there was never a mean or a bad word coming from her lips. She always liked me. There was never anything phony; she was always accepting me as I am. Being with her was like peace; just peace; just absolute peace.

Therapist: So in many ways you have been looking for her over the years.

Mr. L.: Yea. I think I've found her (with conviction and recovering composure). I think I have.

He then spoke of Aunt Emma's unexpected death from a brain tumor and reviewed the detachment he experienced upon leaving her after those summer visits with her. It became increasingly clear that he had been looking for a direct replacement all these years, and internally feeling that she would be found somewhere. The therapist made it clear that Aunt Emma could never be found alive again, even though he might feel this to be possible. The therapist then sug-

gested that the anger for her dying, both unrecognized and uninte-
grated, was expressed by avoiding her family and perhaps getting
into a rage when situations such as scenes in his own home reminded
him of Aunt Emma. His wife spontaneously associated from his comment that Aunt Emma's house was messy and not neat to his temper
tantrums, which could be triggered by similar disorder in their own
home. After continued review of this and related issues, Mrs.
Lewis was asked: "What do you think? How do you feel?"

Mrs. L. (with soft, saddened voice): Well, I feel very sorrowful
about the rough times Joe has had, and I understand a lot of things
that I've never been able to understand as long as we've been married, things I have struggled with over and over and kept thinking
if I could just do better, his attitude was going to be different.

Therapist: You see, if you could have been his aunt . . .

Mrs. L.: Yes, this is what I realize, this is what I was struggling
against all that time, and I didn't even know what I was struggling
against.

Mr. L. (with humor): It's like a murder mystery. Who's to know
it's your aunt? You know, if you listed all the causes . . .

Mrs. L.: In other words . . .

Mr. L.: For years . . .

Mrs. L. (with agitation): I always felt, in order to accomplish anything in this situation, I had to do more than anybody else. I had to
be saintly. I didn't, you know, insofar as I was in any way personally able to be. But I never was able really to feel free to be, you
know, to be well, relaxed, or natural. I always had this feeling, I
would try, and I would try, and it would not result in what I would
think it would.

Therapist: What it sounds like is, and this is just one aspect, but
it seems that in some ways he wanted you to be his aunt.

Mrs. L. (tone of relief): Yes, of course.

Therapist: And he was furious at you that you weren't.

Mrs. L.: Yes, and I never could understand why he got furious at
me. I never could understand this. It's puzzled me as long as we've

been married. Why you would get so furious at me, when I was trying so hard, and when I really cared so much (tearfully).

Mr. L. (quizzically): You really think, I mean, are you sure
you're . . .

Therapist: Go to the cemetery in Charlottesville, and you'll find
out.

Mr. L.: Charlotte.

Therapist: -ville.

Mrs. L.: It's just Charlotte, where his aunt is buried.

Therapist: Oh, it's Charlotte, too?

Mr. L.: Sure, what else? You guys are so delighted when you find
some sort of little nugget. You know, what the hell?

Therapist: How do you feel towards me now?

Mr. L.: Bemused.

Therapist: What else? Annoyed?

Mr. L.: Oh no, no. I have felt annoyed toward you at the last one.
I don't feel annoyed. I feel, you know, I think, I think you're a very
good man. I think you know your business and you really are good
at what you do. I think you're tops, but I have a certain skepticism
about these little nuggets. Although I will say, looking back, she
has three names I could have called her. No one else ever called
her Charlotte. So why do I call her Charlotte?

Therapist: So you accuse me of those nuggets that you're . . .

Mr. L.: Nuggetism.

Therapist: Nuggetism. But you sort of picked out one of three nuggets yourself.

Mr. L.: So, I mean, maybe there's something to it. But there's all
a good reason.

Therapist: There's always a good reason.

Mr. L.: See, for example, I didn't call her by her first name because she didn't like that. I didn't call her by Michael because that's the aggressive, dynamic part of her. So I called her by Charlotte, which is the name that stood for me, I guess, for my aunt (laughing to self, delighted with his deductions).

Therapist: If you want to find out what your aunt still means to you, you go to the cemetery in Charlotte yourself and you'll find out for yourself.

Mr. L. (with concern): I'll probably crack up.

Therapist: You won't crack up. You'll just sort of catch up with yourself.

Mr. L. (quietly): Okay. I'll do that. I've never gone to cemeteries or anybody's grave. She's the only one that really matters. You know, Doc, you're a pretty good unraveler. That's funny. You know it's a funny thing, because until today I never even mentioned what this girl's name was . . . to my wife or anybody else, so maybe that has something to do with it, too. I don't know. People get so messed up. I feel peaceful now, relieved, like having been through constipation or something. (sighs)

Therapist: Our time is just about up now. Do you want to come back?

Mr. L.: Not really.

Therapist: I can appreciate that. Would you come back?

Mr. L.: Yeah.

Therapist: I think you've got to do a lot of hard thinking about what happened in the past, and about your aunt. She's with you. And all you have to do is go down to Charlotte, and you'll find out. I'm not saying you should, but if you want to test this out for yourself where it counts for you . . .

Mr. L.: How did people survive before you guys discovered these little gems?

Therapist: Oh, they didn't survive. They just kept on fighting.

Mr. L.: Well, what happens when you're at complete rest?

Therapist: You're never really at complete rest.

Mr. L.: In other words, you're going to make me so peaceful that I'm no longer sick enough to try for, you know . . .

Therapist: You never get really complete rest. You're just sort of aware of that someone you loved is not here anymore. You still miss them. At least you can put it in some perspective.

Mr. L.: That's the funniest thing, the names. Do you mean that because this girl's name was Charlotte was why this happened? Because it's never happened before to me on a trip. She has the same color eyes. She has the same color hair.

Therapist: The next thing you'll say is she's your aunt. I mean, the way you're sort of tallying this up.

Mr. L. (with magnanimity): I'm trying, you know, trying to help you.

Therapist: Help me? Help you. We're not here to help me. (To Mrs. L.) Do you want to come back?

Mrs. L. (saddened): Yes, I do.

Mr. L.: Why does she have to come back? I'm the guy who's unfilled . . .

Mrs. L. (sobbing): No, because this is helping me so much to understand things that have puzzled me for so long, and I never could cope with, and I didn't know what to do about. That's good enough for me.

Therapist: Maybe get a chance to know your husband a little better.

Mrs. L.: You said it.

Therapist: And get him to know himself too.

Mrs. L.: You said it. I agree with you one hundred percent, 'cause if anybody told me this is what would happen today, I never would have believed it in a million years.

Mr. L. (speaking provocatively into microphone): Well, these things are completely unrehearsed.

Mrs. L.: I want to understand them.

Mr. L.: I'm so confused I don't know what day it is.

Therapist: Monday.

(End of session)

There were seven subsequent meetings with the Lewises during the following thirty months. At the next meeting, they jointly began to consolidate what each had learned about Mr. Lewis's difficult past and how it related to their current difficulties. Also, Mr. Lewis recalled with great bitterness how angry he had felt at his family for desecrating his aunt's memory by haggling over funds for her burial while her recently dead body was lying on the floor in the living room. As he continued to review and integrate the loss of his beloved aunt, he concurrently developed a more realistic perspective about Charlotte, seeing imperfections in her character and behavior associated with a lessened idealization of her. It took about four months of working this through, primarily on his own, with a more compassionate wife, before he gave up his relationship with Charlotte. He and his wife began to develop an increasing positive mutuality; Mr. Lewis now regards her as a friend and companion whose counsel he solicits and respects. They have kept in touch with the therapist through letters, admitting that there are still problems in their relationship, but that now they are able to cope with them.

DISCUSSION

This case demonstrates that hidden, intense grief, unrecognized and thus unresolved, has a latent strength, the presence of which can be revealed by "operational mourning." First seeking for a loss, and then empathically converging on the underlying anguish and pain, elicited from Mr. Lewis the sort of convulsive bitter sobbing commonly observed in children. It was as if emotional pus were discharged, thus neutralizing what apparently was a fixation point in his own development. Of note was Mr. Lewis's spontaneous reference, about nine months after the intense grief reaction referred to above, to visiting his daughter at college. He then reviewed how, for the first time, he had felt like a father, and no longer regarded his daughter as his contemporary. A continuing problem, which however, has somewhat lessened in intensity lately, is an apparent envy Mr. Lewis feels toward his own sons, related in part to the fact that they have married parents. This became apparent at an early meeting, after he poignantly recounted his anguish and distress at being a bastard.

There are numerous elements involved in the complicated management of a case such as this. Mrs. Lewis had reviewed her latent grief, related principally to her mother's suicide, in the second and third meetings — before we discovered Mr. Lewis's hidden grief. Though this seemed to evoke an empathic response in him, it seemed at the same time to promote increased momentum for his divorce. This was suggested at the beginning of the fourth conjoint session when he said that that meeting was to be the last. It appeared crucial that a review of his experiences re loss be attempted, so as to balance what had been achieved with his wife.

The process of "operational mourning" is one in which considerable research is required to determine the secondary derivatives, such as those in areas of the subject's work habits. It appears that a chain reaction effect of a positive emollient sort trickles down to the children, who at times display less disturbing behavior, even though they are not present. Eighteen months after the induced grief reaction, Mr. Lewis described how he found himself able to delegate responsibility in his business to others, feeling capable of coping with the possibility that he might lose in a venture with a client. And he and his wife felt at that time that they had a real honeymoon. He also expressed a feeling of increased freedom from a variable gnawing guilt about his having a harmonious marriage although his parents had not. Longitudinal studies are indicated in such cases to determine the nature of the transgenerational impact of the resolution of marital disharmony on the children, in terms of mate selection and the kinds of coping observed when such children are married and have children of their own.

The role of empathy is regarded as pivotal, insofar as it appears in the nature of an antibiotic in neutralizing the infectious disabling contagion stemming from unresolved internal pain. Mr. Lewis indicated quite clearly that his intense expression of grief engendered in him a feeling of being at peace — the feeling he stated he had when in the company of his beloved aunt. In mourning his aunt more completely twenty-eight years later, he gave up the need to find a direct replacement for her. In a sense, he had an opportunity to start anew, by grieving at once for his aunt, for the little boy he had been, and for himself in the present. His struggle not to be like his father yielded to his becoming freer internally to become more like the man and father he respected. This could only emerge when he could acknowledge the depth of his dependency needs and see himself both accepted and respected in his grief.

Omitted here because of time is a consideration of Mrs. Lewis's background of two suicides insofar as these events and her relations with her parents contributed to her needs in the "symbiotic conflict." The recent studies in bereavement and mental illness by Parkes (1965a, 1965b) underscore the continued need to be aware of the multifarious ways in which grief will be expressed. When grief is hidden and obscured by intense preoccupation and concern with present-day experiences, it is most difficult to learn of its existence. Helene Deutsch (1937) asserted that "the process of mourning as a reaction to the real loss of a loved person must be carried to completion," and thus suggested that incomplete mourning is related to residual states of psychic distress.

Too often we become addicted to the magical nature of words in the definition and description of relational concepts, in a manner analogous to that of the physical scientist. Words distill out the transactional and experiential essence of living experience. I have been guided in some measure here by Alfred North Whitehead (1953) who, in his focus of attention on the obscuring, distorting aspects of language, said: "I insist on the radically untidy, ill-adjusted character of the fields of actual experience from which science starts. To grasp this fundamental truth is the first step in wisdom." This fact, he feels, is concealed by language, which "foists on us exact concepts as though they represented the immediate deliverance of experience."

SUMMARY

A rationale for conjoint marital therapy is described. Focus here is on the relevance of hitherto unrecognized and incompletely mourned losses in relation to fixations in marital partners, mate selection, and a style of marital harmony and incompatibility. The importance of an affective, empathic frame of reference is described, as is the technique of operational mourning in neutralizing the long-term effects of hidden grief. This approach appears to be one worthy of continued exploration and research.

REFERENCES

Chessick, R. D. Empathy and love in psychotherapy. Amer. J. Psychother., 1965, 19, 205-219.

Deutsch, Helene. Absence of grief. Psychoanal. Quart., 1937, 6, 12-22.

Edelson, M. The termination of intensive psychotherapy. Springfield, Ill.: C. C. Thomas, 1963.

Engel, G. Toward a classification of affects. In P. H. Knapp (Ed.),
Expression of the emotions in man. New York: Int. Univer.
Press, 1963. Pp. 266-299.

Greenson, R.R. The problem of working through. Paper read in
part at the annual meeting of the Amer. Psychoanal. Ass., Los
Angeles, May 1964.

Grotjahn, M. Psychoanalysis and the family neurosis. New York:
W.W. Norton, 1960.

Katz, R. L. Empathy, its nature and uses. New York: The Free
Press of Glencoe, 1963.

Loewald, H. On the therapeutic action of psychoanalysis. Int. J.
Psychoanal., 1960, 41, 16-33.

Parkes, C.M. Bereavement and mental illness: part one, a clinical
study of the grief of bereaved psychiatric patients. Brit. J.
med. Psychol., 1965a, 38, 1-12.

Parkes, C.M. Bereavement and mental illness: part two, a classification of bereavement reactions. Brit. J. med. Psychol.,
1965b, 38, 13-26.

Watson, A. S. The conjoint psychotherapy of marriage partners.
Amer. J. Orthopsychiat., 1963, 33, 912-922.

Whitehead, A. N. The organization of thought from the aims of
education and other essays. In An Anthology selected by
F. S. C. Northrop & Mason W. Gross. New York: Macmillan,
1953. Pp. 139-154.

CO-THERAPY TEAMWORK RELATIONSHIPS IN FAMILY PSYCHOTHERAPY[1]

David Rubinstein, M.D., and Oscar R. Weiner, M.D.

The technique of utilizing more than one therapist in the psychotherapeutic situation has been increasingly utilized in recent years. The purposes and rationale for such a technique varied according to the kind of patients involved, the particular philosophy of the therapist, and the therapeutic problems being dealt with. The multiple-therapy technique usually involves a single patient being treated by two therapists, either simultaneously, conjointly, or alternately. The therapists may operate together on a consultative or full-time basis. It seems that, originally, the primary aim was to include a trainee in the therapeutic session for teaching purposes, but it became immediately clear that these "joint interviews" helped to accelerate the therapeutic process (Reeve, 1939; Hadden, 1947). The multiple aims and variations have produced a whole gamut of names to characterize the technique: multiple therapy, co-therapy, role-divided therapy, three-cornered therapy, three-cornered interview, joint interview, co-operative psychotherapy, and dual-leadership therapy. These variations do not always denote the same meaning nor do they represent the same technique and/or rationale. It has been noted (Dreikurs, 1950; Dreikurs et al., 1952) that Adler and his associates at the Vienna Child Guidance Clinic were the first to utilize the principles of multiple therapy in the management of children who presented special therapeutic problems. They reported that these children seemed to respond more effectively when their problems were discussed in front of them by more than one therapist (Adler, 1930). "Multiple therapy" was utilized for a different purpose by Whitaker et al. (1950) and by Hayward et al. (1952).

---

[1] This paper was written in collaboration with I. Boszormenyi-Nagy, Margaret Dealy Griffel, J. L. Framo, Geraldine Lincoln, L. R. Robinson, and G. H. Zuk. The views expressed in this paper represent, in general, the result of joint discussion of the group. There is not, however, unanimous agreement on every point, and therefore the authors accept main responsibility for the statements expressed herein.

They proposed bringing a second therapist into the treatment session with an individual patient in order to successfully break the therapeutic impasse. In very sick patients, the transference relationship with a single therapist becomes so highly intensified that the therapeutic process may come to a standstill. The introduction of a simultaneous second therapist seemingly breaks the impasse, in that the illusional quality of the transference becomes more evident and treatment may start to move ahead again.

This technique has not been limited to the treatment of individual patients; it was soon applied to group psychotherapy. All the vicissitudes of the group's processes experienced in the context of multiple therapy have since been the subject of numerous papers published in the last ten years (Lundin and Aronov, 1952; Demarest and Teichner, 1954; Klapman and Meyer, 1957; Kassoff, 1958; Adler and Berman, 1960; Gans, 1962; Mintz, 1963, 1965).

The use of two therapists has been the preferred technique in family therapy (Boszormenyi-Nagy, 1965; Framo, 1962, 1965). Although there have been some attempts to differentiate between the two terms "multiple therapy" and "co-therapy" (Mullen and Sanguiliano, 1960), the present trend is to include both under the same concept. We prefer to utilize the term "co-therapy" because we believe it more accurately describes the mutual relationship established between the therapists involved. As utilized in this paper, "co-therapy" is defined as the simultaneous treatment of an individual, a group, or a family by two or more therapists.

This paper is a reflection of the work and experiences of our group at the Eastern Pennsylvania Psychiatric Institute in the study and treatment of family processes. We will attempt to deal, in this paper, with some aspects of the deep dynamics of the co-therapy team relationship in family therapy. We present here a cross-section of a process in our thinking that is still in evolution. It is not our intention to present a statistical evaluation of co-therapy as compared to single therapy, nor to defend this approach as the best one. We do not know of any study aimed at evaluating both types of technique. Although our first experience was with adolescent schizophrenic females and their families, we have now expanded our treatment endeavors to families with designated patients of both sexes and varying symptomatology throughout the range of psychopathology.

SETTING

Two members of our group select each other as co-therapists to interview, evaluate, and treat a family.[2] All sessions are taped,

---

[2] Our group has been headed by Dr. Ivan Boszormenyi-Nagy. Some members of this group participate in a family therapy project at the Philadelphia Psychiatric Center, directed by Dr. Alfred Friedman.

and can be observed through a one-way mirror. When families are evaluated, the rest of the therapy staff observes, and following the session we meet to discuss the various aspects of the family dynamics, the team dynamics, the prognosis, strategies, and so on. If one team has special difficulties with the family or difficulties within the team itself during the course of family therapy, then observation of a session by the whole group is requested to help out with suggestions to solve the difficulty. In this manner, our group serves as its own supervisor. The therapy staff also meets in conference twice weekly in order to discuss new concepts and new observations, to consult about a family, to discuss our group and team problems, to plan new projects, and so on. We feel that in these group sessions many of our conflicts have been exposed and worked through. The team itself meets after each family session for a variable amount of time in order to discuss problems that arose during the session.

Our group consists of members from different professional backgrounds. Psychiatrists and psychologists are the two main disciplines. The differences in training and background contribute to the divergent therapeutic approaches, interests, and goals in the therapeutic process. However, the main divergence stems from personality differences among the group's members (e.g., some therapists are more emotionally "free" and some are more restrained). The overall effect is that the group, as a whole, blends different interests and becomes integrated into a unit that at times struggles internally, but, on the whole, remains creative and quite cohesive.

RATIONALE FOR TEAMWORK IN FAMILY PSYCHOTHERAPY

The intervention into a family system for the purpose of studying its processes and trying to change its pathological dynamics is an extremely difficult undertaking. During all these years, our project has utilized a team of two therapists per family. We do not propose here that using two therapists per family is the only way to work; we are aware that many single therapists have worked with a family successfully. Still, the use of co-therapists has been our practice; we have learned a great deal about the dynamic process between therapists, and how this relates to the therapy process of the family. The co-therapy team relationship is merely one component part of a complicated transactional therapy process that we are artificially abstracting for exposition purposes. Due to the fact that we explore these families in depth and over a long period of time, the intensification of needs in the therapists that eventuates must be taken into account in the therapeutic process.

We feel that if one therapist were to deal alone with the intense negative transference of a family system, the result might be overwhelming for the therapist. Family therapy can arouse more disturbing feelings in the therapist than either individual or group therapy. Either positive or negative transference feelings from the therapist to the whole family or part of it are bound to appear. These feelings are based not only on what the family is producing but also on resurgence of old feelings that the therapists had in their own families of origin. The presence of another therapist helps to check and counterbalance all these transference phenomena, either positive, negative, or ambivalent. The added circumstance that the team meets after and between sessions to discuss mutual thoughts and feelings permits both members to become aware of and work through some of these transference feelings, and, further, keeps a check on the possibility of either one becoming "swallowed up" by the family system.

Co-therapists can support one another by talking to each other in a calm way in the face of intense family anxiety. This exercises a very strong control over the family system and permits more efficient psychotherapeutic intervention. This type of closeness certainly acts as a "buffer" against the feeling of helplessness that may often be experienced by the single therapist working alone with a family. The family, as a pathologic system of interaction, has had much experience in arousing the anxieties of other people, agencies, and the community. This new situation, in which they meet a team of therapists whose anxiety is not so easily provoked, is a very relieving experience to the family.

It is logical to assume that the situation of working with a team of two therapists recreates more approximately the original situation of the two parents to the family system. This is especially true if one therapist is a man and one a woman (Sonne and Lincoln, 1965a). Transference phenomena to these two "parents" are therefore easily provoked and exposed. However, it has been our experience that sex difference in the team is not an absolute requirement for the attainment of these transference phenomena. The family tends to transfer the original feelings about their own parents even though both therapists are males. Curious enough to be mentioned is the fact that, so far as we know, two females rarely get together for the purposes of co-therapy in family psychotherapy. We have speculated on reasons for this state of affairs, but have come to no definite conclusions.

We have observed quite frequently that the presence of two therapists allows the family to express positive feelings to one therapist while showing the negative feelings of the relationship to the other. The therapy situation also permits the family members to shift their feelings, and to show ambivalence towards each therapist. At other times, the family develops a multiple transference relationship to both therapists, whereby each member of the team is seen as representing one or various aspects of the multiple transference needs of the family. This sharing and splitting of the family's transferred feelings is an important therapeutic tool.

We have observed that the therapist's need for the family he is treating is expressed through a "mourning period" that follows upon an abrupt or premature termination of treatment. It is easier on him to assimilate the "loss" of the family if there is a co-therapist who remains after these sudden terminations. It is also obvious that having a co-therapist in the transactional process of family therapy brings both members closer together by their mutual sharing of responsibility and experience with the family. Sharing the responsibility with another therapist increases the sense of security in handling intricate family transactions, and therefore permits a more relaxed attitude. This closeness allows several necessary, positive things to happen: for example, the family can be "given up" when necessary. It is better for the attachment to be stronger between the therapists than between therapist and family. A single therapist may get so much gratification from treating a family that it it may hinder and disguise the need for termination of the treatment. The therapists' dependency on the family may weaken his position as therapist.

Like Dreikurs et al. (1952), in their comments on the advantages of multiple therapy for individual psychotherapy, we could describe some of the advantages of applying co-therapy to the treatment of a family. The combination of knowledge and constant consultation between both therapists leads to more accuracy in diagnosis, understanding of the dynamics, and a choice of therapeutic approaches. No matter how experienced a family therapist may be, the opportunity for checking his appraisals and interpretations is necessary. New viewpoints and different insights help to strengthen and increase one's own evaluations and techniques.

Family groups, as well as individuals, tend to utilize a particular kind of irrational logic to serve their own rationalizations and needs and to raise their self-esteem, thus keeping the family system intact. The grossest alterations of thinking may be manifested, often to the point of paranoid-like beliefs shared by the whole family group. A single therapist can be seduced into sharing and confirming the most bizarre of family beliefs. The presence of a co-therapist helps to prevent this possibility. At the same time, the need for a single therapist to get a family "well" and thus enhance his own self-esteem can hinder many of his therapeutic resources and bias some of his viewpoints. The strong relationship to the co-therapist can help to shift the narcissistic need gratification for the family.

As we have mentioned earlier, family therapy sessions can produce great strain in the therapist. There are times when the therapist needs to withdraw from the intense emotion. He may need to work through some internal struggle aroused by the ongoing session. He cannot do this when he is the sole therapist, for the family process requires full-time attention. A co-therapist may take over if he senses the other's need to retreat temporarily.[3] In this fashion, a therapist can allow himself to enjoy both aspects of his activity, and be active or inactive as his needs may dictate. By alternating passivity and aggressiveness in the therapeutic process, one is able to evoke a more complete encounter with the family and one has more opportunity to explore oneself as a person. Naturally, it requires a lot of confidence and reliance on one's team member to be able to allow for this alternation of activity and passivity.

Some therapists welcome both the possibility of playing different roles to the family and the advantage of having an opportunity for a nonstereotyped position. Playing the patient's game and utilizing the patient's distorted logic has been a frequent gimmick in the therapeutic process. This can be more easily done if there is a co-therapist who can occupy the counter-position. While one co-therapist "plays" the patient, the other co-therapist "plays" the therapist's normal rational role. Through this approach, the family members may get a more objective understanding of their own actions.

A few observations about the influence of the major group on the functioning of that team might be helpful at this point. We have stated that team difficulties may, at times, be clarified by being discussed in the presence of the major group. These discussions have been most helpful during the first stages of team formation, at times when everyone's inexperience is relieved by the sharing within the group. We have often played back a tape of a family therapy session in which there are evidences of team dysfunction. These group conferences have, at times, been most helpful in diagnosing the difficulty. The group, as an objective observer, has been able to point out the dynamics of difficulties observed in the intrateam relationships. Furthermore, the team may be able to discuss, in the presence of the group, some of their mutual feelings and speculations. However, this kind of "group control" seems to have its

---

[3] It should be made clear that the therapists are usually not so aware of each other on a conscious level. Most of their mutual awareness and communication goes on at a preconscious level. Therapists are much more consciously involved, generally speaking, with the family and its members than with each other.

problems as well. We have noticed that occasionally the major group
may pose a hindrance in the working-through of the team process.
The group, with its own process, sometimes disturbs the establishment of a sound process in the team. We have observed that the
group's intrusion into the team's relationships sometimes results
in greater dissonance rather than in harmony. This is probably a
result of both an overdefensiveness on the part of the team, and an
overcritical attitude on the part of the group. On those occasions,
it is advisable for the team members to work through their team
process between themselves, through repeated meetings. At these
team meetings, the therapists confer about their mutual feelings,
their thoughts about the family and about each other, and may also
discuss their private lives and families of origin. This method of
monitoring also keeps a check on interfering transferences and
counter-transferences. Team meetings are necessary even if there
are no difficulties, so that pitfalls can be anticipated and averted
and the team relationship can be strengthened.

DYNAMICS OF TEAM RELATIONSHIPS

Because our major experience has been with co-therapy relationships, we would like to transmit some of our thoughts about
the dynamics of the team and how they are manifested. We will attempt to discuss the disadvantages as well as the advantages of
working as a team.

SPLITTING OR DISSOCIATION OF THE TEAM

We would first like to make a distinction here between "splitting"
and "dissociation" of the team. By "splitting" we mean the transactional phenomenon whereby the team members become separated
from a common viewpoint or from a coordinated strategy, or dis-
agree about the goals of either a single session or the long-term
strategy. We do not include here the purposeful splitting that is
planned by both therapists as a technical maneuver in order to reach
a certain result and bypass the family's defenses. In this latter
case, planned "splitting" is to the advantage of the team and increases its resourcefulness.

By "dissociation" we mean another transactional phenomenon,
in which both team members are not identified enough with each
other. Dissociation is characterized by a lack of coordination, an
absence of interlocking strategies, and a failure to support each
other on the corresponding maneuvers, interpretations, or immediate goals. It is seen most frequently in teams whose members lack

experience with each other; the therapists have not yet fully met as two persons, and they are going through the process of testing each other. It requires a certain length of time to progress beyond this stage. For various reasons, usually due to basic personality differences, this stage is sometimes not passed, the dissociation is not resolved, and the split becomes permanent. The usual end result is the premature interruption or termination of the family therapy.

Splitting of the team may take different forms and shows itself in curious ways. We could not possibly go through all of them here, but some are worthwhile mentioning. Splitting may present itself in the form of the therapists, working at two different, noncomplementary levels. For example, one therapist insists on pursuing the exploration of the symptoms and behavior of an _individual_, and ignoring the rest of the family, while the other therapist ignores this endeavor and attempts to explore the marital relationship between the parents. The therapists may compete with each other to make their viewpoints prevail.

Another difference which leads frequently to splitting is the disagreement in goals between team members. We have already mentioned that one co-therapist may be interested in uncovering unconscious material and breaking down defenses; he ignores the presenting symptoms. His primary goal is to do a reconstructive type of psychotherapy within the family system. Meanwhile, the other therapist may primarily be interested in pursuing the symptoms of the individual members in order to suppress them, even at the risk of increasing defenses or providing new ones for the family. The team members may thus undercut each other in their efforts. As soon as one makes an interpretation in line with his own trend of thought, the other may undermine it by drifting away, not following it at all, or by introducing his own completely different ideas. It is true that the family tends to select one of the therapists as the leader of the whole therapeutic experience, but it is up to the team members themselves to be aware of this maneuver and prevent it from happening.

A common occurrence in teamwork difficulty, which leads inevitably to a split in the team relationships, is due to strong narcissistic needs in one or both of the co-therapists. The unconscious need to believe that the family they are treating is primarily _his_ family leads to a reaction of aloofness, detachment, and withdrawal in the other team member, who cannot successfully compete in such a maneuver. This kind of phenomenon often occurs when one of the two members is, or has been, involved in individual psychotherapy with one of the members of the family. The family tends to address him as _the_ therapist and to maintain this image throughout the family

sessions, perpetuating the assumption that the primary patient is
the patient and that they are present only to help him! In the mean-
time, the other therapist has to contend with the feeling that there
are private communications between his co-therapist and the family
from which he is excluded. The family tries to divide and conquer
by calling one of the therapists on the telephone, sending private
letters, or having "secretive" talks after the therapy session is
over. It is imperative that these efforts on the part of the family
should be counteracted by the sharing of "private" communications
between both therapists, and by the exposure of these maneuvers in
the family sessions. These counter-maneuvers are aimed at discouraging the family from the splitting maneuvers. Similar feelings
of isolation may be due to different value systems, which the family
may have based on differences of professional background (psychiatrist and social worker), or religion (Jewish, Catholic, or Protestant), or race (white, Negro, or other).

A different kind of competition between team members develops
in the process of training. Rubinstein (1964) has pointed out that the
trainee learns from the instructor through a step-by-step experience.
At the beginning of his teamwork relationship with the instructor,
there is a definite process of identification. After a short time, however, the trainee, by competing with the instructor, develops his own
style of working in the team. He learns to be himself in order to be
better than his instructor. After he is confident of his role and identity, he functions more effectively as part of the team. After this is
achieved, a better functioning team is established. Some difficulties
may arise while the process of competition is going on; both team
members must be aware of the need to work through the ensuing
splits in order to minimize the effect on the therapeutic process.
Experience has proven that splitting of the team has a definite effect
on the family and its treatment. An outstanding and frequent consequence is the premature termination of family therapy. Feelings developed in the intra-team relationship are easily transferred to the
family, and the family finally may be found to be "unchangeable,"
"boring," or "especially resistant to change." The impasse developed in the intra-team relationship usually manifests itself as a
therapeutic impasse with the family, and no progress occurs despite
the passage of time. Finally, the therapists give up working with the
family as a result of having given up their attempts to work through
their mutual difficulties.

The course of treatment is frequently a good indicator of team
difficulties, and this is especially true of the progress of the primary patient. Sudden and apparently unexplained bouts of anxiety
and reappearance of symptoms may be an indication of the sensitivity
of the family to the therapists' intra-team conflicts.

TRANSFERENCE-COUNTERTRANSFERENCE
PHENOMENA WITHIN THE TEAM

There is another aspect of the team relationship which may not be reality-determined. Distortion may occur as a result of the projection onto the team relationship of the unrealistic attitudes of either co-therapist. The co-therapists in a team are not an exception to these transference phenomena. They may transfer to each other irrational behavior, and their relationship may lead not into a co-therapy team but into a co-transference team. Each team member, in turn, is the object of the feed-back countertransference reactions aroused unconsciously in his co-therapist. Such a development blocks the therapeutic resourcefulness of a team, as it tends to fixate in a deadlock of shared transference-countertransference relationships.

We believe that transference phenomena have positive as well as negative implications. We have wondered if transference phenomena can be considered ultimately as forms of resistance toward achieving a more mature relationship between team members. As long as I am disguising my co-therapist under a mask made up of my own internal imagoes, I cannot accomplish a mature relationship with him. He is not himself to me, but one of my imagoes. I do not relate to him as a separate individual but as an impersonation of some aspect of myself. Therefore, clarification of these types of relationships has to take place before I can relate to him as a person. Furthermore, before he becomes a real person, a real co-therapist, he must cease to be a part of myself. If I transfer to him the unresolved conflicts I experienced with my father, he will be of limited value to me as a real co-therapist. However, if we are both aware of this, we have a good starting point for solving this type of relationship.

In similar fashion, competitive feelings due to old sibling rivalry or stemming from earlier peer relationships may be reenacted through transference to the co-therapist. A therapist interested in proving that he is better or wiser than his co-therapist in order to reassure himself, or to gain the family's approval, may feel that his interpretations and approaches are the correct ones, while at the same time he may disapprove, strongly but secretly, the other's actions because the other "reminds" him so much of some internal imagoes. Furthermore, we have observed that the complicated transactional experience that presents itself in co-therapy teamwork with a family lends itself to the peculiar phenomenon of transferring the transference, using the co-therapist or the family as an intermediary. For example, co-therapist A may have transference feelings toward the family in treatment, but may not always express them in that direction. Instead, they are oriented in the direction of co-therapist B, who becomes the intermediary object of the projected feel-ings. This is best illustrated in the discussion of scapegoating be-low. On the other hand, co-therapist B can be spared from the en-acting of disturbing transference feelings, which in turn may be transferred to the family. We feel that this interesting phenomenon of "double-transference" should be kept in mind since it may lead to confusion as to the real source of attitudes and feelings.

SCAPEGOATING WITHIN THE TEAM

Scapegoating may occur within the team, in its relationship to the family. One team member may scapegoat the other member in order to gain favor from the family. The family is interested in splitting the team as a means of resisting change in the family sys-tem. One therapist, more interested in getting gratification and recognition from the family, complies with the family's demands and unconsciously creates a split within the team. This is easily carried out by working on another level, or by undercutting the other's in-terpretations or trends of thoughts, or by differing on goals, and so on. As a result, he plays the "good one," while the co-therapist is forced to take the role of the "bad one." He offers the co-therapist as a "sacrificial lamb" to the family. We feel that this is done to protect himself from the family's hostilities as well as to gain in their favor. The hostility is directed instead to the other therapist.

We have to consider here three main points about team scape-goating: The first is, how does the co-therapist react to being scape-goated by his team member? If he accepts this role passively, and even enjoys it, we could ask the logical question: What is he gratify-ing in himself? The second point is to consider how frequently this phenomenon occurs in teamwork with families. We can envision that both team members may shift in this role, using each other as tem-porary scapegoats. The effect of shifting scapegoating roles may be that each takes turns in using the other team member as an avenue for closeness to the family. Finally, what are the feelings created in the therapist who scapegoats his co-therapist? Getting more from the family, being closer to them, and feeling that he has betrayed his loyalty to his team-member must create some guilt feelings in him. A common defense to these guilt feelings would be to feel even more hostile. This increased hostility may be overt or covert, and may be manifested towards the co-therapist, the family, or the major group. As we mentioned before, hostility in the team relationship is condu-cive to further scapegoating. Scapegoating establishes a vicious cy-cle which has an unfortunate byproduct: the premature termination of psychotherapy with the family, and therefore, the end of the team work.

A last word about this topic should be added. Competition between team members can lead to a creative process rather than a negative one, if it is utilized in the service of the therapy. Competitive feelings may be a source of gratification and may stimulate improvement in the team's capacity to function.

In summary, a major requirement for teamwork is the ability to trust one's co-therapist. Each therapist has to feel, not only that his flank is protected, but also that he can rely on his co-worker, who is undergoing this pleasure-pain experience with him.

A final word. We are aware that the process of effective team relationship cannot take place as soon as two people start to work together. It requires time for the maturation process to occur. Ideally, a few years of mutual experience are needed. Like a married couple, co-therapists have to learn not to fight fruitlessly, but instead to share and enjoy whatever each can offer the other. After having played together for a long time, they will have learned the rules of their own game and will be able to become an efficient team.

DISCUSSION

Because of what has been said up to now, the reader may have been exposed to a confusing experience. In the first part of our paper we described, under the heading of rationale for teamwork, some of the main advantages of doing family therapy as a team, but the benefits of multiple therapists are well known in a variety of therapeutic contexts. There are numerous papers that underscore similar viewpoints. However, in reviewing the literature on this subject, we were surprised to see that not too much mention had been made previously about the mutability of the dynamics involved in teamwork relationships. This was the purpose of the second part of our paper. The therapist who becomes aware of all the advantages, but does not bear in mind other aspects involved, may attempt to practice teamwork but find himself confronted with a series of discouraging problems. We therefore decided to include in this paper some of our own experiences and observations, and some suggestions about how to cope with the difficulties involved.

We feel that teamwork offers a very strong avenue of approach to many problems of psychotherapy, especially in family therapy. It is only through honesty in describing, examining, and analyzing our own experiences in the most objective way possible, that we can make use of co-therapy's fullest power. We do not intend to discourage the beginner by highlighting all the roadblocks. Nor is it our intention to "double-bind" him by offering first all the advantages and then discouraging him with all the difficulties. Co-therapy is a relatively new approach and its potential has not yet been explored. We feel that with some families, and in certain therapeutic situations, it is the best way we know of handling problems and bringing about change. We acknowledge those therapists who do not feel enthusiastic about it and who prefer to continue as single therapists. We agree with them that there are many ways of skinning a cat. We do feel that, once the team members become aware of the difficulties they are encountering in their relationship, and once they have the courage of working it through between themselves, benefits accrue in therapeutic work with the family. In our view, a "mature" team is much stronger and can bring out more change in the family process than can a single therapist.

On the other hand, we recognize that the kinds of dynamics referred to in this paper are ones we have observed in our own team-work. We have observed similar phenomena while supervising trainees in teamwork, either as co-therapists of one of us, or as team members were observing or supervising. We do not agree, though, that the dynamics described here are common to all teams who work as co-therapists. We assume that many teams would not encounter the difficulties or dynamics we describe here, probably for several reasons. One possibility is that some teams work at a more superficial level, and therefore have no need for deep exploration of the family dynamics or of the team's process. Another possibility is that the goals that the therapists set in family therapy may be completely different from the ones we work toward (Boszormenyi-Nagy, 1965). There are some therapists who aim toward improvement of patterns of communication within the family system; there are other therapists who conduct a brief but intensive exploration of the family dynamics, offering the family concrete suggestions about how to solve their immediate problems. We can understand that in such cases a team process does not have a chance to develop, because the type of work does not require it. In our experience, where family treatment goes on for a prolonged time and where deep exploration and meaningful changes in the family process are our goals, the team process becomes a critical ingredient in the entire therapy process.

Smoothly working co-therapy is not an easy thing to achieve. As we see it, to reach its greatest effectiveness, a certain process has to take place between the team members: various aspects of individual and interpersonal dynamics have to be taken into account. Our main purpose in stressing this point is an educational one; it is especially intended for and addressed to those interested in starting co-therapy teamwork. Quite often we have observed trainees getting together and announcing that they have formed a team "to treat a family." Our reaction includes statements of caution and encouragement. Co-therapy is a magnificent device for teaching and for mutual training, but it should not be taken lightly. The trainee should become aware of the difficulties involved and make provisions for working them through either with his instructor, his supervisor, or his co-therapist. The gratifications and learning experiences to be expected from co-therapy work with families are worth the effort involved in understanding and solving the implied difficulties.

SUMMARY

This paper attempts to describe the dynamics of co-therapy in family psychotherapy as experienced through our work at the Eastern Pennsylvania Psychiatric Institute. The setting is described in detail, and some of the major advantages in using co-therapy are listed and analyzed. Some of the recognized advantages of teamwork described in this paper are: the clarification of transference relationships, the sharing of responsibilities, the recreation of a model for a healthier relationship, and the mutual learning from the mutual monitoring of thoughts and feelings.

We stress some of the transactional dynamics that may pose difficulties for teamwork, and we suggest ways of attempting to solve them. "Splitting" and dissociation of the team, competitiveness between team members, transference phenomena within the team, and scapegoating experiences are some of the difficulties of teamwork dealt with in this paper.

We feel that co-therapy offers a challenging and promising therapeutic approach that has not been fully explored. A trainee who attempts co-therapy should bear in mind the important transactional experiences he is encountering, which may have an influence on the outcome of the therapeutic effort.

REFERENCES

Adler, A. The education of children (translated by E. & F. Jensen). New York: Greenberg Publishers, 1930.

Adler, J., & Berman, I. R. Multiple leadership in group treatment of delinquent adolescents. Int. J. Gr. Psychother., 1960, 10, 213-226.

Boszormenyi-Nagy, I. Intensive family therapy as process. In I. Boszormenyi-Nagy & J. Framo (Eds.), Intensive family therapy: theoretical and practical aspects. New York: Harper and Row, 1965. Pp. 87-142.

Demarest, E. W., & Teicher, A. Transference in group therapy: its use by co-therapists of opposite sexes. Psychiatry, 1954, 17, 187-202.

Dreikurs, R. Techniques and dynamics of multiple psychotherapy. Psychiat. Quart., 1950, 24, 788-799.

Dreikurs, R., et al. Patient-therapist relationship in multiple psychotherapy. I. Its advantages to the therapist. Psychiat. Quart., 1952, 26, 219-227.

Dreikurs, R., et al. Patient-therapist relationship in multiple psychotherapy. II. Its advantages for the patient. Psychiat. Quart., 1952, 26, 590-596.

Framo, J. L. The theory of the technique of family treatment of schizophrenia. Fam. Proc., 1962, 1, 119-131.

Framo, J. L. Rationale and techniques of intensive family therapy. In I. Boszormenyi-Nagy & J. Framo (Eds.), Intensive family therapy: theoretical and practical aspects. New York: Harper and Row, 1965. Pp. 143-212.

Gans, R. W. Group co-therapists and the therapeutic situation: a critical evaluation. Int. J. Gr. Psychother., 1962, 12, 82-88.

Hadden, S. B. The utilization of a therapy group in teaching psychotherapy. Amer. J. Psychiat., 1947, 103, 644-648.

Hayward, M. L., et al. Some values of the use of multiple therapists in the treatment of the psychoses. Psychiat. Quart., 1952, 26, 244-249.

Klapman, J. W., & Meyer, Ruth E. The team approach in group psychotherapy. Dis. nerv. Syst., 1957, 18, 95-99.

Kassoff, A. I. Advantages of multiple therapists in a group of severely acting-out adolescent boys. Int. J. Gr. Psychother., 1958, 8, 70-75.

Lundin, W. H., & Aronov, B. M. The use of co-therapists in group psychotherapy. J. cons. Psychol., 1952, 16, 76-80.

Mintz, Elizabeth E. Special values of co-therapists in group psychotherapy. Int. J. Gr. Psychother., 1963, 13, 127-132.

Mintz, Elizabeth E. Transference in co-therapy groups. J. consult. Psychol., 1963, 27, 34-39.

Mullen, H., & Sanguiliano, Iris. Multiple psychotherapeutic practice: preliminary report. Amer. J. Psychother., 1960, 14, 550-565.

Reeve, G. H. Trends in therapy. V. A method of coordinated treatment. Amer. J. Orthopsychiat., 1939, 9, 743-747.

Rubinstein, D. Family therapy. Int. Psychiat. Clin., 1964, 1 (2), 431-442.

Sonne, J. C., & Lincoln, Geraldine. Heterosexual co-therapy team experiences during family therapy. Fam. Proc., 1965, 4, 177-197.

Whitaker, C., et al. The psychotherapeutic impasse. Amer. J. Orthopsychiat., 1950, 20, 641-647.

THE ORIGIN OF ADOLESCENT DISTURBANCES IN THE FAMILY:
Some Considerations in Theory and Implications for Therapy[1]

Roger L. Shapiro, M.D.

Contemporary personality theory of adolescence looks both to determinants in the current experience of the adolescent and to determinants in his developmental experience to understand adolescent disturbance (Shapiro, 1963). The study of the current family relations of the adolescent helps to identify the nature of these determinants. It provides data about current highly important object relationships of the adolescent and their roles in inhibiting or distorting phase-appropriate development. It also provides a basis for inference about what the quality of these relationships was in the infantile period and during childhood, making possible a more discriminating and reliable formulation of the genetic determinants of the disturbance than could be obtained from history alone.

The formulation of the importance of current family relations to the personality development of the adolescent comes from considerations regarding the drive and ego epigenesis of that developmental phase and the altered relation to reality that this epigenesis makes possible.

Consideration of the drive epigenesis of puberty centers around the transition from a pregenital to a genital drive organization and the altered relation to libidinal objects demanded by this transition. Anna Freud (1958) has pointed out that the relationship to the parents is in the center of these alterations, with drive development reviving old patterns of oedipal anxiety and stimulating defenses that have a new characteristic. This is the predominance of defenses against the existence of the oedipal objects themselves and the attempt at solution of this problem by the finding of new objects. Pathological outcome in adolescence is regularly associated with difficulty in the al-

[1] This paper comes from work done in association with Carmen Cabrera, M.A., Alan Lazerson, M.D., Alma Steinberg, B.S., Irvin Taube, M.D., and Wolfgang Weigert. M.D.

teration of object relations which the drive development demands. Withdrawal of libidinal investment from parents and reinvestment of libido in new objects is one of the complex tasks of adolescence, a task that has many vicissitudes and much potentiality for pathological outcome. The characteristics of the parent-adolescent relationship in cases of pathological outcome provide data of great relevance for an understanding of the libidinal meaning of the parents to the adolescent and the structure of the libidinal problem in the adolescent.

Consideration of the ego epigenesis of puberty derives from formulations of Inhelder and Piaget (1958) regarding new cognitive capacities in the sphere of logical thinking that develop in early adolescence, and from formulations of Hartmann (1950) and Jacobson (1961) regarding the increasing ego autonomy that characterizes this phase. I have suggested in a recent paper (Shapiro, 1963) that the consistent finding of a change in the nature of abstract thought in early adolescence, with the development of hypothesis formation and the utilization of hypothetico-deductive reasoning and experimental proof, justifies the assumption that autonomous ego development occurs in this phase. This assumption defines the basis in ego epigenesis for the observations of personality growth conceptualized by Jacobson (1961) as remodeling of psychic structure and increasing secondary autonomy of the ego, and by Erikson (1956) as the establishment of the sense of ego identity. These new capacities are another foundation of the alteration in the nature of the adolescent's relationship to his parents specifically, and in his object relations generally. Pathological outcome in adolescence has, as another determinant, relationship characteristics within the family that work against the evolving capacity for autonomous functioning in the ego of the adolescent and may draw this capacity into conflict. The new order of abstract thinking in the adolescent allows him a new freedom in the conceptualization of himself in relation to his parents and to society. It provides the adolescent with a new potentiality for assessing the positions taken by his parents, and relating these to the rest of what he sees in reality. It provides him with a new basis for differentiating himself from his parents and aligning himself with new objects and institutions. Parental reaction to this new potentiality in the adolescent has great effect upon the nature of the development of ego autonomy in the adolescent. Parent-adolescent interaction over issues of autonomy then becomes another phase-specific area which may illuminate some aspects of disturbances of adolescence.

Formulation of the altered relation to reality, made possible by the drive and the ego epigenesis of puberty, has derived from conceptualizations of Erik Erikson (1950, 1956, 1958) relating to the

establishment of ego identity as the psychosocial crisis of adolescence. The relation of the adolescent's concept of himself to the concept of him implicit in the behavior of meaningful others towards
him constitutes the essential experience from which ego identity
grows. This relation of self definition to social definition is the essence of the core of identity of the individual in every psychosocial
phase. However, identity consolidation becomes an ascendent task
of the ego in adolescence, and arises from the new drive and ego capacities of this developmental phase. The altered self definition demanded by the drive development of puberty, coupled with the new
conceptual capacities of the ego, allows the adolescent to integrate
complex internal changes with a changing social recognition of his
growth. At the same time, the adolescent's ability to conceptualize
external reality is altering. His new capacities in the realm of logical thinking, and his abilities for hypothesis formation and generalization, allow him a new perspective of his family, of society, of the
past and of the future, as well as a new view of himself in the context of this perspective. The psychosocial task of adolescence—the
establishment of ego identity—is incomplete and lacking in integration
in cases of pathological outcome conceptualized by Erikson as cases
of identity diffusion. The relevance of parent-adolescent interaction
to identity diffusion and of parental delineation of the adolescent to
the adolescent self-definition is a central issue in the diffusion of
identity of the adolescent. The relationships within the family then
become psychosocial events contributing to identity consolidation or
diffusion, and these events can be observed with the hypothesis that
they constitute important determinants of adolescent disturbance.

Studies of the family relations of adolescents have been conducted
by various research groups, with some differences in methodology.
I shall presently discuss the research of my group at the National
Institute of Mental Health, in which attention has been directed to
behavior within the family, and where the disturbed adolescent and
his parents are observed in interaction. In other family studies,
the adolescent and one or both parents have generally been studied
and treated individually, and the interrelations between parental personality disorders and adolescent personality disorders formulated
from the material of the individual therapy. This was true of the
Johnson-Szurek (1942, 1956) group at the Institute for Juvenile Research in Chicago in the 1930's and 1940's (see the papers by Johnson, 1949, and by Szurek et al., 1942). This group arrived at the
important formulation that parents may find gratification of their
own poorly integrated, forbidden impulses in the acting-out of the
adolescent through their conscious, or more often unconscious, per-
missiveness or inconsistency toward the adolescent in these spheres

of behavior. Their study of antisocial adolescents was done through collaboration of the therapists doing individual psychoanalytic psychotherapy with the adolescent and the parent most involved in the acting-out.

The current research project on adolescence of the Hampstead Child-Therapy Clinic goes beyond the emphasis on the antisocial adolescent and employs the technique of simultaneous analysis of adolescents and their mothers to highlight, in a variety of cases, the points of interaction between the abnormalities of mother and child. In a discussion of this research, Anna Freud (1960) emphasizes the importance of replacing the vague generalization derived from child guidance work to the effect that most mental disturbances of children can be traced back to the disturbances of their parents, by precise analytic findings that detail the complexities of the influence of the mother's actions, her manifest attitude, and her conscious and unconscious fantasies—influences that are neither straightforward nor uniform. Anna Freud makes the observation that the disturbances of the children can be similar to those of the mother or can be of a completely different nature. They may or may not show the characteristic consequences of identification, of the overlapping of fantasy activity, or of folie a deux phenomena that characterize the cases from the Hampstead series reported by Burlingham (1955), Hellman (1960), and Levy (1960). The children may show indirect consequences of an illness in the mother that interferes with her capacity for effective mothering, rather than direct reactions to the mother's symptoms. Anna Freud goes on to state that the understanding of the interaction between parents and their children is of the highest importance, and not only where the first foundations of the personality or the roots of mental illness are concerned. As the child moves forward on the developmental scale, each step demands the giving up of former positions and gains, not only from the child himself but also from the parent. She states that it is only in the most healthy and normal cases that both sides—parents and child—wholly welcome the progressive move and enjoy the child's increasing maturity and gradually increasing libidinal and moral independence. More often, it is one or the other partner who lags behind, the child being unable to free himself from fixations or the parent clinging to attitudes of protectiveness or mothering that have become unjustified. In the worst cases, mother and child may join forces in a regressive move. Such interlocking, she states, becomes particularly fateful with the onset of puberty. Here the simultaneous analyses of mothers and their children have proved helpful in specifying the various manners in which individual adolescents strive to free themselves from the infantile object ties to their parents. Finally, Anna

Freud makes the important observation that no more than a dim impression of the parent's responses is received in those cases where the adolescent alone is in treatment; however, simultaneous analyses make it possible to trace the contribution made by both sides to the sources of failure of this particular developmental task.

My group at the National Institute of Mental Health, working from these considerations in theory, has added two aspects to the study of the family of the disturbed adolescent. First, we have required the participation of both parents and any adolescent siblings in our study, thus providing the possibility for evaluation of the contribution of each family member to the personality difficulties of any other. Second, we have made regular and systematic observations of the family group in interaction, as well as making assessments of the individual psychology of the parents and the adolescent, and considering the interrelationship of the individual psychological systems.

We have studied a series of 25 late adolescents (between the ages of 17 and 19) and their families. These are cases in which the adolescent has had a severe emotional disturbance as a result of his first prolonged separation from his parents in the first year of residence at a university, which has resulted in his being required to withdraw from school. The adolescents have had a variety of diagnoses, from acute psychoses to borderline states, with severe symptom neuroses and character disorders of the acting-out or inhibited varieties. In all of these cases, we have combined individual two- or three-hour weekly psychotherapy sessions with the adolescents with weekly sessions for the parents as a marital couple and weekly family group therapy.

Our research focus has been on the family group sessions. Our method makes it possible to directly observe behavior within the family group which contains in action the expression of the individual psychodynamics of the family members. This allows a new order of specification and documentation of the psychological operations of the parents with the adolescent. These behaviors can be detailed, and their impact directly assessed. Instead of stopping at a formulation of the intrapsychic organization of the parents and the adolescent, with hypotheses about how the one affects the other, we are able to go a step further and to observe these systems in interaction. This allows us to formulate, from observations of actual behavior, mechanisms that have been derived in other ways in other personality development research. It enables us to make a series of precise observations about the manner in which specific intrapsychic organization is expressed in behavior within a particular family group.

In our study of adolescent personality development, we are attempting to clarify the impact of characteristic parental behavior with the adolescent upon adolescent personality formation. We organize our observations of behavior through the use of the concept of delineation, which I shall presently define. A central hypothesis of our study has been that there is a significant relationship between parental delineation of the adolescent and adolescent identity formation. Our hypothesis further states that in families where there is serious psychological disturbance in the adolescent, there will be evidence of striking distortions, inconsistencies, and contradictions in parental delineation of the adolescent. Our study of the parent-adolescent relationship includes questions about the kinds of parents who are particularly vulnerable to various manifestations of adolescent development, the manner in which these vulnerabilities are expressed—and here we use the language of delineation—and the effects of these modes of parental behavior on the personality functioning of the adolescent.

By "delineation," we mean the view or image one person has of the other person, as revealed explicitly or implicitly in the behavior of the one person with the other person. In the language of ego psychology, it is behavior that contains the expression of an object representation and the ego organization mobilized in relation to this object representation. Various ego functions are mobilized in relation to object representation and behavior with an object. For example, the characteristics of autonomous ego functioning or state of ego regression effect the behavior of delineation. A highly important subgroup of delineations consists of those we call defensive delineations. When behavior of an individual with an object contains evidence of distortion of the object related to the individual's defensive organization, then defensive delineation exists. The concept of defensive delineation thus represents an integration of two structural concepts in ego psychology. It includes behavioral referents both of the concept of object representation and of defensive organization. Defensive delineation is a conceptualization of those situations in which defense alters the behavioral referents of object representation. It is a response to the behavior of the other person that stimulates anxiety in the one person and gives rise to defensive operations, which are revealed in the nature and style of his delineation of the other person.

The concept of delineation provides a bridge between the intrapsychic and the interpersonal spheres, with similarities to that bridge provided by the theory of transference in the conceptualization of the psychoanalytic relationship. Transference is a conceptualization of the effect of earlier object relationships and related defensive organization upon a current regressive object relationship. This effect is manifested in characteristic idiosyncratic distortions of behavior in the current object relationship. This is also the way we conceptualize the structure of defensive delineation.

We employ the following method in the analysis of family interaction for delineation. We isolate excerpts of interaction during family sessions that are characteristic of the parent-adolescent relationships. In the analysis of these samples we ask the following questions:

1. What is the situation in reality in which these interactions occur? What is the nature of the actual events and issues with which the family members are dealing? What is the adolescent's behavior in the reality context under discussion?

2. What delineations of the adolescent by each parent can be inferred from this particular interaction?

3. Is there an apparent distortion in the parent's view of the adolescent? This may be a clear and obvious disjunction between the view of the adolescent expressed by the parent and that seen by the observer. It may become evident only when the delineation is viewed in the context of a particular reality situation and of the specific behavior in reality of the adolescent. It may become evident from contradiction or bias expressed in delineation. The parent's inappropriate, biased, exaggerated, or idiosyncratic view of the adolescent can be defined by an observer. If the delineations contain evidence of distortion, then the inference of defensive delineation is made.

4. What hypotheses about the determinants and structure of defensive delineations can be formulated? These inferences are made clinically from the material of the family session. They are compared to formulations from research interviews and psychological tests of the parents, which define areas of conflict and need as well as organization of defenses. If there is good correspondence between the dynamics of defensive delineation and evidence from the individual assessment about individual psychodynamics, then we can assume that the delineation is a manifestation of relatively enduring parental character structure. This supports the argument that defensive delineation is not simply a reflection of the adolescent's actual characteristics but represents an expression of the parent's needs and defensive organization. These lead to characteristic emphases and distortions of delineations of the adolescent.

Our use of the concept of delineation will be clarified by two examples of interaction from one of our family groups. This is the family of a deeply anxious and inhibited, highly narcissistic, passively aggressive boy of 19 with symptoms of depression, exhibitionism, and school failure. The first excerpt, taken from a family session that occurred about six months after treatment began, indicates an aspect of the father's delineation of the adolescent.

ISSUES AND EVENTS (EXCERPT 1)

This family session was conducted just before David was to resume a full academic program, having successfully completed a part-time academic program during the summer. He is to leave the hospital to live in the college dormitory but will continue in therapy as an outpatient. In the previous family session David had, in a provocative way, expressed ambivalence about leaving the hospital and returning to school.

EXCERPT 1:

Father: Do you like school or you don't like school? Do you like to go now to school?

Mother: You ended last session by saying you don't know if you really want to go to school.

Father: You have to make up your mind and it's not just . . .

David: But it's not school that's the issue, the way I see it. It's my negative way of doing anything—like going to camp—if you have to force me to go to camp then obviously you have to force me to work, you have to force me to play, you have to force me to eat; you have to force me to do anything.

Father: You see, if I give you this food in the basket—then I better not give you—the cleaning up afterwards.

David: So you do it yourself.

Father: So if you want to go to school and not to make the grade and not to study, better not start it.

David: I remember I did that in the kitchen and Sarah would say: "If you are that hungry, make something yourself instead of always coming and begging for a sandwich or something." So I would make a mess of the kitchen and between the two of you, you would just realize somebody's got to take care of the poor kid or else he'll starve to death.

Father: You lost a year, your whole year now was a big struggle.
This summer I was against your study and according to the doctors,
you were okay. Now I am again questioning, I am questioning although
you have a dormitory and have a schedule again, like with the German, I think he is not qualified to study. If he can come up with remarks like this after he did well during the summer, in German,
and that a dry subject completely, just words—it is something—and
I'm questioning now, not because I want to bring out all this negative
that you should fight me, but I am really thinking that maybe you are
not qualified to go to college.

David: Well, I don't know . . .

Father (interrupting): It seems to me, Doctor . . .

David (interrupting): It seems to me this is an example . . .

Father: If he could at the last minute turn over the whole—you know
the cow what gives beautiful, the whole time, good milk and then the
last minute she turns it over, the whole business—the pail—so the
same thing is with David. After we talked, and after we paid in, and
after everything is prepared, then he just says maybe he doesn't want
it, so—so now I am questioning that he needs it altogether.

DELINEATIONS OF DAVID BY THE FATHER (EXCERPT 1)

1. David can't decide whether he does or does not want to return
to school.
2. David is unwilling to exert effort and unable to persevere if
any demand is made on him.
3. David is prone to start things and not to finish them, and
should not start school if he isn't going to make the grade.
4. David is lazy and likely to spoil whatever he attempts, and
after a big struggle lost an entire year in school.
5. David was not ready to go to summer school, although the
doctors said he was ready. Now he again is not ready.
6. David did well during the summer, but if he can come up
with doubts now about school after succeeding, he is not qualified
for college.
7. David is like the cow that gives beautiful milk and then kicks
over the pail. He promises to produce and to give and then he frus-
trates and destroys.

APPARENT DISTORTIONS SUGGESTING DEFENSIVE DELINEATION (EXCERPT 1)

1. The father's pessimism about David's capacity to succeed seems exaggerated in light of his recent success in summer school.

2. The father seems to be reacting with great anxiety to David's provocative expression of ambivalence about returning to school. This reaction seems excessive. The imagery of milk produced by David to feed his father and the expectation that David will kick over the pail to frustrate his father implies a great need on the part of the father to be fed by David's success. His anger at David for chronically frustrating him is evident in this interaction.

3. Contradictory delineations with regard to success are seen, in this interaction, in the predominance of delineations that ignore the success of the summer and define David as not qualified for college.

4. The imagery of the cow and the milk implies a feminine definition of David.

HYPOTHESES ABOUT THE DETERMINANTS AND STRUCTURE OF DEFENSIVE DELINEATION (EXCERPT 1)

1. The father seems to have both a great wish to be fed by his son's success and great apprehension that his son will not nurture him with success but will frustrate him by his failure. The hypersensitivity to frustration by his son suggests that the father's need to be gratified by him is great, and implies an inordinate degree of dependency on the part of the father as well as great anxiety when his sources of dependent gratification are threatened.

2. The father is clearly ambivalent about his son's success of the summer. This may be determined by competitive feeling toward the son, which may also result in his feminine definition of him.

3. The father may see David's departure from the protection of the hospital as an event that will lead to David's making increased demands upon him.

Projective tests and research interviews with the father provide detailed substantiation and further elaboration of the dynamics of defensive delineations inferred from these interactions.

Another excerpt will illustrate an aspect of the mother's delineation of the adolescent. It is taken from a family group session that occurred about a year after the beginning of family therapy.

ISSUES AND EVENTS (EXCERPT 2)

In the previous family session, one co-therapist (the adolescent's individual therapist) had announced that he would be leaving NIMH in four months. During the evening after that family session, David had been at home, had been depressed, and had made statements to the effect that life was meaningless and the whole world should be destroyed. Two days after that, while driving family members home from the airport, David abruptly changed lanes and entered the right of way of another car, angering the driver.

EXCERPT 2

Mother: Last week at home he came up with a glorious statement of, uh—that the whole world should be destroyed. Uh, he had made this remark—I could think that maybe it had to do with Dr. Crown's leaving; that maybe he's not all well; that he's still sick and needs attention. But he made such a remark about a year ago. And I didn't like it then, but I just thought he was being very flippant and smart.

David: So, so, so!

Mother: But this last week when he mentioned it, it did upset me.

David: Did it really! You didn't seem very upset then. You must have, uh, gotten upset since then. At the time, both you and Daddy thought it very amusing (brief laugh). And Daddy was ready to send me off to, uh . . .

Mother: Amusing? And Daddy thought it was so amusing he was ready to send you off to St. Elizabeth's?

David: But you certainly weren't upset. I mean, I . . .

Mother: Okay. We try to rationalize such talk, and so on, and not to get into a huff and a puff. But the fact still remains.

Therapist: That's a rather characteristic David-sort-of response, though, it seems to me—when your mother brings up an issue of something that's going on in the group, you often minimize it or say that you don't feel it's important or worth discussing or . . .

David: Well, I . . .

Mother: Well, I think a person has a right to differ.

Therapist: Yes—we get a lot of that.

Mother: But—this is so different (slight pause) that it just sounds too destructive—to let it go.

Therapist: This is so different? You mean David's attitude on Sunday?

Mother: Yeah!

David: Actually, it was on Friday evening.

Mother: Well, whenever it was. It probably was Friday because Sunday, when you went to the airport I was worried about just how they would get back.

Father: Hmmm.

Mother (tearfully): And haven't mentioned it—I was worried about them. And the fact that he cut across and there could have been an accident. . . (David snickers). The idea is, "What is life—we all die, and so what? Sooner or later. Might as well push the button and all go together." So I think he made it clear then that if he really has feelings . . . If he feels that way, I can't change him.

David: I've been making remarks like that for years. I mean, how . . . ?

Father: I have my . . . (voice becomes inaudible).

Mother: Well, I'm not finished yet.

David: That's the way I think. Okay.

Mother: I think—I don't know, I may be wrong—I'm just gonna make up a—theory. I think—that maybe possibly, I think everyone fears death to a degree (David laughs); I'm inclined to think that David fears death. I think we have apprehension all over the world—I mean, it's just such an age. And I think especially the youngsters. So why don't we just push the button and get rid of it! But I don't see why— why he should think of pushing the button—in such terms. When the button will be pushed, then you'll be eliminated. We'll be eliminated.

Fine. All right? (David mumbles, "Yes, yes.") Then I'm not so
sure how easily we're eliminated. Plenty remain sick, maimed for
the rest of their lives. (David interjects, "Well...") They just
don't die conveniently for you. Uh—(slight pause, then sighs) I
think he's so afraid of death that he's afraid to live. That's what I
think. And would like everyone else to go with him. Now: this again
may have no connection with my father, but I want to register it for
what it's worth. My father at one time was thinking of committing
suicide. And wanted my mother to go with him. And she didn't
want to go.

DELINEATIONS OF DAVID BY THE MOTHER (EXCERPT 2)

    1. David is potentially explosively destructive.
    2. David is prone to act sick and disturbed to enlist the parents'
care and gain their sympathy.
    3. David requires care and becomes irresponsible and destruc-
tive when he is denied care.
    4. David's destructiveness is threatening and upsetting to his
mother.
    5. David is only being flippant and smart with his threats of
world destruction.
    6. David's instability and poor control warrant sending him to
a mental hospital.
    7. David has a right to differ with his mother unless the differ-
ence is too different and too destructive to let it go.
    8. David is so destructive he almost destroyed his family in an
automobile accident.
    9. David is depressed and potentially self-destructive.
    10. David is despondent and his mother can't change him.
    11. David is too fearful and inhibited to take any action in life
(so afraid of death he's afraid to live).
    12. David intends to eliminate himself and everyone, but plenty
remain sick, maimed for the rest of their lives, and don't die conveniently for him.
    13. David is like her father, who at one time wanted to commit
suicide and take her mother with him.

APPARENT DISTORTIONS SUGGESTING DEFENSIVE
DELINEATION (EXCERPT 2)

    1. The mother's striking and persistent definition of David as
dangerously and unpredictably destructive and self-destructive in

much of this excerpt does not seem warranted by his actual behavior in the events discussed.

2. An alternative quality of delineation of David as manipulative, flippant, pretending to be disturbed, and too fearful and inhibited to take any action in life provides a confusing and contradictory theme of attributions of impotence in counterpoint to the theme of destructiveness throughout this excerpt.

HYPOTHESES ABOUT THE DETERMINANTS AND STRUCTURE OF DEFENSIVE DELINEATIONS (EXCERPT 2)

1. A marked inconsistency is seen between the predominant, apparently exaggerated definition of the adolescent as destructive and self-destructive, and a definition of him as weak, manipulative, and too fearful to act. This suggests a marked ambivalence in the mother about aggression in her son.

2. The apparent exaggeration in the view of her son as aggressive and as anxious seems to result from the mother's tendency to project her own aggression and anxiety onto him.

3. The delineation of her son as destructive and self-destructive is also the consequence of the mother's tendency to project aspects of her depressed father onto her son and to attribute to her son the suicidal actions her father carried out in reality.

Without going into more detail, evaluation of the mother through research interviews and projective tests provided substantiating evidence of a characteristic tendency to project; of readily mobilizable anger, depression, and anxiety; and of great vulnerability to the anger, depression, and anxiety of others.

DISCUSSION

These examples suggest the nature of the view obtained in the family group sessions of the manner in which the parents delineate the adolescent. In families where severe disturbance exists in the adolescent, we have repeatedly seen evidence of anxiety in the parents over the adolescent's expression of his new developmental potentialities. Two areas of adolescent maturation repeatedly give rise to defensive and contradictory parental delineations of the adolescents in our series. These are the new potentiality for individuation and separation from the parents, determined in part by the cognitive development of the adolescent, and the manifestations and new expressions of the adolescent's libidinal development. These general findings are not surprising in themselves. What is of great interest, however, is the detailed study of pattern and styles of parental response to evidence of maturation in the adolescent, the relation of characteristic delineation to defensive need in the parent, and its relation to particular dimensions of disturbance in the adolescent. In our series we find a range of parental behavior. On the one hand there may be evidence of defensive delineation in a particular area, such as sexuality, reflecting a specific parental personality difficulty over adolescent development in that area, with nondefensive and phase-appropriate definition of the adolescent in other areas of functioning. The impact of parental defensive delineations upon the adolescent's functioning can be inferred both from the area of difficulty the adolescent presents and from his defensive style in the management of anxiety. These are cases which would be diagnosed as severe neuroses, where there is no evidence of thought disorder or generalized ego defect but where the disturbance is circumscribed and dealt with in a characteristic way, and where this can be related to circumscribed difficulty in the parent. At the other end of the continuum are families such as those described by Wynne and Singer (1963) at the National Institute of Mental Health, where erratic and autistic parental delineations of the adolescent are a reflection of pervasive thought disorder and an autistic interpretation of reality in the parents. Here the adolescents themselves frequently manifest borderline or psychotic disturbances apparently related to the thought disorder of the parents.

I should like finally to discuss the family group session as a therapeutic instrument which we believe to have a phase-specific usefulness in the treatment of middle and late adolescents. We use the concept of delineation both to organize our understanding of the situation and as an important focus for interpretation.

In our therapeutic design, the weekly parent-adolescent group session supplements two or three hours per week of individual psychotherapy for the adolescent. In our program, the individual therapist of the adolescent is also one of the therapists of the family group. The psychiatric social worker is co-therapist of the family group session, and she also sees the parents as a marital couple in a weekly session outside of the family session.

This structured encounter between adolescents and parents is a highly useful situation in which to clarify and interpret the interrelation between characteristic parental delineation of the adolescent and disturbance in the adolescent. This situation enlists and utilizes the new capacities of the adolescent in the conceptual sphere—the new psychological potentialities for abstraction that bring him for the first time within the range of his parents' level of psychological functioning. The family group session is an excellent situation in which to establish the actuality (Erikson, 1962) of the adolescent's maturation and the idiosyncratic and defensive aspects of the parents' response to it.

In the family session as we utilize it, the therapist orients himself toward the observation of interactions between the parents and the adolescent which illuminate the concept or image each has of the other. In our terminology, he focuses particularly upon the delineations of the adolescent implicit in the behavior of the parents with the adolescent. This is the data upon which the therapist bases his comments. His interpretations are conceptualizations of the evidence about distortions of delineation determined by parental defense and parental need. By making explicit those attitudes of parents toward the adolescent which have been implicit and often unconscious, these interpretations lead to the gradual illumination of various dimensions of relationship of which the participants have been unaware, or about which they have been unclear. The conceptual abilities of the adolescent are enlisted in examining the nature of his parents' image of him and the ways in which this has defined and limited him. His conceptual capacities are also directed toward self-reflection and toward an examination of his behavior toward his parents and the ways in which this provokes particular directions of response in them.

By interpreting evidence of defensive delineation, we are intervening in a way that has many structural parallels to the basis of transference interpretation in individual therapy. We are commenting on the idiosyncratic nature of a relationship in which the patient and the parents become involved and which is a reflection of the view or image each has of the other. The similarity in the two situations is in the focus of both on idiosyncratic behavior that reflects distortions of attitude in relationship, and is identified and called into question by being isolated for comment. In the family group, the behavior is an aspect of the actual relationships being studied, containing attributions determined by internal need of one member about the other member. In individual therapy, the behavior interpreted reflects attributions on the part of the patient towards his therapist, which in turn reflect indirectly the internal images of the parents or other transference figures.

Interpretation of defensive delineation leads to an implicit question about the determinants of distortion. The asking of such a question implies the existence of alternative possibilities of attitude and feeling in the parent. It calls into question the consequences of the parental delineation for the personality functioning of the adolescent. This is a step toward the adolescent's achieving the freedom to explore other possibilities of behavior free of the parents' constricting view of him. The capacity of the adolescent to conceptualize and to abstract is capitalized upon in this process. The conceptual clarity of the therapists in formulating the implications of behavioral interaction between the patient and his parents provides evidence utilized by the adolescent for a new understanding of himself. The family session then becomes an arena for new action of the adolescent in relation to his parents. Correspondingly, the parents are able to understand implications for the adolescent of their behavior and feeling in relation to him. They are able to recognize the elements in their reaction to the adolescent determined by their individual vulnerabilities, although perhaps aggravated by specific aspects of the adolescent's behavior toward them. As this recognition proceeds, the parents, too, are able to experiment with new possibilities of feeling and response, which grow out of a new clarity about the determinants and implications of their characteristic behavior, and can mobilize their capacity for change within the setting of therapy.

What I am describing is obviously a complex process. A parent-adolescent relationship that has given rise to pathological outcome is invariably resistant to change. The resistance to change is seen clearly in stereotyped dimensions of behavior in the family group session, and where it is perceived it is interpreted. This interpretation has as its ally the new developmental capacities of the adolescent and what ability the parents have for reflection, experimentation, and change. The neutrality and conceptual clarity of the therapists support the family members in this effort and provide a model for it. The individual therapy of the adolescent and the therapy of the parents with the social worker further explore the genetics and implications of these resistances and facilitate new dimensions of freedom in the adolescent and the parents, as well as new dimensions of behavior in the family group session. The presence in the session of the therapists supports these directions of new response in both the adolescent and the parents, which then can be continued and built upon in other contacts and in other places.

This effort to define and alter defensive delineation of adolescent by parents and of parents by adolescent is given specific impetus in the family session and is the focus of therapeutic attention in these sessions. Marked shifts in the quality of the adolescent-parent relationship are a characteristic of this developmental phase. This technique of therapy derives its effectiveness from its capacity to mobilize the energies and capacities that accomplish these shifts and characterize this phase. The family session is a setting which can catalyze a developmental trend for both adolescent and parents by focusing on interactions that represent resistances to this trend. It is an aspect of the adolescent's actuality, where new action with figures of great emotional relevance can begin new directions of development.

REFERENCES

Burlingham, Dorothy. Simultaneous analysis of mother and child. Psychoanal. Stud. Child, 1955, 10, 165-186.

Erikson, E. H. Childhood and society. New York: Norton, 1950.

Erikson, E. H. The problem of ego identity. J. Amer. psychoanal. Ass., 1956, 4, 56-121.

Erikson, E. H. Young man Luther; a study in psychoanalysis and history. New York: Norton, 1958.

Erikson, E. H. Reality and actuality. J. Amer. psychoanal. Ass., 1962, 10, 451-474.

Freud, Anna. Adolescence. Psychoanal. Stud. Child, 1958, 13, 255-278.

Freud, Anna. Introduction to: Levy, Kata. Simultaneous analysis of a mother and her adolescent daughter. Psychoanal. Stud. Child, 1960, 15, 378-380.

Hartmann, H. Comments on the psychoanalytic theory of the ego. Psychoanal. Stud. Child, 1950, 5, 74-96.

Hellman, Ilse. Simultaneous analysis of mother and child. Psychoanal. Stud. Child, 1960, 15, 359-377.

Inhelder, Bärbel, & Piaget, J. The growth of logical thinking from childhood to adolescence; an essay on the construction of formal operational structures. (Translated by A. Parsons & S. Milgram.) New York: Basic Books, 1958.

Jacobson, Edith. Adolescent moods and the remodeling of psychic structures in adolescence. Psychoanal. Stud. Child, 1961, 16. 164-183.

Johnson, Adelaide M. Sanctions for superego lucunae of adolescents. In K. R. Eissler (Ed.), Searchlights on delinquency. New York: Int. Univer. Press, 1949. Pp. 225-245.

Levy, Kata. Simultaneous analysis of a mother and her adolescent daughter: the mother's contribution to the loosening of the infantile object tie. Psychoanal. Stud. Child, 1960, 15, 378-391.

Shapiro, R. L. Adolescence and the psychology of the ego. Psychiatry, 1963, 26, 77-87.

Szurek, S., et al. Collaborative psychiatric therapy of parent-child problems. Amer. J. Orthopsychiat., 1942, 12, 511-516.

Wynne, L. C., & Singer, Margaret T. Thought disorder and family relations of schizophrenics: I. A research strategy. II. Classification of forms of thinking. Arch. gen. Psychiat., 1963, 9, 191-206.

THE SECRET AGENDA OF THE THERAPIST DOING COUPLES THERAPY

John Warkentin, M. D. , Ph. D. , and Carl A. Whitaker, M. D.

In his recent book, Bernard Greene (1965) states in the editorial introduction that the <u>methods</u> of therapists differ widely, but that their <u>goals</u> are essentially the same. This statement is in error, as we see it. The goals of therapists are as different as their methods, and their means determine their ending. In this paper we want to emphasize the importance of the therapist's attitudes and his personal assumptions. Let us illustrate briefly:

There are therapists who are genuinely persuaded that they themselves know the way to a good life, and their goal is to help the patient find his way to the same good life as that recognized by the therapist.

There are other therapists who are just as genuinely persuaded that they cannot direct the patient at all in the way that he should go, that they cannot know the goal he should seek, and that the therapist's task is to encourage persistently the patient's search for a way of life that will be consonant with the patient's particular situation, his personal history, and being.

Still other therapists are profoundly convinced that the only good life for the patient is one in which he seeks his own maximum personal growth and development, irrespective of his situation and of the pain he may cause to people around him. This kind of therapist often sees as a clear goal the complete renunciation of all relatives by the patient, or at least of those relatives who are disapproved of by the therapist. But this is in direct opposition to yet other therapists who seek as the ultimate outcome of their therapeutic task the compliant adjustment and accommodation of the patient into the social setting where he happens to find himself.

These few examples make it clear that the therapist's bias and his personal life and values will determine the goals of his particular psychotherapy. This is quite clear in a city like Atlanta, where the two dozen therapists know each other so well that we sometimes recognize each other's patients socially by their manner and speech, since these patients reflect the life philosophy of their particular therapist.

What we have just said means that there is some good common sense in the questioning of prospective patients as to what kind of therapist they should select. Therefore, we therapists need to let ourselves be known, since our own inner values and agenda for the therapeutic task will have such a tremendous influence in the lives of our patients. In private, a respected therapist recently made the extreme statement: "It just doesn't matter what 'school' the therapist belongs to, or what techniques he uses with the patient, or even what words he says; all that matters is his personal being and stature and maturity."

When we began to write down our own personal secret agenda for the therapeutic task with a patient, it sounded so religious that we became quite hopeless of expressing our attitudes directly. We switched to another approach, an effort to describe what we have learned during twenty years of working together as equal co-therapists, much of that time in treating married couples in multiple therapy. The characteristic setting was this: there would be four people in the room or the interview, the married couple, and we two therapists. We spoke of this as a "four-way interview."

Through the years, we often thought out loud together after the patients had left the room. These repeated "autopsies" constituted an expression of our attitudes. The rest of this paper will present a summary of the many post-mortems of interviews, and the comments made during the evenings and Sundays when we thought about them further. They will show some of our own secret agenda, at least by example.

As we reevaluate our experience, we find that our professional attitudes toward the treatment of families in distress are profoundly influenced by the patterns of our own personal living. We see as "healthy" those aspects of marriage that we find pleasing in the experience with our own family. An experience that we do not enjoy in our own family living we call "psychopathologic." Hence we conclude that the personal experience of the therapist extensively determines his work in family therapy.

Our operational assumptions, as we state them below, are the conclusions we have come to as we considered both our personal family experiences and our work with patients. It was particularly in our participation together in multiple therapy, where the "marriage" between us two "parent-therapists" was repeatedly challenged by couples and families, that we formulated several orienting assumptions that we now present. These are as follows:

1. We assume that marital partners have chosen each other with great wisdom—with the wisdom of social propriety, with the wisdom of their bodies, and with the wisdom of their unconscious motives. The exquisite accuracy of marital choice repeatedly amazes us. Even where psychological sickness is present in the choosing, this does not appear to alter the validity of the love or of the marriage itself.

2. We assume that people are good for each other according to the degree that they are intimate together. Marriage is the vehicle and epitome of adult intimacy, established by long-standing custom. It is the one acceptable great arena for experiencing human closeness.

3. We assume that in marriage the whole is greater than the sum of its two parts—that marriage is a whole field of dynamic forces. When we treat a couple in therapy, we speak of the three patients: the husband, the wife, and the marriage. The force or power of the marriage is greater than the algebraic sum—greater than the positive and negative summations of the two people in it.

4. We assume that marriage must become characteristically a sexual relationship or else it becomes a perverse relationship. Dynamic forces in the field of marriage other than sexual forces are secondary. For example, a major age difference between two marital partners, if it becomes the primary axis in the dynamics of the marriage, makes it perverse and sick. However, the marriage can be profoundly satisfying despite a major age difference, if the relationship is characteristically sexually loving.

5. We assume that the feeling relationship between the marital partners is kept continuously balanced, mutual, and reciprocal, both as to type and intensity. As a couple get more and more "married," they seem to agree on a "feeling temperature" which they regulate between them. The emotional thermostat can then be reset only by agreement of both parties; otherwise, if one tries to be "too hot," the other will compensate by being "too cold," thus maintaining a stable overall temperature in the marriage. The feeling flow in a marriage as a whole can be changed only by the participation and support of both partners. (We are aware that the spoken assertions and the behavioral presentation of the two partners may be very different from the underlying feeling tones we are here discussing.)

6. We assume that the usual rules of human social behavior do not apply to marriage, nor to other intimate relationships. For example, fairness is not appropriate. "All is fair in love and war," and marriage is both. Another example: consistency is impossible in feeling relationships. Furthermore, such other considerations

as decency, face-saving, and factual honesty are all of minor significance in marriage.

7. We assume that a normal marriage progresses through a series of impasses as the years go by.[1] For example, when people "fall in love," they experience a bilateral transference relationship with hysterical dynamics in the forefront. The transferences are then gradually exhausted within about ten years, producing an inevitable impasse due to the detumescence of "being in love." At this ten-year point, which we call the "ten-year syndrome," there is likely to be a "civil war" which results in the freeing of both "slaves." If at this ten-year level the partners then find a deeper person-to-person love for each other, they may well live for ten more years before the next impasse arises. This next impasse may develop at about the time they lose their children. However, if they do not resolve their "civil war" at the ten-year level, and just continue living under the same roof, such a continued impasse is likely to result in a perversion of their relationship.

We can state this assumption in another way: It is only after a couple has "fallen out of love" that an adult, warm, loving person-to-person marital relationship is possible for them. In our culture, the ten-year syndrome is probably the first opportunity for a couple to have a really wholehearted marriage.

8. We assume that both marital partners bring their own secret goals to their association, and that these secret goals supersede all the obvious realities. These secret purposes, partially unknown to the partners themselves, determine the dynamic lines of force in the whole field of their marriage. It is as if the two partners constitute the two poles of a magnet, with invisible lines of force between them that only on occasion come to their conscious attention.

Our patients come into psychotherapy with these secret hopes, and they expect the therapist to help them realize them. We have detected such secret marital goals in patients as the following: that marriage should provide greater comfort and happiness with less effort than any previous experience; or, more sophisticated people may expect that marriage will somehow offer the means of increasing freedom from childhood attachments and attitudes; or, that the marriage should help a person to become less ambivalent in making personal decisions. The young bride or groom may secretly expect that the marriage should activate personal emotional growth, by increasing personal toughness when this may be called for in the interests of personal economy. In short, the young husband and the

---

[1] The authors suggested this in more detail at the A.P.A. Regional Research Conference, Galveston, Texas, in February 1965, in "Serial impasses in marriage."

young wife, each having their own secret goals for the good life together, may make such exorbitant demands on the marriage that their very hopes are bound to cause difficulty.

9. We assume that the course of marriage hinges on the conscious determination of the two people to remain intimately related. This means that we consider such problems as sexual difficulty, interfering relatives, and conflict of value systems as "grist for the mill" in psychotherapy, but only so long as the couple is willing to struggle toward the goal of learning to love each other.

10. Finally, we assume that human character structure is so sturdy and substantial that is is unlikely to change much through the years. Therefore, we assume that a person who gets a divorce and then looks for a "better" partner, is very likely to find one who is a reasonable facsimile of the first marital partner. We would expect that the struggle in a person's second marriage would eventually be very similar to that in the first marriage. We are not surprised by the comment of a patient who was in his sixth marriage when he said: "If I could have been as understanding in my first marriage as I am now, there would never have been a second marriage." This particular man recognized quite clearly that he had married six different women who all fitted the same type of character outline, and that he was probably most fortunate with the first one. The authors agreed with him.

We have gradually been brought to the conviction that the current marriage of a new couple in psychotherapy is probably the best one they can achieve in their lifetimes. We see it as our task in psychotherapy to help them explore and experience the heights and the depths of their relationship and to strengthen their resolve to cultivate their intimacy.

REFERENCE

Greene, B. L. (Ed.), The psychotherapies of marital disharmony. New York: Free Press, 1965.